THE SAVAGE CELL

THE
SAVAGE
CELL

*A Report on Cancer
and Cancer Research*

PAT McGRADY

BASIC BOOKS, INC., PUBLISHERS
New York

This book was written
during several leaves of absence
by the author from his position
as science editor of the American Cancer Society.
His views are his own;
they do not necessarily reflect
the policies of the American Cancer Society.

DEDICATION

A book of this kind is the product of the work and devotion of many people. To them it is dedicated—

The thousands of scientists throughout the world who for many years have helped the writer in gathering and interpreting information;

The few scientists who have reviewed this entire manuscript and suggested corrections and changes;

The many in government, academic, and clinical research centers who have read portions pertaining to their specialty and proposed changes;

Those colleagues in the American Cancer Society who have encouraged the writer, and the volunteer workers whose tireless efforts made possible much of the research described in these pages;

A critical and kind first reader, my wife Grace.

It also is dedicated to Annie, who, like many other patients, might have lived much longer and died more gently if she had had competent medical help from the onset of symptoms and during the course of her cancer.

PREFACE

The first draft of *The Savage Cell* was written on a Fulbright fellowship to France during the 1950–51 academic year. The second and final draft was written during leaves of absence in the summers of 1962 and 1963, and this was edited during the spring of 1964.

There is only a faint resemblance between the first and second drafts. The principal reason for this is that, in the intervening decade, the concepts of cancer and the countenance of cancer research had changed a great deal. The scientific explosion, which reached its peak in this interval, opened up vast new vistas of knowledge which invalidated many of the old beliefs about cancer and enabled researchers to begin to define in fairly precise chemical terms the processes by which cells grow, specialize, age and die. Not only had emphasis shifted from one phase of cancer investigation to another, but each research specialty had changed. The Mendelian geneticist was finding it difficult to understand the new molecular geneticist; biologists were becoming biochemists; biochemists were being graduated into biophysics; and scientists who failed to learn the language of triplet codes and the mechanisms of energy transfer were becoming anachronistic. Even bright high school students and intelligent laymen had started to discuss DNA and RNA.

Such is the pace of basic research that, during the months between finishing the final draft of this manuscript and the editing of it, there was need for numerous insertions. Some of the questions posed during the writing of it in 1963 were answered at the spring meetings of 1964. It would be unrealistic to believe that all the information in these pages, the interpretations of data, the emphasis on some findings and the relatively casual treatment of others, and, above all, the synthesis of a story based on the work of many thousands of scientists will be valid a decade hence. It would be equally unrealistic, however, to believe that a report on cancer research should be held back until that day in the dim future when all problems will be solved, all the data will fit neatly into infallible principles, and cancer no longer will be a major threat to life. Important developments have taken place in research; some of them could lead to the control of cancer; others have solved the perplexing problems of other diseases.

This story of cancer and cancer research is the product of almost seventeen years of investigation as science editor of the American Cancer Society. The society has raised no objection to its being written; but, understanding the controversial nature of some of it, the society properly insists that it be made clear that the writer's attitudes are his own and do not necessarily reflect the policies of the society or the views of its officers. The account is based on interviews and discussions over the years with many hundreds of scientists and physicians, on bushels of notes, and on a careful and constant review of current scientific and medical literature.

Cancer research is not entirely a matter of the manpower, money and machines mobilized against a disease. Only in part is it an adventure in search and discovery and an effort to separate eternal truths from the ephemeral clues spewing out of laboratories. Part of it is the problem of transferring to sick humans the benefits derived tediously or fortuitously from test tube and animal experiments. Cancer research is in large measure a conflict of ideas, a struggle between minds, a desperate defense of ideals against the tyranny of professional conformity, mediocrity, materialism, and venality. The physical, chemical, and mathematical equations can be worked out and applied only when a complex human equation is balanced.

A comprehensive report on efforts to control cancer must take into account the human side of the problem. The lives of many people depend, not only on the brilliance of the scientists, but also on the judgment of those who administer research, the enterprise of those responsible for applying it to humans, the pressures and counterpressures of professional organizations and industries, the intelligence and integrity of government agencies, and the competence of the individual physician to treat the individual patient.

In reviewing the original manuscript, some disturbing facts came to light. In the swift current of new developments, many significant discoveries of ten, twenty, and fifty years ago have been swept away. Intriguing leads to the nature or control of cancer have been forsaken in the limbo of literature. Some of the discoveries of bygone days are now being rediscovered as new and startling facts by a generation which apparently did not take time to explore background material. Many of the facts of virus behavior in mammalian cells, for instance, were elucidated twenty years ago in studies of viruses which infect bacteria. More to be deplored than the need for these rediscoveries is the fact that entire important lines of research have been lost or abandoned.

In daring to offer a report on cancer research, the writer must first answer many questions: For whom is he writing? Will he attempt to

instruct—to dramatize—to defend unpopular views—to criticize an entrenched system? How deeply will he delve? How broadly will he explore?
How simple or technical will the story be? How much detail will he
include?

The first question was the easiest. This report is for anyone who can
read; the public at large supports research handsomely and will live with
or die of the fruits of science. The account necessarily includes some
technical material, but I believe that each term which may be strange to
the average reader is amply and often graphically defined.

A great deal of detail has been omitted because of space requirements.
It would have been easier and more satisfactory to have written twenty-
nine books than twenty-nine chapters. The development of new instruments and investigative techniques which made possible many of the
achievements mentioned here has not been described, and neither have
many of the alert observations by some which led to award-winning work
by others. In a great majority of instances, only one of a team or group
of scientists has been identified with a piece of work, and in some cases
not even the institution has been named. A complete bibliography would
occupy a volume many times the size of this book.

Where a scientist would use the escape hatch of "it is tempting to
speculate . . ." without actually committing himself, I have speculated
boldly and without apology. I have avoided a thousand "human-interest"
stories which would have enlivened this book; there was no room for them.

This report gives a sketchy idea of work in the biochemistry of cancer,
essentially the chemistry of life, which is coming to light with breathtaking
speed. Because cancer is related to the processes of evolution and the
development of the embryo, it has been necessary to explore those fields.
Much of cancer research is in areas of better-understood diseases—genetic,
congenital, infectious, immune, degenerative, and other—and I have not
hesitated to describe the parallels. The report, I felt, should be as broad
and as deep as the sophisticated reader would care to have it; any simpler
course would have resulted in a superficial treatment of an important
subject.

It has been a distasteful duty in writing this manuscript to point out
that all doctors are not the same. There are in the United States great
physicians, bad physicians, and a wide range of medical talent between
these two extremes. This statement will be resented by the inferior
physicians, and it will not please the mediocre doctors and the organizations which protect them. Some will object to the thesis that any kind of
cancer calls for the best possible treatment. Doctors as well as patients
must take the blame for deadly delays, and doctors alone are responsible
for wrong diagnoses and incorrect treatment. The question we faced
here was whether to appease large elements within the medical profession

by remaining silent or to speak out and try to save some of the 90,000 to 145,000 lives lost annually to cancer because of patient negligence and physician incompetence.

The decision to write a book of this kind is not a happy one. There is the formidable prospect of inevitable error in attempting to go into technical detail of some of the many scientific and medical matters discussed, the certainty of objections to one's translations from Sciencese to English, and the outrage of some scientists whose pure research has been subjected to interpretation and implications. Throughout, one must try to distinguish the scientific enthusiast from the addict to understatement, the respectable fraud from the bona fide investigator, the fact from the artifact, valid and informed criticism from cynical iconoclasm.

In this quandary, I have been helped by distinguished physicians and scientists; a few have reviewed the entire manuscript, and many others have corrected chapters and portions of chapters pertaining to their specialty. Many have offered excellent counsel on opinions expressed. On reflection, I decided not to thank these advisors by name in this book because, in the minds of some readers, they might be charged with the errors it may still contain and they might seem committed to the writer's attitudes—with some of which each reviewer very well might disagree.

Despite all the pitfalls, *The Savage Cell* had to be written. I do not regret that I wrote it.

For those interested in further detail on various aspects of cancer, there are good books on each phase of the problem. To mention a few authors: Lauren V. Ackerman and Juan A. del Regato, *Cancer* (Mosby); Greer Williams, *Virus Hunters* (Knopf); E. Boyland *et al On Cancer and Hormones* (University of Chicago); Charles S. Cameron, *The Truth about Cancer* (Prentice-Hall); Warren H. Cole *et al. The Dissemination of Cancer, Prevention and Therapy* (Appleton); Freddy Homburger, *Biologic Basis of Cancer Management* (Hoeber-Harper); C. Oberling, *The Riddle of Cancer* (Yale); George T. Pack and Irving M. Ariel, several volumes on specific cancer problems (Hoeber-Harper); Ludwik Gross, *Oncogenic Viruses* (Pergamon); Morris Pollard, *Perspectives in Virology* (Burgess; Wiley); Wendell M. Stanley and G. Valens Evans, *Viruses and the Nature of Life* (Dutton). Paul E. Steiner, *Cancer: Race and Geography* (Williams and Wilkins); Ruth M. Graham, *Cytologic Diagnosis of Cancer* (Little); Harris Busch, *Nucleus of the Cancer Cell* (Academic Press); Gregory Pincus, *Biological Activities of Steroids in Relation to Cancer* (Academic Press), and E. V. Cowdry, *Cancer Cells* (Saunders). Numerous symposiums on cancer subjects have been held by the New York Academy of Sciences, Ciba, and the M. D. Anderson Hospital, and they are worth serious attention.

Among the journals and periodicals I have found helpful in keeping current with events in cancer research are *Acta Cytologica; Acta of the International Union against Cancer; Journal of the American Geriatrics Society;* the *American Journals—of Clinical Pathology, of Medicine, of Obstetrics and Gynecology, of Pathology, of Public Health,* and *of Surgery; The Journal of the American Medical Association; Annals of Internal Medicine; Annals of Surgery; Archives of Internal Medicine; Blood; British Medical Journal; British Journal of Radiology; CA— Bulletin of Cancer Progress; California Medicine; Cancer; Cancer Bulletin; Cancer Research; Ciba Clinical Symposia; Cytologia; GP.; Geriatrics; Health Bulletin; Human Biology; Journals—of Biological Chemistry, of Cell Biology, of Clinical Endocrinology and Metabolism, of Experimental Medicine, of Gerontology, of Immunology, of Laboratory and Clinical Medicine, and of Urology; Der Krebsarzt; Lancet; Leukemia Abstracts; MD, Medical News Magazine; Medical Economics; Medical Science; Medical Tribune; Medical World News; Nature; New England Journal of Medicine; New York Academy of Sciences, Transactions; Obstetrics and Gynecology; Pfizer Spectrum; Population Bulletin; Psychosomatic Medicine; Radiology; Science; Science News Letter; Scientific American; Society for Experimental Biology and Medicine, Proceedings; Surgery, Gynecology, and Obstetrics; Tobacco; Today's Health; Transplantation Bulletin, U.S. Department of Health, Education, and Welfare—Monthly Vital Statistics Report; U.S. National Cancer Institute Journal; U.S.P.H.S. Public Health Reports; Virology; World Health Organization—Rapport Épidémiologique et Démographique;* and journals of some state medical societies, publications of some local medical societies, and of a number of medical schools, pharmaceutical houses, and research institutions.

New York City   PAT MCGRADY
June 1964

CONTENTS

THE SAVAGE CELL

CHAPTER 1

WHAT IS CANCER?

Cancer is almost as old and as ubiquitous as life. It is as new as tomorrow's obituaries. A disease of civilization, its toll has mounted relentlessly through recorded history. With the conquest of other diseases, cancer has become epidemic—during the twentieth century its claim on human life has risen rapidly from relative obscurity to an awesome eminence, second only to heart and circulatory diseases in modern countries.

The scientific effort to identify cancer, to establish its causes and to find new ways to cure it is the boldest, most ambitious adventure ever undertaken in science. Cancer research is putting together a gigantic jigsaw puzzle—as big as space, as detailed as the tiniest particle of the atom, as complex as the sequence of the countless chemical and physical events called life. This supreme challenge to the brilliance of man's composite mind comes in all the colors of genes, enzymes, hormones, emotions, and environment. When the curved and jagged pieces finally are put together, when all the shades and shadows are blended, we shall know the road over which each man came into being, the chemistry of life, the distortions of disease and the irreversible reactions of death.

Even now the first steps to this end have been made. In the test tube man has done what God once did—with the aid of enzymes, he has formed life's basic ingredients, nucleic acids, made them multiply, and directed them to produce proteins. In the laboratory, he has produced, prevented, and cured animal cancers with a quasi-divine authority.

Someday the laboratory advances, now being achieved at a rate so rapid that no one can hope to keep current with even the more significant discoveries, will be applied to medicine. Man then may have to find new

1

things to die of, because in solving the cancer problem, science will have discovered, as by-products, the key to infectious, hereditary, hormonal, and other ailments, and perhaps even a means of delaying for a while the disasters of old age.

It should be made clear at the outset that some kinds of cancer are curable—much more so than the common cold, which as yet remains incurable by any medical means. The American Cancer Society states that one of every three cancer patients is "saved," which means alive five years after surgical or radiation treatment. Many more—perhaps one-third or one-half of those who now die—could be cured if patients would only call their symptoms to the attention of physicians, and if the physicians would promptly refer the patients to specialists competent to diagnose and treat the cancers.

The problem of educating the public to behave intelligently in the presence of cancer and of equipping the medical profession with the heads, hearts, and hands to properly use the techniques now available is as formidable as the research quest for new means of diagnosing and curing cancer.

The status of cancer research is one of more or less ordered chaos, of statistical paradoxes, of ideological conflict and experimental contradictions and, as the prospect of what some call a "breakthrough" becomes more real, of deepening competition among research groups and intense rivalry among individual scientists. In recent years there have been cycles of impending triumph and disillusionment, each crest higher and each trough deeper than the last. There also has been an uneasy feeling that the critical clue—a central piece of the jigsaw puzzle which would make all the other pieces fall into place—may lie forgotten or ignored and buried under the rising mountains of medical and scientific literature.

Specialization—which someone once defined as knowing more and more about less and less until ultimately one knows everything about nothing—is rapidly dividing science into smaller and smaller compartments. Curse or blessing, this is a necessity; science, which suddenly has become each nation's promise of prestige and hope of survival, is spewing out facts and figures in such volume that experts in each field find it necessary to concentrate on ever-narrowing lanes of interest. Chemistry is divided into dozens of branches; and chemists in one specialty find it difficult to communicate with chemists in another field.

It is possible that one man, with exclusive and specialized knowledge, could be the unwitting custodian of the key to cancer—and, because of his ignorance of its relationship to other areas of research, might never recognize the significance of his treasure. Even more likely is the possibility that the extensive bits of knowledge needed to control cancer repose unrelated in the minds of many scientists of widely divergent specialties.

An amazing thing about cancer is that more is known about it than about any other disease. Cancer has had more study from scientists, more treatment from physicians, and more attention from bewildered laymen than any other health problem.

And yet no one knows precisely what cancer is.

The leading authorities are not helpful. One often quoted investigator, Dr. D. W. Smithers of the Royal Cancer Hospital, London, has noted the numerous disagreements in the diagnosis of tumors and has recommended abandonment of the word *cancer* in "communications having some pretense to scientific reporting . . . since the term can have no precise boundaries this side of death." Dr. Leslie Foulds, also a London cancer expert, when asked which feature marks a cell as malignant said, "Whether it kills the patient or not."

Cancer is Latin for "crab"; and *carcinoma,* the word applied to a common type of cancer, is derived from the Greek word for crab. The word is meant to describe the supposed clawlike roots of malignant tumors or the tentaclelike radiation of great veins from a tumor. Like many medical and scientific terms which enshroud living science and changing concepts in a dead language, the word is fundamentally meaningless and misleading. So far as science is concerned, cancer might just as well be called "The Thing"—or, to preserve the pretensions of the wordsmiths who coin scientific jargon, *res,* or *id,* which are Latin for "thing" and "it."

Dr. Michael B. Shimkin, now of Temple University and for many years connected with the National Cancer Institute, U.S. Public Health Service —a scientist, physician, epidemiologist, former editor of the *Journal of the National Cancer Institute,* and down-to-earth scholar, defines it this way:

Cancer is a popular generic term for malignant neoplasms [new growths or tumors], a great group of diseases of unknown—and probably multiple—causes, occurring in all human and animal populations and arising in all tissues composed of potentially dividing cells. The basic characteristic of cancer is the transmissible abnormality in cells that is manifested by reduced control over growth and function, leading to serious adverse effects on the host through invasive growth and metastasis.

To still other authorities, cancer is variously a half-smothered cell, a missing, extra, or displaced gene, a distorted nucleic acid, a defective enzyme, an abnormal gland or unbalanced hormonal system, a dietary indiscretion, a virus in disguise, a weakened or corrupted immunity, overworked emotions, an abused habit, an accident of birth, overexposure to a chemical or ray in our environment, a contaminating microbe, a cell which has learned the secret of eternal youth, or an inevitable consequence of the aging process. In this respect, the cancer scholars are like the legendary blind men who sought to describe an elephant. All of them could be right.

For purposes of expediency and explanation, we will define cancer as a savage cell which somehow evades the laws of the body, corrupts the forces which normally protect the body, invades the well-ordered society of cells surrounding it, colonizes distant areas and, as a finale to its cannibalistic orgy of flesh consuming flesh, commits suicide by destroying its host.

Just as there are many kinds of social savagery, so are there many kinds of cancer. Some cancers are slow to spread and to colonize distant areas; they are highly curable. Others are sure and sudden death. Dr. George E. Moore, director of Roswell Park Memorial Institute, Buffalo, New York, feels that progress in understanding and treating it can be made only when cancer is recognized not as a single disease but as a large group of diseases.

Perhaps the biggest barrier of all to recognizing the idiosyncrasies of the cancer cell is in the prevailing ignorance of the nature of a normal cell. Until the fundamental facts of normal cell life are understood, one can only guess at what makes the cancer cell different. A handful of scientists, for instance, are challenging the basic concept that in growth one cell divides into two, the two into four, and so on. They have produced some suggestive evidence that the normal mammalian cell divides into (a) a parent cell which is capable of further division, and (2) a worker cell which matures (or differentiates, or specializes), does the work required of it, ages, and dies without leaving cell progeny. Dr. Vincent Collins of Baylor University holds that things do go wrong occasionally. He believes that when a cell divides into two worker cells, which age and die but are incapable of further reproduction, this is the process of tissue and host aging; when the cell divides into two nonworking cells, both of which reproduce into daughter cells which also reproduce, they form shapeless masses of useless cells called tumors, including the malignant tumors called cancer. An aging tissue is like a community composed only of old and sterile people; a tumor is a town populated only by a fecund generation of delinquents who have found the secret of eternal youth.

Cancer patients seldom die of the effects of the primary, or original, tumor. Usually it is a metastasis which does them in. Metastases are cancer colonies that form when a cell or chunk of cells drops off the tumor and is carried in lymphatic channels or blood vessels to other parts of the body, where it takes up residence and grows into new tumors. The host can survive in good shape even with large tumors which are contained in the less essential tissues. A tiny tumor can kill when it damages a vital organ.

The body is like a great city. Just as a city can be paralyzed by the breakdown of any of its essential functions, so can the body become sick when cancer impairs an important system or service. In muscle, cancer impedes locomotion; in nerve, communications; in brain, administration; in the digestive tract, food supply; in lungs, fuel; in kidneys, sanitation; in liver and endocrine (hormone-producing) glands, commerce; in skin, shelter; in bone marrow and lymphatic tissues which manufacture blood cells, the transport system and police force.

When cancer strikes one organ, the whole body may become sick; when it blocks a vital function, the whole body dies. By the same token, any sick system impairs the whole body's natural resistance to cancer; malignant disease moves fastest in bodies too young, too weak, too abused, too tired, too sick, or too old to defend themselves.

Scientists have induced cancer in animals by many means. They have made cancer inevitable from the moment of conception by mating cancer-susceptible males with cancer-prone females and by delaying fertilization —by allowing the ovum to become overripe before introducing the sperm. They have done it by injecting or feeding animals with any of several hundred chemicals, or by exposing them to rays. They have done it by adding chemical insult to physical injury, by injecting hormones, or by removing or transplanting hormone-producing glands. They have produced cancer by feeding liver poisons while withholding essential vitamins. They have done it with a variety of infections. And they have transformed normal cells in laboratory dishes by introducing into the medium the gene (DNA) or protein-producing (RNA) nucleic acids from cancer cells. Dr. Jorgen Fogh of the Sloan-Kettering Institute has shown that, if normal cells are removed from the body and grown in tissue culture, one in every several thousand cells will become malignant—it will develop into a cancer when injected back into an animal.

Some experts contend that one cannot tell by looking at a single cell whether or not it is cancer. Most cancer cells closely resemble cells of the tissues from which they arise. Some cancer cells are grotesque, but so are some benign cells.

Dr. E. V. Cowdry, Washington University's eminent authority on cancer cells, has reported that there are exceptions—and sometimes numerous exceptions—to every characteristic attributed to cancer cells. In broad general terms, cancer cells usually are rounded, plump but not necessarily large; they contain king-size cores, or nuclei, composed of stuff much less sticky than the material in normal nuclei; they lack polarity, or orientation, with neighboring normal cells; and they are improvident (they store little material), motile, adaptable to various environments, poorly regulated by the cell community, highly individualistic, vulnerable to mutation-causing (mutagenic) chemicals and rays, antagonistic to cells of other cancers and, perhaps, poison producing.

No man can answer with conviction the question: what is cancer?

An equally important question—from a practical as well as a fundamental philosophical point of view—is: why is cancer?

The savage in cellular society may be motivated by the selfsame circumstances—whatever they may be—that produce savages in human society.

In a sense, the cancer cell stands alone against a corporate society which wants none of it and would destroy it. It turns back the clock of evolution, adopts the primitive code of early life forms, reproduces rapidly because in a hostile host there is safety in numbers, and sets out to exploit the discipline imposed on normal cells. It no longer is fixed to a status in cellular society; it moves with the freedom of a bacterium and pillages with the conscience of a parasite. The skills the malignant cell seeks to develop are those which enable it to paralyze its normal neighbors and invade and despoil their precincts.

Perhaps it could be argued that the savage cell is a symbol not so much of its own sickness as of a sick host. Its vigorous growth may represent an effort to compensate for the disability of a host system and its effervescent youth a rebellion against the decay and inevitable death of a diseased and aging body.

CHAPTER 2

THE COSTS OF CANCER

Insurance-company figures have indicated that in hours lost from work and other financial effects, cancer costs the United States each year more than $12 billion.

This is the least of its costs. The truly extortionate price is in human beings—mothers, fathers, wives, husbands, sons, and daughters—lost to the disease, many of them in untimely deaths.

Cancer is a leading destroyer of life—all kinds of life. So far as is known, cancer may affect every animal species that walks, crawls, flies, swims, or burrows under the earth. Many plants—perhaps all kinds—have tumors. And, except for laboratory animals deliberately bred for their susceptibility to cancer, or animals in which virus-caused cancers rage periodically like a conflagration, man is its most frequent victim.

An important question is: how many people die of cancer? The answer is important, because without it there can be no measure of the problem and no standards of success in solving it.

The American Cancer Society offers these figures for the year 1964: stricken by cancer—540,000 people in the United States; of these, about 360,000 would be dead—possibly 80 or 90 per cent of or with cancer —within five years and 180,000 would be cured of cancer or dead, cancer-free, of other diseases. About 290,000 were earmarked for death by cancer in 1964—155,000 men, 130,000 women and almost 5,000 children. Since the turn of the century cancer deaths increased from 64 for every 100,000 Americans to more than 150.

These figures are approximations—and, at least for morbidity (disease prevalence) and mortality (death rate), conservative. A lot of cancers,

7

deliberately or through ignorance, are called by other names on death certificates.

There are many contradictions and much confusion in cancer statistics. This is due, in large part, to the number of variables involved. There are, for instance, such factors as incidence, multiple (independent) cancers in a single individual, prevention, accuracy of diagnosis, longevity, cure, survival rate and duration, mortality, and death by other causes. A change in any one factor influences others. Prophylactic hysterectomy, or removal of the uterus, for precancerous sores (prevention) depresses incidence, mortality and cure rates. Death by unrelated heart disease in a patient harboring an incurable cancer—does this statistic belong in the cancer mortality column or another? Is a patient who has been cured of breast cancer but killed by a completely different brain tumor listed as a cure, a cancer death, or both? As is becoming quite apparent, there is a considerable difference between being cured of cancer and surviving five years with cancer still present. And the longer one lives the greater the risk of developing cancer and dying of it. An equation embracing all these and other variables may seem to contradict itself in showing morbidity, mortality, cure and survival rates all rising simultaneously. That, however, is the situation.

More than all others, statisticians themselves are most embarrassed by the inadequacy of available data.

A truly anomalous statistical situation exists in the ratio of male and female cancers. Until 1949, more women than men died of cancer. At that point two potent factors reversed the trend: (1) the rocketing rise in lung cancer among men (doubling with every decade), and (2) the rapidly decreasing death rate among women. The drop in female deaths was due largely to a mysterious decline in cancers of the uterus, stomach, and liver. For reasons completely unknown to science, cancers of these sites had decreased about 50 per cent over a quarter of a century. While American men shared the decrease in liver and stomach cancers, the increase in cancer of the male lung more than offset this blessing; lung cancer in men is epidemic and only 5 per cent curable. In the early 1960s, the incidence of cancer still was higher in women than among men (the average American woman was living to age seventy-four, while the average man attained only about sixty-seven years—giving women an increased cancer risk with their greater age); but cancer killed more men than women (about 54 men to 46 women).

This is a sample of the reasons why statisticians often are at odds with each other, why various sets of figures cannot be compared and why laymen interested in following statistical trends usually give up in despair.

Back in 1952, Dr. Paul E. Steiner, pathologist, delivered a provocative and prophetic address as retiring president of the American Association for Cancer Research.

He told the assembled scientists that estimates of the cancer death rate had been much too low—his own autopsies and several other large series showed that the true mortality was 20 or 25 per cent greater than official figures indicated.

He charged that the cause inscribed on death certificates—on which official vital statistics were based—was in error in many cases. He estimated that cancer was cited mistakenly for other diseases in less than 5 per cent of the cases, while other diseases were given erroneously—deliberately or unwittingly—in perhaps 20 per cent of the cases when cancer was the actual cause of death.

He set forth a series of Utopian conditions—in which (1) patients had regular checkups, promptly reported any symptom of cancer to their doctors, faithfully followed the doctor's orders and could and would spend the sizable sums needed for the best medical care, and (2) doctors quickly and competently would undertake the very best diagnostic and treatment measures. Under these conditions, he predicted, the cure rates could be doubled.

Even in his Utopia, however, two cancer patients in three still would die of their disease. The only hope for the doomed two-thirds rested with research.

American Cancer Society statisticians agreed in principle, if not in estimates, with Dr. Steiner. They said that in 1952 one in four was being cured, that another one in four could be cured by application of medical means then available and that two in four could not be saved by the best of skills and all the measures then possible.

Various kinds of cancer, Dr. Steiner said, would respond in different degrees, in his theoretical Utopia. In the order of their importance in mortality tables, these were the then prevailing cure percentages for various cancers and the potential curability under ideal conditions: Cancer of the stomach cures would rise from 5 to 35 per cent, large intestine 15 to 65, lymphatic (including leukemia) 0 to 0, lung 5 to 50, uterus 20 to 75, brain 10 to 20, prostate 7 to 25, breast 20 to 75, pancreas 1 to 5, ovary 15 to 30, skin 85 to 98, soft connective tissue 15 to 25, mouth 15 to 40, esophagus 3 to 20, kidney 10 to 20, larynx 20 to 75, bone 5 to 15, liver 1 to 2, and all other types 10 to 25.

Referring to the great majority of cancers which even in Utopia would remain incurable, Dr. Steiner advised his fellow scientists, "Here is the size of our enemy. The problem remaining for research is more than six times the cure rate now prevailing and more than three times that now theoretically possible under optimum conditions of education and cooperation."

Dr. Steiner contended that even in 1952, without benefit of breakthroughs or dramatic developments, some advances were being made in curing cancer. He said: "Progress in the past has been slow in human cancer, but it has been steady. Decade by decade, things get better. We are fighting for small percentages in each type of cancer and are grateful for the sum of numerous small conquests. Decade by decade, they add up to perceptible, if not entirely satisfactory, sums."

A decade later, in 1962, much of what Dr. Steiner said had become obvious. It was clear that cancer prevalence and mortality had been underestimated in official statistics; education, in alerting the public to the signs and symptoms of cancer, and in instructing the medical profession in modern diagnosis and treatment, while still far from perfect, had increased the cure rate. The major job still remained for research, however.

At the turn of the century, a diagnosis of cancer was virtually a death sentence. Nevertheless, surgeons operated and radiologists, by trial and error, tested and gradually improved treatment with X rays and radium. By 1937 the boast became: one in seven patients is cured of cancer. By 1948 some said the salvage had become one in four. And in 1962 the official cure rate reached Dr. Steiner's theoretical limits—one in three. Improvements in diagnosis and treatment—the fruits of research—had expanded the potential of education. The degree of success, the sum of the slow but steady percentage point gains envisioned by Dr. Steiner, startled even the statisticians. Spectacular advances had been made against a few cancers—none at all against others.

The figures cited by Dr. Steiner were estimates. The figures issued today as official are estimates; and while they represent the best available evidence of current cancer morbidity and mortality, they still require a sizable margin for error. By and large, they probably understate the cancer problem.

Even pathologists—the ultimate authorities as to whether or not it's cancer—make occasional errors in diagnosis. Physicians, many of whom still diagnose without recourse to the microscope and whose death-certificate statements often are not checked by autopsies, make many honest mistakes. And physicians, for various reasons, sometimes deliberately and falsely cite a disease other than cancer on the death certificate.

Why should a physician willfully lie about his patient's cancer? In the first place, he can reason that the stated cause of death is less a lie than technicality—cancer patients almost always die of pneumonia, the impairment of a vital organ, or other debilities and disabilities which are a consequence of their disease rather than of cancer itself. Sometimes the physician sees fit to perpetuate after death a conspiracy of silence initiated at the time of diagnosis—the patient is not told he has cancer, and perhaps only one member of the family is let in on the burdensome secret. Especially in backward communities where cancer still is regarded as an inherited, transmissible, or loathesome disease, the doctor lies to insure the marriage-ability of sons and daughters of the patient and to protect the family from calumny. Under these and other circumstances, the patient very often goes to his grave without knowing cancer is the cause; family members and friends wonder why he does not respond to treatment; and vital statistics are distorted.

Efforts to restore the integrity of cancer statistics are being made at this writing. Recognizing the unreliability of cancer data, the Federal Government's National Cancer Institute in 1956 initiated an "End Results Evaluation Program." This involves a study of 212,638 cancer patients in ninety-nine hospitals in the United States. The idea is to measure the survival of the patients with regard to the kind and stage of cancer and the type of treatment given.

The first "end results" reported in 1960 in some respects were appalling. Themselves questionable because of their preliminary nature and the mixture of microscopically confirmed and unconfirmed cancers, the figures seemed to show nevertheless that (1) cure rates for some kinds of cancer had been exaggerated, and (2) the fundamental yardstick of progress in controlling cancer—the "five-year cure"—was itself a treacherous standard.

Science and medicine many years ago accepted arbitrarily five years as the measure of a cancer cure—if the disease did not recur within five years following treatment, the patient was considered cured. This was done in full knowledge of the rapid or slow courses of various kinds of cancer; many physicians feel, for instance, that lung cancer patients who survive three years after surgery without symptoms of recurrence are out of the woods, while those with thyroid cancer may have a recurrence ten or twenty years following treatment. Despite these vagaries, the five-year cure rate has served a useful purpose in measuring over-all progress against the disease.

The first "end results" report indicated that women who had survived cancer of the breast or uterus for five years had a risk of death during the next five years well in excess of that of other women in the same age bracket but without a history of cancer. In a few kinds of cancer, the report indicated, five-year survival rates had gone down, rather than up. This—probably a statistical illusion due to errors in earlier data, errors in the report itself or both—showed that for women whose cancers were diagnosed before 1950 as against those diagnosed after 1950, five-year survival decreased (statistically) from 36 to 34 per cent for cancer of the tongue, from 31 to 27 per cent in chronic lymphatic leukemia, from 13 to 6 per cent in acute lymphatic leukemia, and from 5 to 0 per cent in acute myeloid leukemia; in men, five-year survival reductions in cases diagnosed before and after 1950 were from 80 to 71 per cent for basal-cell skin cancers and from 20 to 18 per cent in chronic lymphatic leukemia.

In almost all other cancers, survival rates rose by at least a few percentage points. Here, too, however, there may have been a statistical mirage: survival is measured usually from diagnosis or treatment; and, naturally, the earlier the diagnosis and treatment the longer the survival—statistically. Inasmuch as the public has become progressively cancer-conscious and more inclined to call symptoms to the doctor's attention early, survival should lengthen automatically.

A massive study undertaken in 1960 by the American Cancer Society of more than one million people who have reached the "cancer age" (middle age) eventually will improve the accuracy of statistics on the cancer incidence, mortality, survival, and cure rates in the United States. The subjects, presumably healthy, have been checked for past diseases, personal habits and characteristics, exposure to possible cancer-causing agents and many other factors. They are being restudied yearly. As they develop cancer, as many of them now are, the type of tumor, the kind of treatment, the stage of the disease and its course—to cure, or death—are noted. Eventually the project, the most ambitious ever undertaken in the field of epidemiology, is expected to tell not only how many and what percentages die of cancer but also to afford clues as to what kinds of people are most prone to various types of cancer and the most effective treatment for each.

Despite all the shortcomings of statistics, there is no doubt about the enormity of the cancer problem. Sooner or later it will become a matter of personal concern to almost every person. According to present trends, cancer will come grimly, unpredictably, perhaps randomly, to one of every four Americans now alive. Its lethal touch will be felt in two of every three families.

Moreover, the incidence and death rates continue to rise rapidly and relentlessly as they have through recorded history. During the last twenty years the cancer death rate has risen six times faster than the rate for heart disease. Only part of the rise can be attributed to the fact that diagnosis is improving and the human lifespan lengthening; much of the increase is mystifying.

Usually for reasons unknown, cancer statistics fluctuate: one kind of cancer will relent for a year, a few years or a longer period, while other types with startling suddenness will increase. The most pronounced increases have been in lung cancer among men (which most authorities attribute in large part to cigarette smoking) and in children's cancers (for which no satisfactory explanation is offered and which may be notoriously underdiagnosed).

Cancer statistics are influenced considerably by geography. Cancer deaths in the United States are most frequent in the New England, Middle Atlantic and East North Central states and least frequent in the Rocky Mountain, Southwest and Southern (except for Atlantic Seaboard) states. The Pacific Coast, South Atlantic Coast, and West North Central states are a middle ground in mortality figures. These rates are "age-adjusted," meaning that allowance has been made for long average lifespans in areas like the Midwest (over sixty-eight years) and short lifespans in the Southwest (sixty-four years and under. A seeming anomaly—the highest cancer death rates are in areas with the greatest concentration of doctors and hospitals —can be explained in part by the fact that cancer patients migrate to these centers to be treated and, when treatment is unsuccessful, to die. In some areas, low cancer rates may merely reflect poor diagnosis.

Has cancer's cold, hard grip on human destiny begun to relax? Perhaps —perhaps a little. More than one million cured cancer patients in the United States alone can attest to this. What's more, the number and percentage of cures are rising slowly but steadily. Most of the fortunate former patients, to be sure, had cancers which were accessible, readily diagnosed, and responsive to surgery or X rays. While almost all incurable cancers remain incurable still, ease and comfort have been given to most of these patients, and their useful lives have been lengthened, often without great pain. To those who have learned to live each day for itself, these small advances are a blessing. There is no prospect at present that science and medicine ever will invest man with immortality.

Meanwhile in thousands of laboratories new concepts of cancer are emerging, and new treatments are being devised. The greatest successes are against tumors growing in laboratory dishes and in experimental animals. It seems inevitable that some of these results someday will be applied clinically to prolong human life, relieve man of his pains and terrors, and enrich him with health and new degrees of productivity.

CHAPTER 3

EPIDEMIOLOGY OF CANCER

Until 1935 there was very little cancer among animals in the Philadelphia Zoo. This was regarded as one of the proofs that wild animals never developed cancer. At this time, the zoo improved the diet. All walking, crawling, and flying creatures which earlier had been dying of malnutrition and related diseases began to live much longer—and the cancer rate in all species promptly started to soar.

These events afforded a clue as to why wild animals seldom die of cancer—they simply don't live long enough to attain the "cancer age." When wild animals lose their ability to fight or flee they soon become dinner for a stronger, faster, hungry predator.

Animal and human studies are beginning to explain why cancer is a "disease of civilization," why it is most prevalent in areas of good eating, good housing, and good medical care. In regions where people die early of malnutrition, infections, warfare, cannibalism, addictions, poor medical attention or filth, the cancer death rate is very low. During the 1930s and 1940s the lifespan in India was 33 years, in Mexico 38, and in Egypt 36; cancer was not an important public health problem. In the last decade or two, with the lifespan lengthening, cancer has become an increasingly serious matter in all these countries.

More than two million people die of cancer each year throughout the world. At any given time five million have cancer, and four or five times that number have precancerous conditions—although many of these do not develop into cancer.

Cancer is a completely democratic disease. When people live long enough, no one is immune. Of every three homes, cancer visits two. In a typical small town of 1,000 population during the course of a year, three new cancer cases will crop up. Of these, two will be dead within five years and one will be cured. Of the 1,000 people, 250 eventually will develop cancer and 150 will die of it. The cancer rates for a city of one million population can be computed by multiplying these figures by 1,000.

Obituaries are a constant reminder of cancer's ubiquity. In little more than a year or two, the disease claimed Pope John XXIII; Israel's second president Yitzhak Ben-Zvi; screen personalities Boris Morros, Jack Carson, Hoot Gibson, Gary Cooper, Charles Laughton, Zasu Pitts, Dick Powell, Frank Borzage; writers Clifford Odets, Oliver LaFarge, Ludwig Bemelmans, Van Wyck Brooks, Boris Pasternak; artist William Baziotes, educator Dr. A. Whitney Griswold, pianist Alec Templeton, industrialist Irving Sands Olds, banker George Whitney, football idol Ernie Davis, Dr. Tom Dooley, scientist Enrico Fermi, premiers Hans Christian Hansen and Hitoshi Oshida, political figures Sam Rayburn and John Foster Dulles, Broadway's Oscar Hammerstein 2nd, and Guthrie McClintic. While the deaths of those and many other famous "names" shock the public into cancer consciousness, cancer usually can be found in one's own neighborhood or in one's own circle of friends and relatives.

The United States' cancer death rate is only a little above the average for all modern nations. With the age factor standardized, the World Health Organization calculated cancer came to this degree (in terms of annual cancer deaths per 100,000 population) to various countries: Austria 177, Scotland 176, Finland 171, Switzerland 164, England and Wales 161, German Federal Republic 158, Netherlands 156, Chile 153, United States 141, Northern Ireland 140, France and Canada 139, Israel (Jewish population) 138, Norway 134, Australia and New Zealand 130, Sweden 127, Italy 121, Japan 119, Puerto Rico 119, Trinidad and Tobago 103, Guatemala 95, Portugal 85, and Ceylon 29.

In all modern countries, the cancer death rate for women varies only a little, although it is somewhat low in France and a bit high in Denmark. Male cancer mortalities range widely from country to country. In almost all nations except Portugal, Columbia, Denmark and Israel, the age-adjusted death rate is higher for men than women.

World Health Organization charts show an enormous geographical difference in the frequency of cancer of various sites—one country may have ten, twenty, or more times as much of a certain kind of cancer as another country shows. Cancer of the mouth and pharynx is very high in Ireland (almost four-to-one in men over women), high in Switzerland and England and low in Columbia, Venezuela, Israel, and Japan. Cancer of the esophagus is very high in France and Switzerland. Intestinal cancer (to which women are the more susceptible) is high in Belgium, France, England, Scotland, and New Zealand and low in Japan, Finland, and Portugal, while cancer of the rectum is high in Denmark and England and very low in Chile and Columbia. Cancer of the larynx is high among Frenchmen and low in the Scandinavian countries. Lung cancer (pretty much a male disease) is most common in England, Scotland, Switzerland, and Denmark and low in Japan. Cervical cancer is high in Portugal, England, Scotland, Norway, and Switzerland and low in Ireland, Japan, Italy, and Israel, but cancer of the body of the uterus is high in Japan, West Germany, Austria, Belgium, and France and low in Israel, Norway, Portugal, New Zealand, and the Netherlands. Bladder cancer is high in England and low in Japan. Thyroid cancer is high in Austria and Switzerland and low in Germany, Belgium, France, Netherlands, and Australia. Leukemia is highest in the United States, Denmark, and Sweden and low in Columbia and Ceylon.

Whatever the variations and the broad latitude for statistical error, the "war against cancer" in all modern countries is still a losing one. In a single year, 1963, cancer deaths in the United States almost equaled the total number (291,000) of Americans killed in combat during the entire three years and nine months of participation in World War II. The cost is exorbitant whether it is in the high cancer areas like the Northeastern states where mortality ranges from 140 to 170 per 100,000 population, or Alaska, where the rate is only about 68.

If man can learn how cancer picks and chooses among the populations, it may become possible to protect many of the intended victims. In more than 90 per cent of the cases, the causes of cancer probably are external.

Studies of the distribution of other diseases among various ethnic, occupational, racial, socioeconomic, religious, geographical and other groups have helped eliminate many once-formidable recurrent epidemics.

Two observations enabled the English general physician, Edward Jenner, to produce a safe and effective vaccine for smallpox: (1) victims who survived one attack of smallpox did not again develop the disease, and (2) milkmaids, who had experienced the mild effects of cowpox, were immune to smallpox. The prevalence of many infections among the poor in squalid quarters and of venereal infections among the promiscuous was the basis for the revolutionary dogma of hygiene laid down in the eighteenth century by the scourged German prophet, Johann Peter Frank. Earlier epidemiological observations enabled the Burgundian, Louis Pasteur, to control anthrax (common among wool sorters) and rabies (from bites of dogs and other animals), and permitted the small-town German medical officer Robert Koch to promulgate the preventive principles of disinfection and sanitation which suppressed cholera (in water), bubonic plague (from rat fleas), and sleeping sickness (carried by the tse-tse fly). From the seventeenth century, when the first real effort in the public health statistics was begun, until today, epidemiology has helped resolve the problems of one great pestilence after another.

Now on an ever-enlarging scale epidemiology is pitted against the many mysteries of cancer. Never in the history of medicine has a problem appeared so difficult, so bewildering—or so intriguing.

Cancer is ruthlessly, or scrupulously, impartial in the number of lives it exacts from modern societies. The disease comes with almost random frequency to man and woman, saint and sinner, prince and pauper, worker and loafer, city man, and farmer. Only in the body site it attacks does cancer discriminate between races, nationalities, religions and socioeconomic groups. And, only in some cases is there a good rationale for its lethal selections.

One of the more reasonable explanations is for skin cancer. The fairer the skin the more susceptible it is to cancer induced by weather and the rays of the sun. There is more than twice as much sunshine and six times as much skin cancer in the United States Southwest as in the Great Lakes region. The most frequent victims are red-haired or blond, blue-eyed, freckling people of Scandinavian, British, Scotch, and Irish descent.

A puzzling predilection is for breast cancer. In Japan this disease is rare—almost one-eighth as frequent as in the United States. In terms of deaths per year per 100,000 women, Japan has only 3.4, Greece 3.8, and Poland 5.2. At the other end of the scale, the breast cancer rates are for the United States 25.9, England and Wales 37.5, Scotland 33.5, Denmark 33.7, Belgium 31.4 and Switzerland 31. While there is no acceptable explanation for the geographical, racial or national proneness to breast cancer, there is a correlation, noted in several studies, with marital status; breast cancer is most frequent in this order: among (1) spinsters, (2) women who marry late and have no or few children, and (3) women who have few children and do not nurse them. None of these seems to be a factor in the worldwide distribution of breast cancer, however. The rate at which people age may be a factor. One autopsy study at Johns Hopkins University showed conditions suspected of being precancerous in the breasts of almost every very old woman examined.

One of the more marked phenomena is the rarity of cancer of the uterine cervix among Jewish women, not only in Israel but elsewhere throughout the world. A Boston study indicated that these tumors are nine times as common among non-Jews as among Jews. The reason most often given for this is male circumcision among Jews. Some of the data and conclusions are disputed, however. A survey in Buffalo showed that most wives really do not know whether or not their husbands are circumcized (their answers to this question proved at variance with the results of physical examinations of the husbands in a high percentage of cases). A series of physical examinations showed that men too are often wrong in statements as to whether or not they have been circumcized—in many cases the surgery of the religious ritual is of a token nature and does not constitute complete circumcision. Other investigators have found that carcinogens (chemicals which cause cancer when applied to animals) do exist in the smegma which collects under the prepuce of men who do not cleanse themselves thoroughly and regularly. It is possible that feminine hygiene and sexual abstinence during and after menstrual periods, as required by religious law, may account for the depressed rate of cervical cancer among Jewish women.

Researchers have reported that cancer of the prostate is relatively rare and of the penis nonexistent among Jewish men in New York. While circumcision may account for the latter, answers probably lie elsewhere for prostatic cancer's absence.

An investigation of 84,341 white men and women who died in New York between 1953 and 1958 showed that Jewish men had less than the normal frequency of cancers of the mouth, pharynx, esophagus, gallbladder, larynx, lung, prostate, skin, and genitalia and a higher than normal incidence of cancers of the large intestine, kidney, brain, thyroid, lymphatic tissues (including leukemia and Hodgkin's disease), and breast. The same study indicated a much lower than normal uterine cervical cancer rate and higher than normal incidence of cancer of the liver and pancreas among Jewish women. While Jews had a low incidence of skin cancer generally, they had more melanoma, the pigmented cancer which often arises from dark moles, than was found among other New Yorkers.

Cervical cancer shows both a religious and a racial partisanship; but it is difficult to consider this an example of biological bias or privilege. Studies have shown that the uterine cervix disease is almost nonexistent among Roman Catholic nuns and unusually high among American Negroes. While cervical cancers decreased about 50 per cent among American white women between 1930 and 1960, it relented only 25 per cent among Negro women. Part of the answer to this probably lies in the field of trauma— the unrepaired uterine injuries involved in reproduction may lead to cancer.

Stomach cancer is unusually common in Iceland, Chile, Japan, the Scandinavian countries, and Northern Russia. One-half of all cancers in men are of the stomach in some areas. What do these regions have in common? Hot food and drinks—and these are the causes, some say. Others say fish; and still others say smoked food. A few have wondered whether the sharp changes in seasons—ulcers act up most during season changes— might have something to do with this startlingly high cancer rate. Still others feel that poor diets may be the cause.

The Navajo Indians have been reported remarkably free of almost all kinds of cancer. One reason for this is that they die young—lacking modern medicine, hygiene, and sanitation, they are less than 50 per cent as successful as their white neighbors in attaining the age of forty-five years. For those Navajoes who die older than forty-five, the cause-of-death statistics are very unreliable—one investigator found that death certificates in more than one-half of the cases were signed by physicians who had not attended the patients.

Cancer of the esophagus poses several riddles: In Curaçao it comprises 10 per cent of all cancers, in Cuba 1.47 per cent, and in Jamaica and Venezuela less than 1 per cent. In India it is four times as common as stomach cancer; in the United States the reverse is true. In Curaçao and the Caribbean it affects three men to every two women; among Bantus, fourteen men to every woman. Where is the common denominator among the victims—and among the resistant?

In Southern and Western parts of Africa, liver cancer comes early in life and is very common; 90 per cent of all cancers in some Bantu tribes are of the liver. Dr. Paul E. Steiner found that under the microscope African liver cancers were the same as liver cancers among white residents of Chicago or Philadelphia. In Africa, however, the black victims died at an average age of 37.6 years—two decades younger than the average Caucasian liver cancer patient either in the United States or in Africa. The most frequent guess is that this is due in large part to inadequate diets, which injure the liver directly and impair the liver's normal regulation of hormones (many worn-out hormones are dismantled in the liver) and production of infection-resisting chemicals. In areas which have become industrialized, there have been improvements of the diet, and doctors now are seeing less liver cancer and more hyperthyroidism, diabetes, peptic ulcer, heart disease, and hypertension. One cannot avoid the thought that with continued improvement in living standards, Africans and others now subject to cirrhosis and liver cancer may live long enough to develop a variety of cancers. Some sources have said that the African areas—including Algeria, Senegal, Sudan and Southern Rhodesia—are part of a "liver cancer belt," which also encompasses Java, Indonesia, China, Japan, and Korea.

Cancers of the pharynx, nose, and mouth are common in China and a few other Asiatic areas. Some of these have been attributed to chewing betelnut, inverse smoking (with the lighted end of the cigar in the mouth) or sucking a mixture of lime and tobacco. Similar cancers abound in Scandinavians, especially Swedish women who have never heard of betelnut or inverse smoking.

Many other geographical concentrations of various kinds of cancer have been reported. The basic data range from fairly reliable to completely undependable. And the proposed rationales range from logically plausible to highly improbable.

The apparently high incidence of thyroid cancer in the goiter belts of the world logically may be due to iodine deficiencies. Cancers of the belly skin reasonably are laid to the comforts of kangri, the wicker baskets of glowing charcoal worn by Kashmir natives. Other skin cancers appear to be caused by stove couches, called *kairo* in Japan and *kang* in China.

Something in poverty—would it be early marriage?—brings cervical cancer to the poor, according to a dozen surveys from Tata Memorial Hospital, Bombay, to Memorial Cancer Center, New York. And something in riches—could it be late maturity and marriage?—makes breast cancer prevalent among the well-to-do. To some degree virtually all populations reflect a parallel to the statistical situation in India, where one-half of all cancers among Hindu women (who are poor and marry early) are of the uterine cervix, while one-half of all cancers among Parsee women (who are better off financially, and marry at a later age) are of the breast.

Dr. Walter B. Quisenberry of the Hawaii State Department of Health has reported intriguing observations of the mixed population of his state. Hawaii's population ethnically is 35 per cent Japanese, 23 per cent Caucasian, 18 per cent full or part Hawaiian, 12 per cent Filipino, 6 per cent Chinese, and 6 per cent Samoan, Korean, Puerto Rican, and other national derivations. This conglomeration of racial and national offshoots show these predilections for various kinds of cancer: Stomach cancer is high among Japanese (possibly due to their low socioeconomic status and typical Japanese diet); liver, high among Filipinos (who subsist on a diet high in carbohydrates and low in vitamin B_1); lung, low among Japanese and Filipino men, who are relatively light smokers; breast, five times as low among Japanese women as among other female citizens (Japanese women nurse their infants); large intestine, most frequent among Caucasian women (due, possibly, to their diet and bowel habits); prostate, nine times as frequent among Caucasian as Japanese men (attributed by one source to the regularity with which Japanese men make love and their early mating habits); nasopharynx, high among Chinese who drink often and copiously of hot teas; uterine cervix, most common among Hawaiian and part-Hawaiian women who have poor medical care during and after pregnancy.

In Sumatra, the Chinese and Javanese laborers do the same work, eat much the same rice diets, and live side by side. The Chinese develop much stomach cancer and many ulcers, and the Javanese show very little of either. Does cancer here show an ethnic bias? Or genetic? Is it a matter of temperament?

Or is stomach cancer a dietary affair? This disease is 50 per cent more frequent in Newfoundland, where salt cod is a favorite dish, than in Canada generally.

Early reports from Egypt indicated that the annual cancer death rates per 100,000 populations were: 14.5 for native Egyptians, 16.3 for Moslems, 64.8 for Egypt-born Italians, 80.5 for Christians, and 187.4 for Jews. If there is any accuracy at all to these figures (and, because Egypt did not require a registry of deaths at the time these studies were made, the data may be completely unreliable) there still is no logical conclusion that can be drawn from them.

White United States war veterans showed a high incidence of cancers of exposed areas of the skin (8.45 per cent of all cancers) and Negro veterans very little (0.6 per cent); but the percentages for cancers of unexposed skin areas are reversed completely—0.8 per cent in whites and 9.78 per cent in Negro veterans. Skin sensitivity to sunlight might explain the former phenomenon; but what accounts for the latter?

Scientists at Roswell Park Memorial Institute have studied the cancer incidence in the cosmopolitan population of Buffalo, New York, with emphasis on immigrants from Poland, Italy and Germany, as well as American-born patients. They found that cancers of the stomach, lung, and esophagus were higher in the foreign-born than natives, that Polish-American males were abnormally susceptible to cancer of these three sites, while Italian-Americans were prone to cancers of the bladder, pharynx, and colon, and that German-Americans showed no special susceptibility to any tumor type.

Some relations with socioeconomic status came to light in the Buffalo studies. The poorer the man, the more susceptible he was to cancers of the stomach, liver, esophagus, lung, and larynx; and the poorer the woman, the more prone she was to cancers of the stomach, liver, and cervix. Rich and poor were equally susceptible to cancers of the mouth, bowel, pancreas, body of the uterus, ovary and prostate. Poverty seemed to show only one virtue in these studies—it protected to some degree against cancer of the female breast. Other studies have shown that American Negroes, generally with less socioeconomic status than white citizens, have about 30 per cent less stomach cancer than white people. American Negroes also have less leukemia and cancers of the breast, bladder, lung, and thyroid than American whites but more cancer of the uterus and mouth.

Buffalo urban dwellers have more cancer than do nearby rural people. This is especially true among city men, who show these excesses over country men: Cancer generally 27 per cent, cancer of the esophagus 82 per cent, stomach 10 per cent, lung 37 per cent, larynx 30 per cent, urinary organs 43 per cent, and leukemia 33 per cent. Buffalo city women have only a 15 per cent excess of cancer over rural women; and these sites account for the difference: mouth and pharynx 24 per cent more, digestive system 18 per cent, lung 33 per cent, breast 12 per cent, genital organs 13 per cent, kidney 53 per cent, bladder 21 per cent, skin 13 per cent, and leukemia 10 per cent.

Cancer death rates, generally, are on the rise throughout the world.

This is not true of cancers of specific sites, however. In one area of the world, one kind of cancer will relent while the same cancer pursues its upward trend everywhere else. Sometimes several kinds of cancer will plateau or diminish in the face of a general spurt upward by cancer.

During the past thirty years, deaths from cancer of the uterus have diminished gradually in the United States, England, and Wales. During this same period, mortality from cancer of the breast has remained remarkably steady in these same countries, while cancer of the prostate deaths have risen more or less sporadically. Deaths from leukemia and cancer of the pancreas have risen in males and females almost everywhere; and male deaths from lung cancer have soared. Intestinal cancer deaths have risen rapidly in American Negroes, gone up slowly in American whites, and dropped in England and Wales. In the United States, deaths from liver cancer have decreased almost 50 per cent and from stomach cancer, a big killer, also about 50 per cent in thirty years.

And nobody knows why.

CHAPTER 4

ENVIRONMENT
AND CANCER

Our recent kaleidoscopic passage into four profoundly revolutionary eras
—Industrial, Air, Atomic and Space—has brought with it a host of headaches. Before we had time to adjust to one ephemeral environment, another age was upon us.

Some of the major problems of our accelerating history lie in the
field of public health; among these is the influence of the changing environment on human cancer. This is an area of numerous and formidable
unknown quanities. Enough is known, however, to indicate that we live
in a sea of carcinogens—cancer causers; some of them are natural and
long familiar, while others are the man-made products of modern times.
They are in the food we eat, the water and beverages we drink, the air we
breathe, the habits we develop, the jobs we hold, the drugs and medical
treatments we take, in radiations from the heavens above and the earth
below. They may be inside us—in the mechanics of our emotions, in
the hormones we produce or fail to produce, in our inherited or acci-
dentally disturbed cell chemistry, perhaps even in the cumulative chemical
and physical traumata incurred in the process of growing up and growing
old.

There have been research efforts to identify these dangers and to eliminate
them, but so far the efforts have been weak and, except in a few notable
instances, ineffectual. Laws have been strengthened to ban some carcinogens from commercial products and bar them from natural resources;
but, as against the dizzying pace of developments, current statutes and en-

forcement agencies have fallen farther and farther behind the needs of the times.

It must be made clear at the outset that the evidence against any single substance as causing human cancer is strictly circumstantial. No one yet has taken two or more large groups of matched humans, used some as unexposed controls, and deliberately applied the suspect agents to the others in prescribed doses over set periods.

Circumstantial evidence of cancer causation is available. It is based on human statistical data, animal tests, and chemical structure; and it is regarded by various people as convincing, speculative, or irrelevant, depending on whether they are selling or buying a suspect carcinogen, whether they are naturally credulous, reasonable, skeptical, or cynical and, of course, whether they really know the evidence and can evaluate it. Courts of law, however, regularly send men to the gallows or electric chair on circumstantial evidence more tenuous than the case against some suspect carcinogens still peddled freely and unlabeled on the open market.

Something—or, more likely, some combination of things—causes a large variety of cancer in millions of people each year; regardless of the complexities of the question of carcinogens, the problem is one of deadly reality.

Two sets of circumstances help to confound the issue of what causes cancer in people.

One is human—the honest inability of equally qualified experts to agree on the validity or interpretation of evidence, the pressures and propaganda of industries to protect themselves and their products, and the natural tendency of scientists to surrender to or bitterly resist the pressures. A few researchers have been forced to resign their positions because their findings were unfavorable to an influential industry or product, but their colleagues sometimes argue as to whether true persecution or the scientists' paranoid evangelism was at the root of these incidents.

The second difficulty lies with the suspect substances themselves. It is difficult to ascertain what constitutes a real danger to humans. What is a carcinogen for the goose is not necessarily a carcinogen for the gander. Some carcinogens cause cancers in 80 or 90 per cent of one sex of, let us say, rats and virtually no cancers in littermates of the opposite sex.

Some carcinogens produce a variety of tumors in several species and none at all in others. Some affect only one organ in one species; others attack almost any tissue in several species. And even though a carcinogen induces tumors in a wide variety of mice, rats, dogs, cats, rabbits, guinea pigs, flies, cockroaches, sunflowers, fish, and chickens, almost invariably a few organisms escape. Except in highly inbred strains, susceptibility to cancer varies as much as or more than the carcinogenic agents themselves.

The route of administration—by mouth, or injection into vein, skin, artery or belly cavity, or painting on the skin—is important. Some carcinogens act only if administered in a certain way; others will cause different kinds of cancer when given by different routes.

Some carcinogens act alone. Some must work together. Many must be dissolved in natural fats, oils, or water to take effect; and some are carcinogenic only when altered by body chemistry. Some have an additive effect —that is, two or more of them pool their potency. Some have a synergistic, or multiplying, effect—one may make another five or ten times as potent as it normally is. And in a few combinations, one may cancel out the effects of another. Some carcinogens even suppress the growth of cancers; in a few instances they have been used as anticancer drugs in humans. One class of anticancer drug (aminostilbenes) was tested by British scientists because of its clinical usefulness—and found to be carcinogenic; and another known carcinogen, urethane, was found by the same group to be a good anticancer drug. Both drugs poison the system and have the physiological effect of dietary restriction.

Some carcinogens need something else (itself noncarcinogenic) to promote their action. Creosote and croton oil sometimes are promoters even when they are applied long after the carcinogen. Some chemicals act in concert with physical or chemical injury, cold, heat, growth, aging, genes, hormones, viruses, rays, vitamins or enzymes; and some are inactive unless there is a deficiency of a vitamin, hormone or enzyme.

Carcinogens may have a cumulative effect—lifetime exposure is the thing to be considered, not necessarily a brief encounter. Within the very recent past, however, scientists have built up a resistance to some animal cancers with small doses of the carcinogen prior to the cancer-causing dose; and others have destroyed incipient cancers with enormous doses of the very virus which caused them.

Some of the foremost absurdities in the broad and fertile field of medical fantasy center around carcinogens. They range from soothing assurances by manufacturers and vendors of commercial products to ridiculous declarations by alarmists; from panic printed in public periodicals to childish secrecy—supposedly panic-preventing—by scientists and health agencies. Buck-passing by timid or security-conscious spokesmen who urge the public to consult the family physician (who rarely reviews the broad spectrum of medical and scientific literature), and outbursts by politicians who find ignorance no restraint on oratory have not helped the situation. Much of the polemics is done with bitterness, whether it be a woman inveighing against the perils of aluminum cooking vessels or a researcher propounding his views on protecting the public from disclosure of established scientific fact.

It is unfortunate that there are no practical Marquis of Queensbury rules and no responsible referee—and no prospect of either—in the free-for-alls involving not only carcinogens but also the validity of cancer detection tests and treatments. The most notable instance of Federal action against a carcinogen was in the famous tainted cranberry episode, in which the government's intemperate blast in a naive press against a group of defiant growers had unfortunate consequences. The episode did not win the confidence of the public or the respect of science and medicine.

Referees would be asked to resolve many basic questions on the nature of cancer and carcinogens. One of the most elementary is: what is cancer? Certain common dyes cause bladder cancer in man. The cancers kill, but often they do not metastasize—that is, "seed" or spread to tissues near to and far from the original tumor. Inasmuch as virtually all definitions require that cancer invade and metastasize, is a deadly bladder tumor really cancer? And are the dyes that cause it really carcinogens? Decisions would profoundly affect the classification of several cancers (most commonly, basal-cell skin cancers which usually do not metastasize) and many carcinogens (one authority lists asphalt, coal tar, uranium, nickel, chromates, shale oil, hydrogenated coffee soot, and 3,4-benzypyrene as producing, infiltrating and destructive, but usually nonmetastasizing, cancers).

The problem of preventing exposure to carcinogens hinges on identifying the malignant components of molecules and similarities of biochemical behavior. Is there a "common denominator" among carcinogens? Are all carcinogens chronic irritants? Do all of them mutate body cells? Do the molecules contain areas of unsatisfied valence? Do they bind with proteins and delete them from cells? Do they alter cell metabolism from an oxidative toward a fermentative type of chemistry? Do they or their oxidized products fluoresce or sensitize tissues to light? Do they polymerize cell chemicals—that is, do molehill molecules pile up into mountain molecules by a process similar to that followed in producing plastics? Do they suppress body growth and natural immunity? Are they allergens? Eminent men of science espouse each of these demonstrated or postulated facets of carcinogenesis; equally eminent authorities dispute them. If it could be firmly established that any single theory truly represents the basic mechanism of all cancer production, the road to prevention—and possibly to cure as well—would be shortened.

Important clues to cancer causes could lie in a number of other vague and relatively unexplored areas.

Is there, for instance, such a thing as a "house of cancer"—a house in which an inordinate number of cancer deaths have occurred? There are a number of these eerie residences in which all or almost all the succession of unrelated tenant families for a half-century or more lost at least one member to cancer. Is this sheer coincidence? Or is there something in the structure, the grounds, the air, or the water which is conducive to cancer? In most instances the victims die of cancers of different organs.

Is it mere coincidence that in the class of 1940 of one Maryland high school of 400 students, seven developed leukemia and died of it within a decade? That all victims lived on the same street and sat near one another in class? And three more classmates died of cancers related to leukemia?

A few studies have correlated soil types with cancer deaths. In England, researchers found cancer rates highest in low-lying clay areas seasonally overflowed by the river and lowest rates in high areas. Netherlands investigators found cancer cases concentrated in this order: in peat areas, sea clay, cover sand, sand, and river clay soils. French and Soviet studies showed cancer to be highest in soils rich in magnesium. And a preliminary survey of the United States indicated cancer was most concentrated in areas of high background radiation—the investigator was so taken by the coincidence that he believed he might be able to find uranium deposits in areas having high cancer rates.

Only a good deal more study will indicate whether there is any validity to these impressions. As of this writing the observations belong in the interesting-if-true type of conjecture.

Carcinogens have been recognized for almost 200 years, ever since scrotal cancer in London chimney sweeps was traced to soot.

About thirty years ago, Dr. Riojun Kinosita, then of Osaka University and now of the City of Hope, Duarte, California, opened a new era in cancer investigation by showing that a well-identified food additive of known molecular structure could cause internal cancer. He fed rats butter yellow, and the animals developed liver cancer. For an embarrassingly long time, European and American scientists failed to confirm Dr. Kinosita's highly significant results. It occurred to Dr. Harold Rusch of the University of Wisconsin that a difference in the diet might be at fault—Dr. Kinosita had fed his animals polished rice which is deficient in riboflavin. When Dr. Rusch made his rats riboflavin-deficient and fed them butter yellow, these animals readily developed cancer. The work thus added two more important observations on environmental cancer: (1) butter yellow (or azo dye, as it is known) probably interferes with, or displaces, a vitamin in cell chemistry, and (2) a vitamin deficiency in some way is involved, in some instances, in the basic mechanisms of malignancy.

Many new carcinogens have been identified since Dr. Kinosita's classical work. Some of them are among the 800 artificial chemicals in common use and possibly among the fifty or so introduced each year to the public. The great majority of them are called carcinogens because they cause cancers in experimental animals; most independent scientists in the field consider positive animal tests prima facie evidence of a potential danger to man.

Some of the carcinogens are generally tolerated as a human hazard or, at best, incite only a mild academic debate. These include chimney soot, excessive sunshine, massive or repeated burning, freezing with liquid nitrogen and infection with the blood fluke, *Schistosoma hematobium*. One common denominator among these agents—the one which may discourage heated debate—is the fact that they are not commercial products. Massive or repeated injury, which has been shown to speed the growth of existing cancers but, by itself alone, not to cause cancer, is argued vigorously but only in the courts—with the plaintiff for cancer damages losing more than nine times out of ten.

The path to scientific proof has many pitfalls. Sometimes the statistics are deceptive. For instance, an appallingly high lung-cancer rate is said to prevail around Anaconda, Montana, where copper smelting is virtually the sole industry. Part of the answer could be that the State Tuberculosis Sanitarium, housing patients with many respiratory diseases, happens to be located in the same county. Suspect chemicals have been called toxic or carcinogenic on the basis of uncontrolled animal tests, but a properly conducted experiment might have shown that noninoculated control animals died at the same time in the same way. Culpability of a chemical sometimes is as difficult to prove in retrospect as to predict in advance, because almost invariably the carcinogen has disappeared from the tissue by the time cancer is detectable.

Some theories can be no more reliable than sheer guesses. Some thought many years ago that pessaries, used to prevent conception, might cause uterine cancer. They pointed to the fact that scientists at Johns Hopkins Hospital, by inverting the womb of experimental monkeys and causing a menstrual backflow, had induced endometriosis, in which the trapped uterine lining grew in a malignant manner and invaded most of the pelvic organs. During the last two or three decades of increasing use of pessaries the United States death rate from uterine cervical cancer has gone down by about 50 per cent, and for at least a half-dozen years oral contraceptives seem to have decreased the cervical cancer rate among closely observed populations.

There is obvious validity to the claims of industry that if we were to abandon absolutely the use of all carcinogens, life would become dreary. We would not have, as we know them, paved roads, synthetic automobile tires, oil and gasoline, plastics of many descriptions, many of the metals and alloys in common usage, pesticides, insecticides, fertilizers, cosmetics, detergents, drugs, foods, dyes, and many other essentials as well as time-savers, luxuries, and comforts of modern life. An absolute ban on carcinogens would close down many industries because of the exposure of workers to plant chemicals and of the public to nonradioactive fallout belching from the smokestacks of coke, steel, and chemical plants.

Cancerophobia is a common form of hypochondria; and hypochondria often involves bizarre behavior. The complete hypochondriac might not keep a dog, because these pets can transmit toxoplasma, staphylococcus, and other pathogenic organisms to humans. He might not travel by air if there were a fear (often present in hypochondriacs) of coronary artery troubles, high blood pressure, respiratory disease, anemia, and other conditions for which flying is contraindicated. He might not swim in pools because of contamination, nor in the sea for fear of sharks. He would have difficulty selecting the proper climate—what is beneficial for one disease state usually is bad for another. He probably would find it impossible to dodge the diseases indigenous to his ethnic origins and socio-economic status. The complete hypochondriac has his troubles.

The complete hypochondriac, however, conceivably might outlive the complete daredevil who doesn't distinguish between commercial claims and scientific findings, who blithely dismisses suggestions of potential danger in fallout as pure political propaganda, and who doesn't care much about precautionary labels one way or another.

Some scientists employed or financed by industrial and commercial enterprises have argued variously that (1) statistical or epidemiologic evidence is not proof of the carcinogenicity of a substance, (2) the induction of cancers in experimental animals is not necessarily proof of a health hazard to humans, (3) in the absence of epidemiologic, biological, and chemical evidence of toxicity or carcinogenicity, products should be presumed safe, and (4) in the presence of acceptable proof of carcinogenicity in laboratory animals, there is no harm in "safe doses" for humans. The burden of proof usually is on the public. And so are the costs, in terms of cancer, if the assurances prove ill-founded.

The American Medical Association, in a long uphill and partly successful fight to compel producers to label poisonous chemicals (for one reason, so that the proper antidote can be prescribed in an emergency) ran into vigorous opposition on the grounds that (1) trade secrets would be violated, (2) warning statements are a psychological handicap to sales, and (3) children, who are frequent victims, can't read. The AMA also found that some products were falsely labeled as safe; and, in some cases where labeling was required on products for domestic use, the exported products, unlabeled, were of an inferior grade.

There is no reason to believe that the problem of carcinogens would stir industry's conscience more than the effort to combat toxicity did.

Carcinogens, as a rule, are not considered poisons; carcinogenic doses can be and often are without immediate toxic effects. Laws which govern a poison (defined technically as a substance which in certain doses kills 50 per cent or more of experimental rats within two weeks) cannot apply to carcinogens. Some carcinogens take anywhere from twenty to forty-five years following initial exposure to produce cancers in humans; and some of them have been shown in laboratory animals to be much more potent when administered in small doses over a long period than when the sum of the doses is given in a single large one.

Independent scientists engaged in testing substances for carcinogenicity do not agree often with industrial spokesmen—they advocate more caution before introducing potentially harmful substances on the market. They feel that if the substance serves no useful purpose other than the profits accruing to the producers and sellers it should be withheld until proved safe. Some believe that, even when the substance is useful and no practical and harmless substitute exists, suspicions of carcinogenicity should be resolved before the public is exposed.

Many who test carcinogens question the existence of a "safe" dose. Like the industrial consultants, independent scientists feel that animal tests don't necessarily indicate the degree of danger to man. Their reservations usually are on the conservative or cautious side, however; they point out that arsenic, virtually noncarcinogenic to laboratory animals, is a potent carcinogen in man. They say that dyes which are known to cause bladder cancer in man are weak carcinogens in animals, inducing bladder cancer only in dogs, liver cancer in mice, and generally no tumors in other species. They stress the point that, unlike poisons whose impact usually wears off, the effects of carcinogens are cumulative and irreversible —the first malignant cell may mark the point of no return.

Dr. Wilhelm C. Hueper, a vigorously public-spirited government authority on environmental carcinogens, doesn't think highly of the "safe dose" philosophy. He has said, "The control of environmental cancer hazards could easily be made, by the adoption of a 'safe dose' of carcinogens, into a lottery of human lives." Prof. Eric Boyland, an eminent authority from the Chester Beatty Research Institute in London, feels that "the principal that there is no safe dose is the only prudent one, because it would be impossible to determine this level even if it existed."

Laws designed to protect the public against toxic substances and carcinogens gradually have been strengthened, although they still honor "safe doses." The Food and Drug Law amendments now include a provision that "no additive shall be deemed to be safe if it is found to induce cancer when *ingested* by man or animal, or if it is found, after tests which are appropriate for the evaluation of the safety of food additives, to induce cancer in man or animal." Some independent scientists feel the law is weak—they regard carcinogens as dangerous if they cause cancer when applied by means other than ingestion.

There are dissenting views, a few of them expressed by scientists of some stature in the field of industrial health.

Dr. R. E. Eckardt, director of the Medical Research Division of the Esso Research and Engineering Company, has protested that "there are no magic formulas, no crystal balls, or simple slide rules that will permit the public health official to come up with the answer to the question of whether a given compound will present a cancer hazard to the general public if it is permitted to enter the food supply." He has argued that in the field of food additives—contrary to experience in the oil industry, where animal experiments have helped detect and eliminate hazards—carcinogens must be evaluated "with judgment and wisdom" with regard to the compound's chemical nature, probable concentrations in the food supply, known biological effects in animals, metabolic pathways in man and animals and importance in food technology. He feels that the production of animal cancers by injection is not good evidence that the substance is risky when eaten or inhaled by humans. The law agrees with him by and large.

Dr. Eckardt has cited the need for "vastly expanded" programs of research on carcinogenic mechanisms in animals and epidemiological studies in man. The broad-scale animals investigation, he estimates, would take at least ten years, the human studies perhaps twenty or more. "Until the data are clear-cut and a solution has been found—i.e., either control of the material or its elimination—publicity through newspapers, congressional committees or other types of non-scientific releases can hope to accomplish no useful objective," he has admonished scientists in the journal, *Cancer Research*.

With environmental hazards mounting and cancer deaths increasing, ten or twenty or more years is a long time for the public to wait for warnings of potentially dangerous exposures. Many, in that time, may be done to death by agents they could have avoided had they been cautioned against them. Dr. Eckardt, however, proposes this solution: "Until such time as our knowledge in this field has been vastly increased by the above studies, our effort should be to limit, as far as *practical,* not as far as *possible,* exposure to carcinogens by routes in man which the available experimental evidence in animals by comparable routes suggests might present a hazard to man." He concludes that "if such interim decisions are reached in good faith, with neither hysterical over-concern or complacent under-concern, there is little likelihood that an epidemic-like occurrence of cancers will result in 10–30 years."

For some time cancer has been epidemic, and the epidemic is growing. It seems hardly reasonable to ask the public and Congress to let industry and business have their way, unmolested by the press or governmental inquiry, for an entire human generation.

Unfortunately, there is not enough scientific manpower, enough time, enough money or enough facilities to test more than a minuscule portion of the hundreds of new products constantly coming on the market. The available scientists and their facilities are completely occupied in efforts to determine the possible carcinogenicity of single substances. The infinitely more important question of multiple carcinogens—their additive, synergistic and, to perhaps a small degree, neutralizing effects—concern very few scientists, probably because it is impossible to test any appreciable fraction of the countless combinations. The fact is that the average person is exposed constantly not so much to a single carcinogen but to multiples of them.

CHAPTER 5

FOOD AND CANCER

A few years ago fish became the beneficiaries of technological advances in the science of nutrition. Rainbow trout in United States hatcheries were given a cleverly concocted diet containing traces of arsenicals designed to destroy disease-causing amoebas, sulfa drugs to do away with other infections, oxidized fatty acids, vitamin supplements, and cheap vegetable protein instead of more costly meat protein.

In 1960 scientists were appalled: 80 or 90 per cent of the brood trout kept in hatcheries for three years had developed liver and lung cancer. Fish as young as six or eight months old were coming down with the disease. At this writing, the culpable agent has not been identified. The epidemic could be due to a combination of dietary chemicals, each by itself incapable of promoting cancer to any great degree.

Scientists who have studied this strange situation regard the episode with concern. They say it could happen to humans exposed en masse to untested technical "advances" in nutrition.

Because the victims were fish and no considerable commercial element was involved, the solution was easy. The diet was changed; suspect substances were removed from it. The epidemic subsided.

Dr. Hueper, one of the National Cancer Institute scientists who investigated the matter, pointed out that some elements of the human diet parallel those fed the fish and have been shown in laboratory tests to be carcinogenic. He cited as examples of both accidental and deliberate carcinogens in human food—some of them now restricted or banned— arsenic and such chlorinated hydrocarbon pesticides as DDT and aramite; fungicides like thiourea and thioacetamide; the sweetening agent, phenetyl urea (Dulcin); the flavoring agent, safrol; selenium, a contaminant; and food dyes like oil orange E, oil yellow HA, and butter yellow.

"The occurrence of a catastrophic cancer epidemic among rainbow trout," Dr. Hueper said, "should provide a most forceful stimulus for organizing comprehensive epidemiologic studies on the incidence and site distribution of cancers in human populations especially strongly exposed, for some reason, to the various dietary carcinogens."

In contrast to much of the rest of the world which is still stalked by hunger, nutritional deficiencies, and stark starvation, the United States is richly fed—perhaps overfed. Its fertile lands and superb agricultural and food-processing technology enable the nation not only to feed its own citizens and many millions overseas but to pay food producers handsomely not to grow more than can be marketed.

The secrets of American success are many: spacious and fertile lands, a varied climate, constantly improving conservation practices, mechanization, water, storage, pest and disease control, plant and animal breeding, and, at this writing, industry's expenditure of more than $100 million a year in the development of new food products.

Animals and plants which provide $80 billion worth of food in this age of technology are mated and mutated by geneticists to bring out their best qualities. They are protected from crowding, overabundance, and waste by economists. Engineers shield them from flood and drought, and geologists tease new water supplies out of the earth for them. They are protected against disease, predatory insects and pests by a great array of chemicals. Their earth, enriched with fertilizers, yields ten times the growth possible under primitive farming methods. Their natural beauty and esthetic appeal are maintained with antiaging compounds and enhanced with dyes. They are preserved against decay by freezing, canning, packaging and organism-resisting chemicals. In texture, taste, scent, composition, appearance, and enduring freshness, the seven or eight thousand different articles on the supermarket shelves represent a triumph of human ingenuity as well as a mark of nature's bounty. Two-thirds of these products—increasing at the rate of about twenty-four a day—did not exist fifteen years ago.

By contrast with food-providing and money-making animals, wild creatures have begun to disappear. Pesticides and other chemicals considered essential to modern farm management have poisoned them.

Back in Reconstruction days, Dr. Harvey W. Wiley began to cry out against commercial contamination of the nation's food. His famous Federal "poisons squad" uncovered the use of many toxic substances in commercially processed foods—formaldehyde in milk, cocaine in soft drinks, improper preservatives in catsup and additives in meat as substitutes for good processing practices. Microbes, like those causing tuberculosis and botulism, were found in many foods. It took twenty-three years of energetic investigation and campaigning to finally persuade the government, under President Theodore Roosevelt in 1906, to pass the first Food and Drug Act.

The original law professed to protect all people against injurious food adulterants. Some leeway was allowed, however, if the toxic substances were added in doses tolerated by the young, the old, the weak, and the sick. The leeway was enough to encourage the rapidly changing food industry and various parts of it to maintain strong and constant pressure for relaxation of the act and to violate it when possible. A few strong-willed government employees, generally backed by the courts, held the poison peddlers more or less in check. They enforced as best they could the qualified provision of the 1938 Act that poisonous additives be kept out of food unless they were unavoidable or necessary and, when necessary, kept to a regulated minimum.

Some contaminants could not and cannot be avoided; many more than one million cases of food poisoning (*staphylococcus* and *salmonella* are probably the most common infectious agents) now are estimated to occur annually in the United States. While this figure can be reduced with more careful handling of food, it is unrealistic to believe food poisoning can be eliminated completely. Most of the agents get into the food in the kitchens of careless cooks.

Commissioner of Food and Drugs George P. Larrick, in 1957, urged strengthening and modernization of the law. He said:

We have had some very narrow escapes because of the use of additives that had no place in food. It is inconceivable that this country should continue to expose itself indefinitely to the risks inherent in the present scheme of food control.

He pointed out that the nation's change from an agricultural to an industrial society had made it necessary to transport food long distances and to store it for long periods. But, he insisted, the law should require adequate testing of a chemical before it is used in food.

Commissioner Larrick has said that there is no evidence that any food distributed in the United States "produces cancer when it is eaten." There is undeniable evidence, however, that some substances in human food—noncarcinogenic when fed—cause cancer when injected into animals.

Commissioner Larrick estimated a few years ago that about 400 chemicals were being used for various purposes in food production. He divided the additives into three categories—about 150 of them known to be harmless, another 100 considered "safe" in the quantities in which they are normally used, and the remaining 150 "a scientific no-man's land—our scientists do not know whether they are safe or not, but they suspect some of them ought not to be in use."

The Commissioner agreed with concerned consumers that questionable substances then in use should be tested for toxicity; but he also espoused the contrary contention of commercial interests that useful but poisonous additives should be permitted in foods in "safe tolerances." He took a dim view of legislative proposals that manufacturers be permitted to put a banned chemical on the market and sell it until the Food and Drug Administration succeeded in restraining them in federal courts—an action which might be decided, he said, by "which side has the cleverest lawyer."

While the Commissioner's acceptance of the idea of a "safe dose" of a poison did not please some consumers and scientists, he also gave little comfort to industrial groups like the National Canners Association, which declared itself "adamantly opposed to having any Federal agency determine what the American consumer likes or dislikes or what serves a useful purpose in any food."

In 1958 and 1960, Congress legislated amendments to the Food, Drug and Cosmetic Act which placed a ban on old and new risky additives in food and on substances shown to be carcinogenic when eaten by animals. The FDA was required to take into account the quantity and manner in which an additive is used, as well as its usefulness; FDA denials of marketing privileges could be appealed in Federal courts. The food industry, fearful of a "hard" enforcement policy, resented the indefiniteness of the law. Some scientists, sensing too "soft" an interpretation, also were concerned. No one seemed completely happy about the compromise, which protected neither the public nor what industry calls "free enterprise."

What are food additives? Most simply, they are anything added to food. Some additives are unintentional, more or less unavoidable and deplored by producer, seller, and consumer; these include pesticides, insecticides, fertilizer residues, and bacterial and viral contamination. Many additives are intentional and beneficial, like vitamins occasionally added to compensate for vitamins lost in processing food. Some, including many suspect substances which increase production, improve marketability and serve the producer's and sellers' purposes but are of doubtful value to consumers, are controversial. Then there are widely advertised "miracle ingredients" which often serve no purpose other than to enrich the producer at the expense of credulous consumers.

Additives are used as food stabilizers, preservatives, extenders, disinfectants, antioxidants, thickening, drying or wetting agents, tenderizers, emulsifiers, growth promoters, fumigants, herbicides, defoliants, fungicides, miticides, bleaches, antibiotics, sweeteners, conditioners, colors, and flavors. Foods incorporate plastics, enamels, films, plasticizers, and catalysts from their packages. Machinery oils, cleaners, detergents, metals, and many other adulterants also get into food, and sterilizing radiation and heat processes sometimes produce significant chemical changes in it.

Few of the adulterants or additives are ever in such concentration as to produce an immediate toxic reaction more serious than a transient digestive disturbance; but meal-after-meal exposure to traces of ten, twenty, or thirty different toxins at each sitting very conceivably could result during a lifetime of eating in a variety of chronic conditions. Some of the conditions are reversible; British scientists found, for example, that troublesome rashes and other allergic reactions of mysterious origin promptly disappeared when some patients stopped drinking penicillin-contaminated milk. (United States consumers technically are protected by a law which states that milk produced for 72 hours following the cow's injection with penicillin is nonmarketable.) Other chronic diseases, notably cancer, are insidious in onset and irreversible—once a cancer has started, it grows and spreads in the complete absence of the agent which caused it.

Ordinary and essential foods sometimes will cause cancer if they are given in a bizarre way or in fantastic amounts. Repeated injections of common table salt have induced cancers in mice, and a long-term diet composed chiefly of eggs has wrought cancers in a few chickens and mice.

On the other hand, very small doses of some carcinogens will quickly produce cancer in a predictable percentage of animals. Dr. Charles Huggins of the University of Chicago has induced with carcinogens what some call "instant cancer." After feeding rats a single trace (0.00035 ounce) of a laboratory chemical called DMBA (7,12-dimethtylbenz(a)anthracene), he noted these results: every rat developed breast cancer and died of it, the first tumors appearing in fourteen days after the fateful meal, the last in sixty days. A single large dose of another hydrocarbon, methylcholanthrene, did the same, but slower. So far as anyone knows, neither DMBA nor methylcholanthrene exists in human food; some of their hydrocarbon relatives do, but no one has proved them responsible for human cancers.

Animal experiments and human statistics have shown that excess weight leads to early death from many diseases, including cancer. Lean animals and people are the longest lived.

Simple dietary restriction has reduced the incidence of disease in colonies of cancer-susceptible mice and in others bearing transplanted or chemically induced tumors. A few human studies have indicated that proneness to cancer increases with weight; international observers have reported that among the rare advantages of living in wartime German-occupied Europe and the consequent reduction of calories was a reduction in cancer.

Among the diseases with which excess weight is associated are coronary atherosclerosis, diabetes, diseases of the gall bladder, degenerative arthritis, and hernia, as well as cancer. A study by the Society of Actuaries published in 1959 showed that one in every five American men older than twenty years is at least 10 per cent above average weight. It indicated that even younger men, succumbing to the urge to drive, rather than walk, to the corner drugstore are putting on excess weight, while older men are showing little interest in reducing the pot that tends to develop with increased age. Women, on the other hand, seem to be putting more and more effort into retaining their figures. The rewards and penalties for overweight may be reflected in two charts: One of them shows that women are living six or seven years longer than men; the other shows that while cancer death rates continue their sharp upward trend for men, they have just about leveled off for women.

Cancers must be fed, and they have gluttonous appetites. Several scientists have labeled food with radioactive atoms and traced it through the body's systems, tissues and cells. They have found that cancers commandeer a lion's share of the proteins, nucleic acids, fatty acids, carbohydrates and other dietary elements and use them to grow on; eventually, when the host's waning appetite fails to meet the needs of the large tumors, the cancers draw their nutrients from the host's tissues. This may be the reason why the fattest—and from the cancer's point of view, most generous—host becomes more and more emaciated. Even the forced feeding of patients in late stages of the disease produces only transient benefits, if any; a growing tumor's appetite is hard to satisfy. As one physician has put it: "In terminal patients, quite often, the only really healthy tissue is their tumor."

Dietary deficiencies have been implicated in the onset of some animal cancers. Lack of dietary riboflavin speeds the development of butter-yellow-induced liver cancer in rats; choline deficiency has caused fatty livers and in some instances liver cancers in rats and chickens; niacin deficiency has worked in concert with urethane to produce lung cancer in mice. On the other hand, tumors which develop spontaneously in fruit flies will not appear if there is a deficiency of biotin, pantothenic acid, niacin, or thiamin. Dr. William E. Smith and others at Fairleigh Dickinson University found that supplements of vitamin A acted as a promoting agent in one kind of mouse lung cancer (an epidermoid type induced with methylcholanthrene) but inhibited the development of another type (adenoma).

Other deficiencies, too, may contribute to cancer. Liver cancers have been induced by creating in laboratory animals a deficiency of methionine, a protein constituent. The deficiency is achieved most easily by feeding them an analogue, a false methionine called ethionine. Thyroid cancer is common in "goiter belts"—areas in which there is not enough iodine in the ground, water, and food, and iodine is not added to the diet. Some feel that the prevalence of cancer of the salivary glands in Chinese and Malayans may be due to general malnutrition and that liver disease in South Africa is traceable to meatless diets of cooked meal and sour milk.

There is no doubt that traces of suspect carcinogens are in all sorts of food in modern countries: plastics in packaged foods, hydrocarbons in seafood from polluted waters, naphthalenes applied to prevent premature fruit drop and potato and tomato germination, arsenicals in some wines, tween 60-type emulsifiers in bread, antioxidants in chewing gum, and dyes in candies.

Tannic acid, which has caused cancer when injected into experimental animals, is a natural component of tea, coffee and cocoa. Safrol, a now-banned ingredient of some soft drinks, has induced animal cancers.

Antibiotics, a few of which have been shown to cause animal cancers and many of which can put a sensitized person into shock, are commonly used to enhance the growth of livestock and poultry and to protect chilled and canned meats. Despite the law banning the marketing of milk from recently treated cows, antibiotics used against bovine mastitis do get into the human milk supply (one sampling in Glenville, Illinois, showed sensitizing doses of penicillin in from 3 to 10 per cent of the milk tested).

Male and female hormones are used liberally to enhance the growth and tissue texture of livestock and poultry; and these, in large and regular doses, have caused cancer in experimental animals. Some of the hormone pellets implanted in livestock release high doses of estrogen for six weeks; and estrogen—which exists naturally in small amounts in such foods as peanut butter, milk, eggs, liver, potatoes, yeast and honey—in regular doses may be risky for some humans, although they are beneficial and possibly even cancer-preventing when there is a clear-cut need for the hormone.

It is known that heating destroys some nutrients in foods. Frozen foods and vacuum-packed foods undergo chemical changes, but no one knows whether these actually constitute a hazard to health.

Even cooking meat at high temperatures for long periods has raised suspicions of cancer dangers. Meat oils and fats at extreme temperatures (over 615° F) form at least two hydrocarbons of the kind known to induce cancer in animals. Grease left in the skillet and used over and over again also forms hydrocarbons of a possibly carcinogenic nature. Dr. F. A. Kummerow of the University of Illinois has pointed out that in commercial frying operations, new oil is constantly added to previously used oil remaining in the vat. The mixture, he has shown, contains a substance which multiplies the effect of some carcinogens. He has warned that inasmuch as the cancer-promoting substance is absorbed by fried food and consumed, his laboratory findings "may be of significance to the human diet."

Water contamination ranks with food additives as a health problem. Unlike food, water resources are limited—they cannot be expanded or produced. Water can only be reused; now that this is being done on an increasing scale, it becomes dirtier with each day.

The Division of Water Supply and Pollution Control, U.S. Public Health Service, in 1960 published a summary of 286 reports from 36 states. In a single year 6,300,000 fish were killed by pollutants in 1,153 miles of river, 51 miles of lake and bay shore and 1,407 acres of lakes, reservoirs, and bays. Industrial wastes, then the principal culprit, was responsible for the deaths of 5,460,000 fish. Domestic sewage killed 287,000 and agricultural poisons 73,000.

One year later, in 1961, the toll had more than doubled—15 million fish had been killed by pollutants. In this report, industrial wastes were blamed for only 2.9 million fish deaths, while those killed by agricultural poisons totaled 5.6 million. By 1964, the nation was horrified by the wholesale slaughter of fish in the lower Mississippi; pesticides were blamed. Five per cent of the sole in some Puget Sound areas recently have been found to have cancers; the cause is unknown.

Of equal concern is the poisoning by pollutants of algae and other food for fish. Fish populations, some authorities feel, face extinction from starvation if not from the direct poisoning of themselves and their eggs.

And how about humans? There is no doubt that humans consume the contaminants. The average adult stores between 100 and 200 milligrams of DDT in his fat.

A Government expert, Dr. Harry E. Jordan, has expressed fears of the synergistic, or multiplying, action of these poisons. "An instance recently discovered in the field of insecticides is a case in point," he reported. "Malathion and EPN have been found to be many times more toxic when fed together to rats than was expected from their separate toxicities. There is also the possibility that infants, or pregnant mothers, or persons below par in health, or unduly fatigued, or undernourished may be more susceptible to a chronic toxic action than persons in a more nearly average state of health or activity."

The water pollutants are, many, dangerous, and increasing rapidly as growing industries and expanding populations demand more and more of this precious commodity. And some of them, including some detergents, cause cancer in animals. While the effects are not as apparent or dramatic as the occasional outbreaks of hepatitis caused by toilets draining into water supplies or the more frequent episodes in which water becomes nonpotable because of the stench of disinfectants and contaminants, the long-term results of chronic exposure may be much more serious. It must be remembered that cancer often takes five, ten, twenty or forty years to develop to the point where it becomes detectable.

The water pollution problem has been increasing rapidly with fast-growing industries dumping more and more cyanides, other complex and toxic chemicals, and now, despite controls, allowing radioactive materials to contaminate the streams. It is complicated by the widespread use of arsenicals and other toxic and carcinogenic farm substances which run off the land and the potent carcinogens in road and highway pavement which also are washed into streams.

More than three times as much synthetic detergent as soap now is being used. The detergents stubbornly resist the microorganisms and other agents which decompose soap into innocuous compounds. A detergent often is composed of a half-dozen or more different ingredients, some of them carcinogenic. Although detergents have been in common usage for less than two decades, their concentration in the drinking supply already has reached risky levels and their use still is mounting.

The population explosion already has made the water problem acute in many areas. An average of 30 inches of rainfall in the United States supplies 315 billion gallons a year for national use—plus, of course, much more which is dissipated in runoff or evaporation. The national need now is well over the available supply, with industry claiming more than 160 billion gallons, agriculture 141 and municipalities 22. In some other parts of the world, the water-scarcity problem is much greater.

In the United States the water supply problem can be kept under control for a long time to come by reusing this vital commodity. With reuse, however, the pollution problem becomes more intense.

Among the measures now being undertaken or considered are: (1) increasing the supply by seeding clouds and by desalting sea water (the latter at an estimated cost of from $1.75 to $2.80 per 1,000 gallons); (2) dams and, to prevent evaporation, thin layers of long chain fatty alcohols and other materials on the surface; (3) better urban and rural drainage systems; (4) improved treatment plants and systems; (5) new foaming and absorption methods of removing detergents; and (6) the use of perishable or disposable detergents—based on sugars rather than petroleums, for instance.

The problems of food additives and water pollution are alarming. A comforting statistic should be cited, however: Stomach cancer in the American male and female has declined about 50 per cent during thirty years of increasing food additives and water pollution; if this organ is a target of environmental carcinogens—and no one knows whether or not it is in humans—the effects of modern living are negative or even beneficial. The same can be said of liver cancer; among Americans, this too has been reduced to almost 50 per cent the rate that prevailed a generation ago. It is possible that both these decreases in stomach and liver cancer are due to increasing prosperity and production, and consequently, the better nutrition of the last thirty years.

No man can say for certain whether any or all the technological advances in providing food and water have caused a single case of human cancer. It goes without saying, however, that eating and drinking are lifelong and unbreakable habits; and immediate and considerable study should be given to the acute and long-term effects of modern food and drink on public health.

A start has been made on the problem. Initial investigation has brought forth some disturbing facts.

The Committee on Environmental Health Problems, established by the U.S. Public Health Service in 1961, expressed stern discontent with the safeguards of the nation's food and water supplies. Its Subcommittee on Milk and Food, after a brief but revealing survey, reported early in 1962: "Positive action is needed to stem the trend toward obsolescence of the food protection program in public health agencies, and thus keep pace with the developments in food science and technology. In contrast to the notable progress made in food sanitation during the first half of the twentieth century, this area of Government activity has now become the weakest link in the protection of the nation's food supply." It expressed distress at the rapid rise in acute food poisoning; and it cited the threat of chronic disease resulting from food contamination by insecticides, growth regulators in plants, hormones in animals, dust and fumes from the air, detergents from water, additives used in food formulation, chemicals leached from containers during storage or from faulty utensils during food preparation, and residues of cleaners or sanitizing agents. It professed "growing concern about the radionuclide contamination of milk and other foods by fallout from nuclear explosions, by-products of atomic reactors and residues of radioactive wastes" and added that "the determination of how and when chemicals may be used safely in relation to food is already a major public health problem, and it will become even more important in the future."

The Subcommittee on Water Supply and Pollution Control made these points: (1) many municipalities and industries have resisted constructing waste treatment works, regarding them as a benefit only to someone else downstream; (2) "the public has been allowed to retain too much of the outmoded 'water purifies itself every seven miles' philosophy;" (3) new technologies are producing complex new wastes and products beyond ability to treat or control them, or even detect their presence in water; (4) ground water, often used as a drinking supply, is being contaminated by sewage seepage as suburbs spring up; (5) along the coastal areas, sea water intrudes into the land as ground water is pumped out for use by new and growing communities; (6) in oil areas of the Midwest and Southwest, ground waters are becoming polluted by brine-disposal practices; (7) municipal waste treatments were designed for forty years ago— Chicago, for example, with the best treatment available, pours into the Illinois waterway every day 1,800 tons of sewage solids from one million people; (8) heat, produced by electric power generation, in some areas has reduced by one-half the ability of water to assimilate organic wastes; (9) with increasing demands for water by industry, agriculture and new communities, silt rises in streams, the menace of forest and brush fires increases, irrigation water—used over and over again—becomes laden with deleterious metals and other chemicals; and (10) with increased leisure, growing numbers of sportsmen pollute the waters in which they boat and fish—and in which fish are poisoned by human, industrial, and other wastes.

Thanks largely to the late Rachel Carson and her eloquent *Silent Spring,* an indictment against the indiscriminate use of pesticides, several official bodies have begun to look into the biological consequences of spreading hundreds of millions of pounds of toxic materials over 90,000,-000 acres. Hearings have been held; reports have been written. Some of the highly vocal critics have been silenced by awesome evidence of the disappearance of wild life from the air and the earth and under the waters. At this writing, however, virtually no corrective action has been taken.

Attention has been centered on the acute toxicity of insecticides, fungicides, and herbicides—the immediate and dramatic deaths due to about fifty pesticides now known to be deadly to various species. Even those who have long suspected pesticides as lethal agents have been astonished at their potency. Whereas endrin, for example, is undetectable in milk in concentrations of 10 parts per billion and anything less than that is considered a "safe dose," as little as 0.2 parts per billion have killed fish in laboratory experiments. In the lower Mississippi, when millions of fish were exterminated in 1964, the endrin content measured only 0.025 parts per billion of water.

Scarcely investigated and largely ignored are the very real possibilities that the chronic effects of pesticides—and of other additives, pollutants, and contaminants—may be just as lethal as the acute effects. They could cause cancer, a disease in which the genesis is difficult to trace.

Evidence that pesticides cause cancer is sketchy. It is sketchy because little research has been done in this area. Nevertheless, the few reports which have been made should be enough to alert public health officials to this possible hazard.

Drs. Joseph Song and William E. Harville of the University of Arkansas have succeeded in inducing liver cancer in two mouse strains by feeding them aldrin and dieldrin for a year. Drs. Karl H. Kolmeier and Edwin D. Bayrd of the Mayo Clinic have reported that a boy came down with acute myelogenous leukemia eight months after heavy exposure to an elm spray, and his mother, similarly exposed, developed the same disease after fifty-four months. The Mayo physicians reported that toxic exposure to hexachlorocyclohexane, another insecticide, triggered leukemia in two cousins eight months later.

The Life Sciences Panel of the President's Science Advisory Committee pointed out in 1963 that, though physicians can diagnose pesticide toxicity in acute asthma, "diagnosis is difficult in patients with nonspecific symptoms that may result from unsuspected contamination with pesticides." The panel found no federally sponsored research in the nonspecific effects of chronic exposure to minute amounts of insecticides, and it called for studies to determine the cancer-causing potential of insecticides and their synergism with many commonly used drugs.

At this time, it can be said flatly that food and water contents have not been proved to cause human cancer. The possibility just has not been investigated.

CHAPTER 6

DRUGS AND CANCER

Most "miracle drugs" are ushered in on a wave of public and professional enthusiasm. In time, the enthusiasm ebbs; it subsides gradually as the drug's limitations are recognized, or it collapses completely when the therapeutic dream turns into a nightmare of uncontemplated serious side effects.

This has been the history of most medicines introduced during the last generation. Dangers have been identified in the sulfas and antibiotics which have greatly reduced deaths from microbial infection, the anti-pyretics and analgesics which suppress fever and relieve some symptoms of headache, colds, neuralgia, etc., the tranquilizers, pep-up pills, thyroid suppressants, antimalarials, muscle relaxants, anticonvulsants, antihista-minics, bacteriostatics, diuretics, arsenicals, heavy metals, blood pressure depressants, cholesterol inhibitors, and an impressive list of anticancer preparations. Even aspirin can produce a bad reaction, especially in people with bronchial asthma or digestive-tract bleeding, although it serves a score or more of medicinal ends.

While many of these preparations still are indispensable to the comfort or survival of certain patients, the medical profession has learned through an unbroken series of sobering experiences that it can be injudicious and sometimes fatal to administer almost any drug without first diagnosing the disease and studying the patient. Self-medication is much more hazardous. Bad reactions are startlingly frequent; in 1962, 65 hospitals reported 2,745 cases involving 338 preparations.

Usually an untoward reaction is mild—a red spot or rash, scaling skin, a swollen lymph gland, stomach cramps, vomiting, a touch of temperature

45

or aching joints. Occasionally the reaction is serious—irreversible liver damage and jaundice, the widespread destruction of white blood cells needed to ward off infections, anemia due to red-cell destruction, peripheral neuritis, hemorrhaging of the kidneys or brain. And in some cases, it is rapidly fatal, as in anaphylactic shock when the circulatory system collapses.

Most mild reactions disappear when the drug is discontinued. Sometimes, when the blood or bone marrow is affected, sulfas or antibiotics must be given to conquer infections until the white blood cells are restored; cortisone may be injected to suppress inflammatory conditions; or more heroic measures are called for in shock and other severe sequelae.

The causes of most reactions are no better understood than the medication's mechanisms of healing. In allergic-type reactions, antibodies are believed to form against the drug or a product of it, free or bound to body chemicals; but sound proof of this is lacking. The mechanisms of shock, blindness, sensitivity to light, anemias, hemorrhage, liver damage, and many other reactions still are largely Nature's secrets.

One of the more difficult problems in epidemiology is: Is cancer sometimes iatrogenic? ("Iatrogenic" is another Greek-derived term meaning "doctor-induced" or "drug-induced.") Although there exists among scientists every shade of opinion, as in other areas of environmental studies, there is no general concurrence. A growing number of drugs are suspect, but, though the evidence against each preparation ranges variously from very strong to extremely weak, it is impossible to say with absolute conviction that any drug or procedure causes human cancer.

There is no reliable animal or chemical test which determines whether a substance—drug, food additive, or other compound—poses a cancer threat to man. Some scientists become suspicious of substances which are teratogenic, that is, when given to pregnant animals they cause malformations in the offspring. Because the monsters so produced seldom live long enough to develop cancer, one can only speculate on the synonymy of teratogen and carcinogen. If teratogens are indeed carcinogens, a vast number of chemicals commonly found in food, water, and drugs would be carcinogenic. Though several interesting efforts have been made to correlate carcinogenicity with certain atomic configurations and molecular structure, they too have not yet yielded a method of identifying carcinogens.

Even highly persuasive clinical observations offer no real proof of carcinogenicity. Early in 1964, two Australian physicians, Drs. H. J. Woodliff and Lesley Dougan of the Royal Perth Hospital, Perth, found that five of fifty-five adult acute leukemic patients they had studied had taken phenylbutazone for rheumatoid arthritis and other inflammatory conditions; and three other leukemics had taken the drug, but also had had radiotherapy. The report induced several physicians in the British Isles to comment that some of their acute leukemics also had been taking phenylbutazone before coming down with blood disorders. Only a good deal more investigation and evidence will indicate whether suspicions of phenylbutazone as a leukemogen are justified.

Even though radiation is generally regarded as capable of causing human cancer, there is considerable dispute as to how culpable diagnostic and therapeutic doses of X rays actually are. Northwestern University scientists and others have voiced their suspicions that Thorotrast could be carcinogenic to man. Thorotrast is the material introduced into humans to enable the doctor to see, under the fluoroscope, the contour of blood vessels and the status of such organs as liver, spleen, and lymph nodes. Its radioactive components emit alpha, beta, and gamma radiation; one thorium isotope has a radioactive half-life of 200 years. In thirty-seven cases, tumors of the breast, eyelid, jaw, sinus, lung, spleen and, most importantly, the liver, were reported probably due to injections of Thorotrast. Scientists, confirming the human observations, have traced this injected material to a resting place within the mouse's antibody-producing tissues, the reticuloendothelial system.

Some compounds, most of them not very important in modern medicine, have proved carcinogenic in animal tests: alkaloids from Senecio plants which are used in Africa against the cold, as a stimulant and to combat nightmares in children; ergot, a mixture of alkaloids derived from plant fungi and which induces powerful uterine contractions and constricts blood vessels (it has caused cancer of rat ears); carbamates, like urethane, which have been used more in animals than humans as anesthetics; and, from still very inconclusive evidence, isonicotinic hydrazide, a brilliantly conceived, artificial molecule widely used against tuberculosis.

Perhaps the strongest case against drugs as causing human cancer could be made against arsenic. Many medical writers have cited instances in which arsenicals have seemed to cause specific cases of human cancer. A long list of arsenicals—happily shorter now that more effective drugs have been produced—has been used liberally in times past against a variety of conditions, including malaria, epilepsy, burns, chorea, chronic skin conditions, anemia, syphilis, and cancer. While arsenic has been indicted mainly for cancers of the skin, a few autopsy reports indicate that these tumors sometimes are associated with cancers of the lung and other internal organs. The case against arsenic is disputed, largely on the grounds that it has proved difficult or impossible to induce animal cancers with arsenic—an interesting reversal of industry's argument that agents which induce cancer in animals are not necessarily a cause of cancer in humans.

Another large and very commonly used group of drugs under growing suspicion are the phenols. Phenols, obtained either from coal tars or synthetically, are widely used in antiseptics, germicides, disinfectants, escharotics, and local anesthetics. Carbolic acid is a well-known phenol. Not only do the phenols exist in numerous drugs, but they are widely used in heavy industry and elsewhere as antioxidants, preservatives, and disinfectants. They are in many plastic products; and they abound in smoke polluting the air; every ton of rubbish burned yields eight pounds of phenols.

Some of the effects of phenol become apparent within a short time. Physicians who use phenols as exfoliants to remove wrinkles, brown liver spots, and other evidences of aging are familiar with their rapid and complete destruction of skin—and, occasionally and unfortunately, the pneumonia, pericarditis, gangrene, and ugly scars left by these medications. In recent years, somewhat safer chemicals (like trichloroacetic acid) and abrasive measures (skin planing and wire brushes) have begun to replace phenols in dermatology.

Phenols cause animal cancers. University of Wisconsin scientists, who have done much to establish the molecular structures of compounds likely to make a cell malignant, have tested more than fifty phenols for their ability to induce tumors; more than half of them caused animal cancers. The carcinogenic phenols did violence to enzymes, nerve cells, the circulatory system and a variety of tissues. The Wisconsin scientists concluded after years of work with phenols that, in view of the toxicity and ubiquity of phenols, "the hazards to man must now be considered."

There still is no definite proof, however, that any member of the enormous populations regularly exposed to phenols ever has developed cancer as a consequence of the exposure.

While there is no clinical evidence to suggest that antibiotics cause human cancer, a few scientists have reported inducing malignant tumors in experimental animals with these drugs. Japanese scientists have reported that one strain of actinomycin has induced cancer of connective tissue (sarcoma) at the site of injection in mice; and another group has reported that rats which fed on penicillin-contaminated rice showed liver cancers. A group at the University of Cincinnati has shown that griseofulvin, an oral antibiotic with occasional spectacular effect against some chronic and severe fungal infections of the human skin, accelerates carcinogen-induced cancers of the mouse skin; for this effect, the drug had to be given in large doses and at the right time.

Atabrine, the antimalarial widely used by troops during World War II, was said by one scientist to have enhanced the development of rat liver tumors induced by feeding a butter-yellow-type compound. Others have reported a contrary anticancer effect; when Atabrine was spread on the skin of mice subjected to carcinogenic doses of ultraviolet light, it prevented not only the tumors but even severe sunburn; taken orally, the Atabrine had no effect, good or bad. An ancient and recently revived quick-tanning compound, methoxypsoralen, also showed opposing effects —it sensitized the mouse skin both to sunburn and ultraviolet-induced cancers in one series of experiments and helped prevent skin cancers in others. The few experiments done with photosensitizing drugs have indicated that some agents which cause, or help cause, cancer might prevent the disease if used in another dose, by another route of administration and at another time in the sequence of events leading to malignancy.

So many experimental cancers have been induced by altering the endocrine status of animals—that is, by giving them various hormones or by blocking hormone production (most commonly by removing or destroying glands)—that the most cautious investigators are strongly against the medicinal use of hormones for any but well-defined reasons. They contend that the body's hormonal balance is a delicate one, and it can be disturbed drastically by the intervention of small doses. They have expressed the opinion that some cancers of the female uterus, the male prostate, and the male and female breast might be due to resorting to hormones in the hope of restoring the waning libido, enlarging breasts, or acquiring a smooth skin. A few have challenged the use of estrogens in skin lotions. Others have pointed to the fact that, at autopsy, between 15 and 30 per cent of men over fifty have (usually small) prostatic cancers—a warning against the capricious use of hormones which might make these cancers grow and spread. Many, however, are much more liberal or (considering how little still is known about hormones generally, let alone their relationship to cancer) much more daring.

Medicinal use of plastics is similarly debated. Plastics are used more and more commonly in medicine with each passing year. They become the thread that ties structures together following surgery, dental prostheses, blood extenders, replacements for blood vessels, segments of the digestive tract and even heart valves. They are the containers, catheters, and syringes for medical preparations. Cellophane, polyethylene, polyvinyl chloride, Teflon, nylon, Dacron and polystyrene used as films, fibers, adhesives, and lacquer are generally believed to be carcinogenic only when they block the flow of tissue or body fluids. One study showed that tiny porous plastic disks implanted in the animal skin were carcinogenic, but the larger and more numerous the pores, the less carcinogenic the disks proved to be. Despite their burgeoning use in medicine, however, plastics are still relatively new and their carcinogenic potential is yet to be determined.

Sometimes iatrogenic disease passes almost unnoticed, as quietly and as quickly as it appears. The short-lived offending preparation is recalled, occasionally without even the general medical profession aware of its past dangers and disasters. The death certificates are filled out listing the immediate cause of death but not the culpable agent, and the mistakes are buried with the victims.

Sometimes the recall of a drug is embarrassing, causing a stir which may seem out of all proportion to the damage done. One firm sent widely publicized letters to 243,000 American doctors warning that its antidepression drug had caused a dangerous white blood cell reduction in seven patients, and that four had died. No such effects had been noted in any of the 3,500 patients who had taken it experimentally before it was put on the market. The Food and Drug Administration, however, considers toxicity of this sort high if it occurs to one in 50,000 patients.

Sometimes a drug will do enormous damage over a long period before the word leaks out and the public, as well as the medical profession, is horrified at what has happened. This was the case with the German sleeping pill, thalidomide, which gained ever-widening popularity as a hangoverless sedative between its introduction in 1958 and November, 1961, when it was taken off the market. Somewhere between 3,500 and 5,000 German mothers who had taken these pills during their pregnancies delivered monsters, babies with flipperlike structures for arms such as seals have, and sometimes small stumps for legs. The condition, called phocomelia, was rare among malformations until this episode. The drug interfered with the growth of long bones, probably during the second month of pregnancy. Dr. Frances O. Kelsey, a Food and Drug official, suspicious of the German preparation and standing alone against industrial and political pressures, blocked its production and use in the United States as a hypnotic and sedative. Dr. Helen B. Taussig of Columbia University, who looked into the effects of thalidomide in Europe (a few hundred English infants also were deformed by it) commented that, "We should be grateful the drug was not dreamed up in this country. It could have passed the Food and Drug Administration under our present laws." She predicted that about one-third of the affected infants would die of internal malformations, including those of the small intestine and heart.

The thalidomide episode, Dr. Taussig said, should teach young women to be cautious about new drugs. "Until new laws become effective," she said, "and indeed until research for the proper tests on pregnant animals has been completed, physicians must bear in mind that sleeping tablets, tranquilizers and other apparently innocent drugs may do terrible harm to the rapidly growing embryo and the unborn child."

While thalidomide may have ceased to menace the unborn generation, other preparations and maternal habits are still killing and deforming babies. Congenital malformations constitute the leading cause of death among the newborn. And sometimes they are accompanied by cancer—possibly induced by the same agents.

Of the fifty or more tranquilizers that have come on the market during the last decade, all of them have some side effects if used in sufficient dosage. Some present multiple risks. Among the bad effects are damage to the nervous system, habituation, hypotension, cardiovascular injury, water logging, skin disorders, seizures, liver damage, psychosis, and various degrees of blindness.

Dr. Curt P. Richter, a distinguished scientist at Johns Hopkins Hospital, reported at the National Academy of Sciences a few years ago that rats regularly fed any of a variety of commonly used pills within one to four months developed subtle damage from which they never recovered. The test substances included sulfas, thyroid-suppressants, hormones, sedatives, antipyretics, and others. Behavior charts and autopsies indicated that brain areas, particularly the hypothalamus, were affected. "The damage does not interefere with life," Dr. Richter stated. "It cannot be seen, and the rat appears normal. Its presence can be detected only by taking daily records of spontaneous running activity, food intake and water intake over long periods." The disturbances assumed a rhythmic character, showing themselves in cycles ranging from fourteen to fifty-eight days. He contended that prolonged use of the drugs could produce severe mental and physical changes in man and might be responsible for some human periodic diseases and psychoses.

The dangers of many drugs are known—widely advertised by their producers, in fact. In some instances, drug houses publish pages of printed matter indicating for what and for whom the drug is indicated, adult and pediatric dosage schedules, methods of administration, side effects, the early signs of toxicity, contraindications and other valuable information. Misadventures with various drugs are the subject of many articles in the professional literature. Nevertheless, some doctors through ignorance or carelessness, prescribe them when they are contraindicated, or they fail to caution their patients against the penalties of departing from the prescribed dosages. And the ultimate victims, the consumers, take old, unlabeled drugs from their bathroom shelves or, with drugs bought over the counter, ignore both the large and small print and swallow them on the principle that if a little is good, a lot is better. It is no wonder that about a hundred Americans are known to die annually of overdoses of aspirin and aspirin-type tablets and that many others encounter confusional states and death from uncalculated doses of bromides. These are among the sudden, acute effects of their error.

The chronic effects of ill-advised medication probably are much more common and much less frequently recognized—the blood changes, the eventual central nervous system effects (optic neuritis, convulsions, psychoses, vertigo, deafness, blurred vision and light-headedness), the jaundice of liver damage, the internal allergic responses, the eroded kidneys, the damaged heart and other organs.

Part of the abuse-of-drugs problem rests with the government. This was acknowledged by the Kennedy administration in 1962 when it drafted a bill which imposed new FDA controls. Under the new law, the FDA is empowered to review laboratory and clinical data, rule on both the safety and efficacy of drugs and devices, and withdraw them from the market in the event of substantial doubt of their efficacy or safety.

Another bill applies to cosmetics also. Some of the dyes and other chemicals are suspect of having a carcinogenic potential. Cosmetics containing hormones are considered drugs.

The major part of the solution to drug abuse rests with the medical profession, the pharmaceutical industry, and the public. This is largely a matter of education. It must be pointed out to those who produce, sell, prescribe, administer and use them that drugs have profound and far-reaching effects on the organs and systems of the body, only some of which are now recognized. These effects can be masked, latent, cumulative, untraceable by present means to their source. Good conscience and common sense dictate that they are not to be marketed until laboratory tests and clinical trials have demonstrated their usefulness and short-term and long-term effects; they should not be prescribed without complete information as to what can be expected of them in various kinds of patients. They are not to be given or taken capriciously.

Doctors and patients alike have been warned that virtually all drugs can be dangerous—a cholesterol inhibitor eventually may bring cataracts, hair loss, and impotence; the aspirin which eases a chronic headache eventually may damage the liver; cortisone which relieves rheumatoid arthritis (aspirin is regarded by many as better and safer) may retard wound healing, spread infection, aggravate diabetes, precipitate gout, shorten clotting time and induce depression and psychoses; the pep pills which increase one's physical performance two- or threefold, and some of the pills which bring blessed sleep to the overtense can become habitual and lead to stronger addictions—morphine, for instance.

And as for the array of drugs which man uses regularly or sporadically during his lifetime: do they cause irreversible changes in his metabolism, atrophy his organs and systems of disease-resistance, and eventually induce cancer or accelerate the development of cancers caused by other agents? No one knows. Ignorance, however, is no deterrent to drug use; during the last twenty-three years, the average American has increased his drug purchases by 943 per cent.

There is a great and urgent need for human experimentation with drugs.

The experiments should be done, however, in research centers where qualified scientists are prepared to undertake time-consuming studies of patients, faithfully record their experimental and control data, promptly reverse any untoward effects of their medications, and freely publish their results and observations. This right of experimentation does not rest with the ordinary physician; his job is to learn from the medical literature the benefits he can expect from various preparations and the dangers that lie in them. Scattered through medical literature are numerous tragedies—the deaths that have resulted from intravenous injection of tetracycline into women during the last three months of their pregnancy, the one hundred or more deaths attributed to a commercial preparation which makes the bladder show up under X rays, the defective bone pins and screws which cause severe reactions and infections, the teratogenic effects (in animals) of various antibiotics, the instances of sudden high blood pressure caused by an antidepressive. Certainly the layman who treats himself experimentally has a fool for a doctor and a patient.

The very volume of drugs now being sold gives substance to the suspicion that iatrogenic disease may be much greater than is suspected· During 1962, these *millions* were spent in the United States: $209 for antibiotics, $164 for tranquilizers, $35 for sedatives and hypnotics, $18 for antidepressants, $45 for dermatologic preparations, $60 for corticoid hormones, $45 for antacids, $96 to treat respiratory infections, $144 for vitamins, and $24 for analgesics and narcotics.

The nation's drug bill of close to $2,000,000,000 indicates a rather sick society.

CHAPTER 7

AIR POLLUTION AND CANCER

The atmosphere is being polluted by countless new compounds, many of them foreign to the chemical requirements of life and toxic to the systems they touch. As water pollutants have made streams barren of the fish and smaller life forms which once dwelt in them, as the poisons man has strewn over his plants have depopulated areas of highly essential bacteria, burrowing creatures and bird life, so has air pollution become a menace to all living forms, including man. More and more, it is becoming difficult to hide from, or survive, the trend of the times as directed by the inventiveness of the human mind. Sadder still, the trend has only begun; the already overflowing urban population packed into a minuscule part of the land areas continues to reproduce and concentrate in and around 212 cities, industries are explanding inexorably, and, primarily because of these trends, the air gets dirtier all the time. Its annual pollutants would bury the cities under 21 feet of dangerous debris. Among the pollutants are numerous carcinogens.

The most dramatic consequences of pollution are seen in the recurrent fatal fogs—in 1952 a four-day fog in London cost about 4,000 lives. These disasters have occurred only in cool (but not extremely cold) weather, usually from November through January. Other long and lethal fogs have smothered people in Glasgow in 1901 and 1925, the Meuse Valley, Belgium, in 1930 (60 were suffocated) and Donora, Pennsylvania, in 1948, when 20 died and 5,910 were made more or less acutely ill. These emergencies ended when the sun finally burned through the clouds and stirred up a breeze which blew the fog away.

Los Angeles' famed smog is another type of trouble—only distantly related to the peasoup problem, which presents itself as a rule only in cold weather. Smog occurs 30 to 50 times a year and in warm weather. The air pollutants are different; they have an oxidizing, rather than reducing, effect. And the sun, far from ransoming the human victims, helps produce chemicals which add to their discomfort.

To varying degrees almost all other cities have air-pollution problems. They are particularly painful for the very young, the very old and the ailing.

Clean air is composed of about 78 per cent nitrogen, 21 per cent oxygen, and one per cent argon and assorted other gases; and, depending on the weather, its water content ranges from zero to about four per cent.

About 75 million American automobiles and many industries in various areas alter the composition of the air. They contribute pollutants which are measured in terms of more than a trillion (1,000,000,000,000) cubic feet a day. The smokes and dusts spewed out by exhaust pipes and smokestacks contain carbon monoxide, oxides of nitrogen and sulfur, many descriptions of hydrocarbons, aldehydes, and organic acids. Some of the pollutants are toxic in their original form; others are made toxic by their reaction with other chemicals or by the intervention of such physical agents as sunlight. On various biological systems, the pollutants may act together to produce an additive or a multiplying effect.

There is no dispute as to whether atmospheric pollutants are dangerous to plant and animal life. Crop and cattle losses due to them are enormous, amounting to several billion dollars annually. And there is no argument against what everyone knows and feels—a pile-up of pollutants, which in smog are ten, twenty, or thirty times as thick in normal weather, causes acute discomfort in humans, including eye-smarting, asthmatic and allergic attacks, emphysema distress (which usually clears when the patient is placed in an environment of filtered air) and outbreaks of chronic obstructive lung disease.

Engine exhaust gases are electrically charged, usually positively but occasionally negatively (depending on whether water droplets or carbon particles predominate). Clouds of ions pass as low as 30 feet overhead, especially in the wake of diesel trucks which are not grounded. The charged chemicals could have a profound effect on the metabolism of exposed cells, the normal chemistry of which depends on a balanced ration of ions.

More than 200 hydrocarbons and lead are belched out in exhausts. Carbon monoxide, perhaps the most common gaseous pollutant of the air, crowds oxygen off red blood cells. Ozone, an oxygen molecule which an electric spark endows with three rather than the regular two atoms, is a powerful disinfectant (it kills microbes) and, in well-established doses, kills laboratory animals as well. Formed from peroxides, ozone reacts with other pollutants to produce the compounds which make eyes smart, create haze and give the air a chlorinelike odor.

Nitrogen oxides, which have an affinity for combining with red-cell hemoglobin up to 300,000 times that of oxygen, are known to decrease animals' antibody production and resistance to infection; and, in combination with many hydrocarbons, exert acutely irritating effects on eyes, the respiratory tract, and the circulatory and nervous system.

Sulfur dioxide is the chief irritant in coal smoke; its concentration in the air can be correlated with asthma attacks in adults, but, oddly enough, not in children, and while its corrosive effects on buildings are estimated at about $7 billion a year, there is not even a good guess as to its toll on human life.

The immediate, the acute, the easily traceable effects on living systems may be mild compared to the chronic, long-range, consequences of air pollution. Even in the absence of irritants and chemicals which produce prompt effects, many hazardous chemicals abound in polluted air. They include carcinogens.

Federal government investigations show that city air, on an average, contains sixteen times the amount of known carcinogens found in non-urban air.

Drs. Paul Kotin and Hans Falk, formerly of the University of Southern California and now of the National Cancer Institute, have studied the problem for years. They have concluded that the evidence against air pollution "warrants its incrimination as one of the dominant agents" in lung cancer. The NCI's Dr. Hueper has written that "it is not unlikely that industrial and industry-related air pollutants are partly responsible for the increased frequency of cancers of the lung in most industrialized countries and particularly in their highly industrialized regions."

A California group, headed by Dr. Riojun Kinosita, found that highways, far from the cities, as well as urban streets paved with petroleum asphalt, contain carcinogens. Samples applied to or injected under the skin of mice produced cancers at the site of application. These carcinogens permeate the air in heavy, fast-moving traffic.

Dr. Kotin once created in his laboratory a heaven and a hell for experimental mice susceptible to lung cancer. Heaven was filled with finely filtered air, as sweet and clean as morning on a mountain top. Hell was pervaded by a concentration of the dusts and smokes to which smog-bound populations are exposed. At the end of forty weeks, Dr. Kotin took stock; 63 per cent of the mice in hell had developed lung cancer, as compared with only 13.5 per cent of the Eden dwellers. When influenza virus was added to the polluted air, cancer developed with startling suddenness. Dr.

Kotin has identified in smog concentrates six well-known cancer-producing polycyclic hydrocarbons, and he has established the carcinogenicity of products of another large (aliphatic) class of hydrocarbons which long had been believed innocuous. The aliphatic hydrocarbons are produced by automobile engines, gasoline or diesel. Other scientists have found in concentrated smog many other compounds either known to cause cancer or with a high suspicion of it.

Dr. Ernest L. Wynder of the Sloan-Kettering Institute for Cancer Research has reported that at least twenty-four polynuclear hydrocarbons are in the exhaust of an automobile driven on a city schedule. The known carcinogens among them are from fifty to more than a hundred times as concentrated as in cigarette smoke; by the time they reach the human lung, however, they are diluted thousands of times.

A great deal can be done to keep the air clean; a great deal must be done if the few atmospheric incidents and disasters of the past are not to assume catastrophic frequency in a future which is moving in on us rapidly.

The solution to air pollution, however, cannot be achieved quickly, simply or cheaply. It cannot be attained with the present national annual expenditure of three or four million dollars. The economic damage done by air pollution (in ruined crops, sick and killed livestock, metal corrosion and soiled surfaces, laundry and cleaning bills, and interference with ground and air transport) is estimated at about $12 billion, or $65 for every person. Clean air cannot be obtained by prevailing statutes like Public Law 159, which states that air-pollution control is a state and local responsibility; no local or state government can legislate against pollution sources in another area any more than they can influence the direction of the wind which scatters pollutants over a radius of a hundred or more miles. And the matter cannot be resolved on a local basis.

Some relief might be achieved without further study. In automotive transport, for instance, those who have studied the situation state that several measures can be taken to decrease the emission of the one gallon of fuel in fourteen which remains unburned in passing through the average engine—it is the unburned and partially burned, not the completely burned, gasolines and oils which constitute the poisons. Standards for the combustibility of fuels can be established. Cars and trucks with inefficient engines can be ruled off the roads. Devices, like afterburners, to burn carbon monoxide to carbon dioxide and simple carburetion adjustments, possibly with water injection, to reduce nitrogen oxide emission now seem feasible; field tests of catalytic combustion devices in exhaust pipes have reduced excess nitrogen oxides by 91 per cent, carbon monoxide 75 per cent, and various hydrocarbons 92 per cent.

A substantial start has been made during the last generation to reduce the menace of factory smokes. Smokeless fuels have been substituted for soft coal; tall smokestacks have been built to fumigate more lightly and over wider areas, thereby sparing nearby plant, animal and human populations; and smoke control equipment has been installed to imprison pollutants before they leave stacks. This is only a start, however.

Large particles of soot and dust can be removed by separating them by weight in settling chambers or cyclones, smaller dust particles can be filtered out with cotton, plastics or even glass baghouses similar to those in vacuum cleaners, and very fine electrically charged particles can be removed with electrodes. Even these procedures, however, would have limited effect on the noxious gases, some of which acquire toxicity by the action of sunlight upon them.

The problem of air pollution is not a static one; it changes with the times. In an evolving environment, there can be no prospect of an ultimate solution. Perhaps by the time the emissions of gasoline and diesel engines are cleaned up, highly efficient fuel cells will become the prevailing source of automotive power. In these, chemicals like hydrogen, oxygen, propane, and air will react in an electrolyte solution (perhaps of potassium hydroxide) to produce direct current electricity. Will fuel cell products present a new pollution problem?

And then there is atomic energy, now in its infancy but a fairly certain common power source for the factories, other plants and the vehicles of the fast-advancing future.

CHAPTER 8

OCCUPATION AND CANCER

Most scientific reviews and many popular accounts of occupational cancers give prominent mention to a classical observation in 1775 by the alert London surgeon, Dr. Percival Potts. He noted that many chimney sweeps had cancer of the scrotum and skin, attributed the disease to the accumulation of soot around the crotch and in skin crevices, and suggested that these cancers might be prevented by bathing regularly.

Dr. Lester Breslow, a modern epidemiologist of the California State Department of Health, wishes there was less emphasis on Potts' contribution and on Agricola's report on lung cancer among miners in the fifteenth century. "I believe these examples may convey a false impression by implying that cancer arising from extrinsic agents in the course of work occurs as a rather bizarre phenomenon in distant time, isolated places or unusual circumstances," Dr. Breslow has said. "As a matter of fact, evidence is now rapidly accumulating that many types of cancer can result from exposure to agents encountered in work. Current studies of cancer of the lung, skin, bladder and other sites, as well as leukemia, are yielding this type of information."

Only about twenty occupations are recognized as holding clear carcinogenic dangers. They account for less than 1 per cent of all cancers. Only nine or ten thousand cases of occupational cancer are reported in the world literature.

Strong suspicions, however, attach to a long and lengthening list of other occupations. If and when the suspicions are confirmed, we may find that most or all workers face some cancer hazards. Great or minor exposure to carcinogens exist in all sorts of mine, mill, farm, factory, office, and professional jobs. If one includes the phenomenal uterine cancer rate among prostitutes and the impressive breast cancer rate among nuns, it becomes clear that, as an occupational disease, cancer does not distinguish between widely disparate physical, intellectual, and spiritual fields of endeavor.

Occupational cancer comes not only to those who produce carcinogenic substances but also to those who process them, handle them in other industries, transport them, sell them and use them in the office or home. Innocent bystanders are exposed to the industrial wastes eructed into water and air and strewn recklessly on the land.

Farmers, presumed to lead a healthful outdoor life, spray themselves as well as their crops, and breathe in the toxins with which they sow their lands. Epidemiological studies during the next few years may indicate what modern agriculture has done to farmers' health.

Government estimates indicate that more than one-half of the 70-odd million civilian labor force have "some degree of physiological impairment which could be greatly reduced if adequate knowledge were available." The incidence of silicosis, for instance, went down dramatically with damping procedures against mine and mill dusts, once the disease had been traced to these sources. Similar reductions in occupational cancers might be achieved with definite knowledge of the source of the cancers.

With cancer, however, we are dealing with a great complex of external and internal factors. The best industry could hope for would be the identification and elimination of principal sources of exposure.

The job of reducing deaths by occupational cancers is not made easier by a measure of scientific secrecy maintained by some industries. In too many cases, scientists employed by industry to find and assess the causes of occupational illness do not publish their findings. For understandable reasons, industries are not eager to advertise health hazards in their operation or their products: there are the ever-present possibility of damage suits by workers, handlers and consumers, the difficulties of recruiting men and women for jobs known to be dangerous or unhealthful and the reluctance of dealers and consumers toward products acknowledged to be carcinogen-tainted.

Beyond this, there are all the familiar problems of determining what constitutes a real menace to human health. Perhaps more than in any other area of environmental cancer, the evidence of carcinogenic influences in industrial works and wares is bitterly debated. Epidemiological studies are challenged on the grounds that they have not ruled out many other possible factors; chemical analyses are contested; and animal experiments are pooh-poohed as having little if any relevance to humans.

Occupational health risks resulting in immediate acute illness and sudden death are more or less beyond dispute. There is not much argument that overexposure to halogenated hydrocarbons (like carbon tetrachloride and certain noninflamable solvents, which are used as cleaners in factories and garages, floor waxes, fire extinguishers and intestinal worm killers) is dangerous. Some die suddenly of the acute effect; others become chronically ill from damage to liver, kidneys, heart, blood vessels and nerves, including that bundle of nerves called the brain. Some methyl bromides, chlorides and iodides, used as refrigerants and fumigants, are known to cause at least a few deaths each year from severe injury to liver, kidneys, brain, and lungs. Trichlorethylene, a component in some industrial solvents, household cleaners, and inhaled pain killers and anesthetics, exacts a few more lives by its effects on nerves, heart, kidneys, and other organs. Many other chemicals—like the chlorinated naphthalenes and diphenyls (in electric wires, transformers, and motors), ethyl alcohol (a solvent, antiseptic, Bowery beverage and chemical intermediate), petroleum distillates (like kerosene and gasoline), benzene and turpentine—are acknowledged as causing sudden, severe, and sometimes irreversible illness with overexposure.

To prove that human cancer, occurring five, ten or fifty years after exposure, is due to a specific job or carcinogen is another matter. Animal tumors induced by placing metals—like chromium, cobalt, gold, nickel, platinum, silver, tantalum or cadmium—in tissues usually develop long after local injuries have healed. In some cases the cancers are far from the site of injection.

Some of the chemicals which bring about acute illness also cause cancer. And some of the acute illnesses often are associated with cancer. Uranium miners in a recent United States study were found to have 17.8 times the normal risk of death from failure of the overworked and overgrown right side of the heart and five times the normal risk of lung cancer. It now is known that subtle oxygen-displacing compounds combined with certain lung diseases, like emphysema and lung cancer, cause the right side of the heart to overgrow in pumping additional oxygen-starved blood to the defective lungs. As cause, effect or part of a vicious cycle, many other acute conditions—sudden baldness, skin ulcers, pneumonias, anemias, fatigue, and the like—may be associated with various cancers.

One difficulty in presenting information on occupational carcinogens which can be understood by the potential victim lies in the interchangeable technical names often masking these substances. Harold L. Althouse and Frances Althouse, public health nursing experts, have listed a few synonyms: Anthracene is also known as paranaphthalene and green oil; asphalt as bitumen, judean or petroleum pitch; benzol as benzene, phenyl hydride, and coal naphtha; creosote as liquid pitch oil; mineral oil, crude, as lubricating oil and liquid petroleum; paraffin oil as lube oil, kerosene and motor oil; spindle oil as engine oil, lube oil, and machine oil; arsenic as orpiment, mimetite, sorodite, sperrylite, nicolite, and realgar; asbestos as amosite, tremolite, and amianthus; chromate as chromium trioxide and chromic anhydride, and nickel carbonyl as tetracarbonyl. Trade names compound the confusion.

Despite their technical nomenclature, occupational carcinogens are common, ubiquitous and seemingly harmless. They exist in carbon paper handled by secretaries and creosoted ties laid by railroad workers. They are in automobile tires and bottle stoppers, in paints, in dyes, in roofing materials, and in dozens of kinds of oils and greases. They are in pharmaceuticals and printer's ink, in cleaners and cleansers and cosmetics, in jewelry and other metal manufactures, in many kinds of food, clothing, and shelter.

Sometimes their carcinogenic character comes to light by accident. A University of Wisconsin group found that a shipment of mice they had purchased because they were cancer-resistant came down with lung cancers; investigation showed the disease was due to the fact that the crates in which they had been shipped were creosoted. A Swedish scientist was struck by the statistic that of 500 printers in Stockholm, eight (comprising 6.4 per cent of all lung-cancer patients) had come down with lung cancer within a brief period; he looked up the literature and found that another scientist about thirty years earlier had painted mice's necks with printer's ink and produced cancers of the lung, liver, spleen, and lymphatic system.

Acute clinical observation often affords the clue which leads to cancer causes. Dr. Arthur J. Vorwald, now of Wayne State University, was impressed by reports of precancerous lesions developing in people, mostly in children, who handled beryllium powders spilled from broken fluorescent lighting tubes. After several attempts he induced bone cancers which rapidly spread to the lung, liver, and other sites in beryllium-injected rabbits. Beryllium powders also induced lung cancer in rats. Sensitive to these experiments, manufacturers promptly abandoned the use of beryllium in lighting tubes; and workers who handled beryllium in the manufacture of alloys, steel, X-ray windows, atomic energy devices, and numerous other products were warned by the Atomic Energy Commission to avoid dangerous contamination.

And sometimes the source of cancers comes to light by a combination of clinical observation and logic. Some years after the discovery of radium and X-ray-producing Roentgen tubes at the turn of the century, some of the early developers showed severe burns and a variety of cancers, including leukemia. In modern times, a few scientists felt that dentists and physicians seemed somewhat more susceptible than others to various cancers. They investigated, and their statistical studies showed that physicians using radiation equipment had ten times the cancers developed by physicians who did not use X rays. It became evident that many doctors were not adequately protected from the instruments they used on patients.

Only a small percentage of the chemicals encountered in industry undergo laboratory tests for carcinogenicity. Some of these are checked by independent scientists working for the government or for universities, and these results are freely published in scientific journals. Others are tested by scientists employed by the industries, and their findings can and sometimes do remain the private and confidential property of the employers.

Some cancers have been called occupational in origin without serious challenge. The cited exposures usually have been in the distant past and far places, the carcinogens involved not marketable or the hazards so much a part of the worker's way of life that damage suits were unlikely. The latter include the continuing skin cancers in fishing, farming, and seafaring (due to excessive exposure to sun and weather). Lung cancer has killed up to 50 per cent of uranium miners in Joachimsthal, Czechoslovakia and up to 80 per cent of cobalt miners in Schneeberg, Germany. Less is heard about occupational cancers in modern mining and smelting areas, where the dangers only recently have come to attract public attention. More has been and is being heard about bladder cancer among workers in the dye industry, and more recently among shoe repairers, leather workers and, to less extent, hair dressers, textile workers and coal miners.

Skin cancers are an occupational hazard in the synthetic oil industry. In some companies, elaborate preventive measures have been taken— insistence upon daily showers and frequent washings with strong soap, yellow tags to warn workers of dangerous equipment, protective gloves and clothing, moving workers with warts (which some say occasionally become malignant anywhere from two to twenty years after initial exposure to carcinogens) to unexposed jobs, quarterly or semiannual medical examinations and the prompt treatment of suspicious lesions. The highly carcinogenic residues (which boil at temperatures over 700 degrees Fahrenheit) are sold usually as fuel oils rather than as lubricants to protect consumers. Nevertheless, an unusually high incidence of leukemia has been reported among garage workers and others handling lubricating oils, and this stirs suspicions that sufficient precautions have not been taken.

The list of jobs entailing small or considerable exposure to proven, suspected, and debated carcinogens runs into the hundreds or possibly thousands. Among those exposed to chromium compounds, some of which are more or less generally suspected as carcinogenic to humans (chromate producers have fifteen to forty times the normal rate of lung cancers) are acetylene workers, aniline workers, artificial flower makers, battery (dry) makers, bleachers, blueprint makers, candle (colored) makers, carbon printers (photography), chrome workers, chromium platers, colorers (marble), color makers, compounders (rubber), crayon (colored) makers, dye makers, dyers, electroplaters, enamelers, enamel makers, explosives (pyroxylin) workers, frosters (glass and pottery), furniture polishers, glass colorers, glaze workers (pottery), ink makers, linoleum workers, lithographers, match-factory workers, mixers (rubber), mordanters, painters, paint makers, paperhangers, paper makers, paper-money makers, pencil (colored) makers, photoengravers, photographic workers, photogravure workers, pottery workers, rubber workers, steel (chrome) workers, tannery (chrome) workers, textile printers, vulcanizers, wallpaper printers, waterproofers (paper), wax-ornament workers, welders, and wood stainers.

And chromium is only one of many classes of carcinogens encountered in industrial and other occupations.

Dr. Wilhelm C. Hueper of the NCI has listed these broad categories of chemicals as being carcinogenic—that is, they have caused one kind of cancer or another in laboratory animals: coal tars, petroleum asphalt, paraffin oil, nickel, chromium, uranium, many hydrocarbons, aromatic amines, and polymers. Some of these and a few other industrial compounds have been indicted in epidemiological studies as causing human cancer; arsenic, virtually noncarcinogenic in the laboratory, is considered carcinogenic to man. Many of the compounds, he pointed out, cause skin cancer but, when inhaled as mists or injected, do not cause animal lung cancer.

Dr. Hueper mentioned the presence of the well-known laboratory carcinogen, 3,4-benzpyrene, in soot from coffee factories and in black roasted, "French-type" coffee beans as a possible explanation for the unusually high incidence of lung and bladder cancer in New Orleans. Chemical analysis and animal experiments with other coal tars, he felt, might explain an excess of lung cancer in coke-oven workers, gas-plant retort workers, metallurgical workers (who inhale petroleum oils as sprays or mists), and many others. He regarded as "reliable and valid" epidemiologic evidence that workmen in contact with certain inorganic (noncarbon-containing) chemicals are unusually subject to cancers of the respiratory system; these compounds include arsenical ores and insecticides, asbestos dust in mines, mills and textile factories, nickel, and uranium. Scientists at Roswell Park Memorial Hospital once showed that even money causes cancer: animals with dimes (which contain nickel) implanted under their skins came down with skin cancers. Of a more tenuous nature was the risk of cancer among those exposed to plastics, or polymers, which are in paints, vulcanizers, beer, fruit juice, hair lacquers, other cosmetics and innumerable containers for drugs, food, and other products. Some scientists contend that only solid plastic films are carcinogenic; others say they have produced cancers with water-soluble plastics washed off containers.

A few relatively small-scale studies have brought to light some interesting hints of the liability of several industrial workman groups to different kinds of cancer. An Ohio study of male workers showed high cancer rates generally among construction, electrical, machine, and nonferrous metal workers; low rates, generally, were among stone, clay and glass workers. Broken down into cancer of various sites, the statistics indicated these significant high and low rates—*Digestive tract:* High among manufacturing, nonferrous metal, iron and steel and machine workers, and low among stone, clay and glass workers. *Respiratory tract:* high among mining and quarrying, transportation and communications workers, and low among agricultural, stone, clay and glass workers. *Genital:* high among agricultural, odd jobs, rubber and plastics workers, and low in transportation and communications, iron and steel, nonferrous metal, mining and quarrying workers. *Urinary organs:* high among electrical and machine and nonferrous workers, and low among rubber and plastics workers. *Lip, mouth* and *pharynx:* high among stone, clay and glass, iron and steel workers, and low among mining and quarrying, rubber and plastics workers. *Skin:* high among agricultural, mining and quarrying, construction, stone, clay and glass workers, and low among iron and steel, rubber and plastics workers, electrical and machine and nonferrous metal workers. *Brain* and *central nervous system:* high among rubber plastics, electrical and machine workers, and low among nonferrous metals, sand, clay and glass, agricultural, transportation and communications, mining and quarrying workers.

A small and preliminary study directed by Dr. Breslow brought forth some surprisingly high susceptibilities to lung cancer among welders, steamfitters, bridge-crane operators, asbestos workers, miners of lead, zinc, and copper (but not hardrock mining or gold and silver mining), ship engine room and fireroom workers, painters and hotel and restaurant cooks. Some of these findings were so intriguing that a large-scale study was begun with the help of labor unions.

Several studies now being conducted by the Federal and state governments and by the American Cancer Society eventually may yield dependable information which would make cancer-prevention measures possible.

Meanwhile, the prospect of progress in this area is bleak. Industry's organic wastes have been increasing at the rate of about 50 per cent each decade, and the increase in many synthetic inorganic wastes is much greater. There are no signs that these trends will waver.

Dr. Hueper has few illusions about the difficulties of controlling cancer's environmental causes. He has said, "The principal barriers in accomplishing an effective preventive control of cancers on the basis of existing factual knowledge and of the information which, with moderate effort and sincerity, could be obtained is represented by the continued lack of serious interest of the medical profession in general in the etiology of human cancers, by a still widespread inertia of public health agencies of all levels to develop adequate and effective cancer prevention programs, and by the often obstructive attitude of industrial parties to study occupational hazards and to publish even when investigations have been conducted and the results obtained."

Dr. Breslow has commented:

it is not uncommon to encounter resistance in industry to deal officially even with very small exposure situations. Sometimes there is a reluctance to acknowledge the existence of the problem or to make known what industry has learned about it, for example, data from private investigations. There is a tendency in some countries, including this one, to settle compensation claims outside of the regular processes which come to public attention. Cancer prevention efforts also encounter difficulties in the orientation of labor organizations. Trade unions have tended to stress extra pay for hazardous or suspected hazardous work, rather than emphasize the preventive measures which might be undertaken. Both industry and labor organizations have social obligations to employed workers for the development of cancer prevention measures.

Many steps toward control of occupational illness have been proposed by government and advisory bodies. Until this writing, however, little has been done beyond holding a few conferences.

CHAPTER 9

TOBACCO
AND CANCER

Down through time, cigarettes have been blamed for tuberculosis, nervousness, impotence, indigence, and immoral behavior. Almost all complainants were reformers or obscure medical men with an evangelistic bent.

In 1936, Dr. Alton Ochsner of New Orleans, no reformer for the sake of reform, announced that every one of his lung cancer patients was a heavy cigarette smoker and declared flatly his belief that cigarette smoking was producing a fearsome plague of this disease. A world-renowned surgeon with an engaging sense of humor and eloquent delivery, Dr. Ochsner was given attention. With statistics, sparkling wit, and grim realism, he told his professional and lay audiences that this epidemic would continue to grow until something was done to deter men from smoking their way onto the operating tables and into the graves of the world. Nineteen of every twenty of these patients were dead of their disease within five years—most of them within a year.

Dr. Evarts A. Graham at Washington University was a distinguished surgeon, a fairly heavy cigarette smoker, and, at first, somewhat skeptical of Dr. Ochsner's sobering accounts. With a young associate, Dr. Ernest L. Wynder, he checked available records in 1950 and confirmed Dr. Ochsner's contentions. Dr. Wynder entered a career in epidemiology; he produced damning statistical, chemical, and biological evidence against cigarette smoking as a cause of lung and some other cancers. Dr. Graham quit smoking, but he quit too late. The great surgeon, who had performed the first successful lung removal—from a heavy-smoking fellow physician—developed lung cancer himself, and neither his operation nor any procedure known to medicine could save him. He died of lung cancer a few years after indicting and abandoning the habit.

One by one, various groups and individuals reported observations indicating that cigarette smoking and lung cancer were linked. Dr. Morton L. Levin in Albany added the weight of his studies on behalf of the New York State Health Department.

Despite the mounting evidence, in 1950 there were many nonbelievers within science and medicine as well as among the general public. Two highly skeptical investigators were Dr. Daniel Horn and Dr. E. Cuyler Hammond, the American Cancer Society's epidemiologists. Both cigarette smokers, they felt that all the studies so far undertaken were unreliable because they were small and retrospective—that is, the smoking studies were made among people who already had or had died of lung cancer. They were convinced that a prospective study—in which a large healthy population is followed until a significant percentage develop lung cancer—would show no connection between the habit and the disease. They persuaded the Society that a large prospective study would be in the interests of public health; there was no very strenuous objection from board members and officials from tobacco-growing states. After all, this study once and for all could lay the lie being told about tobacco.

Volunteer workers in nine states were given instruction, and—with each volunteer keeping tabs on ten men—they began the prospective study of 187,766 middle-aged men, who presumably were in good health and whose smoking habits were known.

At the end of twenty months, the first data were collected and submitted to the computer. Halfway through their analysis, Drs. Hammond and Horn quit smoking cigarettes. This first sample showed clearly that lung cancer was frighteningly common among cigarette smokers and extremely rare among nonsmokers. It showed much more: early death from several other causes, including heart disease, also went with cigarette smoking.

The Hammond-Horn study showed that the death rate from all causes mounted with the number of cigarettes smoked; as compared with the rate for nonsmokers, it was 34 per cent higher for those who smoked a half-pack a day and 123 per cent higher for those who smoked two or more packs a day. The death rate differences in lung cancer were spectacular: as compared with the rate for nonsmokers, the mortality was anywhere from ten to sixty-four times as high, depending on how much was smoked.

Cigarette smoking was not the only factor involved in lung cancer. This sample and numerous other studies made before and since it showed that air pollution, urban living, heredity, being born abroad and, possibly, earlier virus infections enter into the picture. But all the other factors together were dwarfed by the enormous, eye-popping impact of cigarette smoking. Cigarette-smoking city people had six times the risk of lung cancer run by nonsmoking city people. Other studies showed that among the foreign born the ratio was four to one between smokers and nonsmokers, native born almost seven to one, and among farmers, ten to one.

There was a salutary note in the cold calculations. Those who quit smoking stood to gain years of health added to their lifespans. In the Hammond-Horn study, those who had stopped light smoking ten or more years earlier had reduced their chances of lung cancer by 85 per cent and heavy smokers 62 per cent. For those who quit smoking, it turned out, death from several causes was deferred appreciably.

Cigar smokers and pipe smokers were almost immune to all the premature ills which befell cigarette smokers. Light cigarette-smokers paid the penalty of their habit, but only in proportion to the number of cigarettes they smoked, the shortness of the butt they finally threw away and the degree to which they inhaled the smoke into their lungs.

The surest way to avoid lung cancer, however, was to abstain entirely from cigarette smoking. A study in Seventh Day Adventist hospitals in California later was conducted by Dr. Ernest Wynder, now of Sloan-Kettering Institute, and others; in this nonsmoking sect, investigators found only two patients with lung cancer—both of them recent converts.

The Hammond-Horn findings posed a difficult decision for the Cancer Society. The results undoubtedly would shake the confidence of millions of people in the cigarettes they smoked. Some would stop smoking; if enough did, this massive industry—which then paid more than two billion dollars in taxes—would suffer, and the livelihoods of an estimated six million people who financed, grew, harvested, packaged, advertised, and sold tobacco would be affected adversely to a large or small degree. On the other hand, the results were so clear-cut and the implications—that about 60 millions then were smoking themselves into untimely graves—so appalling, it was evident that every day of delay would cost many lives.

On other levels, individuals and organizations during the coming years were to face the same dilemma. Medical and scientific groups with the responsibility of counseling the citizenry, individual doctors paid to protect the health of their patients, parents charged with the guidance of their children—for all of them there was a moral obligation to take a stand. The defense of the indicted habit—whether professional and for pay, for capricious or quibbling scientific reasons, or through sheer ignorance of the facts—could have more lethal effect on the population than all the wars of history. Lung cancer alone was killing three times as many Americans as were lost in combat during the Korean war, and, spreading at a frightening rate, this epidemic soon would be killing more than are destroyed in highway accidents.

The Society decided the information should be released at the earliest appropriate medical conference.

The results were disclosed at the 1954 annual meeting of the American Medical Association. Newspapers, radio, and television treated the findings as top news of the day. There was a brief dip in tobacco stocks, followed by a rebound; and for a few months cigarette sales dropped off. Then, as the effects of the scare wore off, sales steadily rose to new all-time highs.

The industry, aware that trouble was in the offing, a short time earlier had begun forming a Scientific Advisory Board of the Tobacco Industry Research Committee, with Dr. Clarence Cook Little as its head. Dr. Little, a geneticist with a record of achievement as one time head of the organization which became the American Cancer Society, former president of the Universities of Michigan and Maine and Director of the Roscoe B. Jackson Memorial Laboratory in Bar Harbor, Maine, organized a board of distinguished scientists; together they planned and put into effect a multimillion-dollar research program. In the decade of its existence, this research program has supported excellent work. A few of its projects have tended to suggest that cigarette smoke contains carcinogens, may be responsible for numerous diseases, and that cigarette smokers, perhaps by nature, are somewhat on the neurotic side.

The major burden of answering the growing indictment of cigarettes was left largely to lay spokesmen for the industry. Newspapers, with what ordinarily is commendable objectivity, for years gave the industry spokesmen equal credence with scientists in their accounts of research developments. The unsophisticated news reader (meaning probably 90 per cent of all news readers) apparently has difficulty in distinguishing the announcement of a research development by a scientist from a purely commerical denial by industry. Were it not for this lack of readership aptitude, or perhaps news editors' failure to spell things out more carefully, news of the harmful effects of cigarettes might have had more impact on tobacco sales and, possibly, on mounting mortality rates. It was left to several magazines—notably the *Reader's Digest*—to present a comprehensive picture of the controversy and to the Consumers Union to add up the facts in a well-documented 218-page report—perhaps one of the most persuasive arguments of all on the demerits of cigarette smoking.

The first Hammond-Horn report had its critics. Foremost among them were industry spokesmen. Mr. Timothy V. Hartnett, representing the industry, criticized the scope of the study as being small (it was the largest of its kind ever undertaken) and of too short duration. When the study was completed after four years of follow-up and the final results completely corrobrated the first findings, Mr. Hartnett listed as criticisms by scientists he did not identify: (1) a mere numerical association does not establish a cause-and-effect relationship; (2) the survey's limitation to smoking habits did not eliminate other possible factors; (3) the people studied were not representative of the total population (it covered urban and rural areas in nine widely scattered states); and (4) the number of lung-cancer deaths was small and the sampling methods not statistically sound. On other occasions, the industry contended that there was no chemical or biological evidence of carcinogens in cigarette smoke.

All of Mr. Hartnett's early criticisms long since have been met. About forty different surveys in the United States and eight or nine other countries have been almost unanimous in showing that cigarette smokers die early, that many of them die of lung cancer and that lung cancer is rare among nonsmokers. Another mammoth survey, headed by the late Dr. Harold F. Dorn of NCI, showed that general death rates of 200,000 veterans holding government life insurance policies were twice as high among heavy smokers as among non-smokers and that for lung cancer the ratio was 16 to 1. Drs. Richard Doll and A. Bradford Hill in a prospective study analyzed the death rates for British doctors between 1951 and 1954 and showed that lung cancer rates mounted steadily with smoking—heavy smokers having 20 times the lung cancer rate of non-smokers.

A breakdown of the Hammond-Horn results showed an increased susceptibility among smokers to other kinds of cancer—among them cancers of the bladder, esophagus, larynx, tongue, mouth, and back of the throat. While several other cancers and many other nonmalignant diseases were not associated with cigarettes, smokers showed high susceptibility to strokes, peptic ulcers, emphysema, and a few seemingly unrelated diseases.

A by-product of the Hammond-Horn study proved to be perhaps more important than its principal objective. It disclosed that heart disease, the Number One killer in modern countries, also went hand in hand with cigarette smoking; the death rate from coronary artery disease was a shocking 70 per cent higher among smokers than nonsmokers. This and other surveys have shown that it helps a great deal to stop smoking before the first heart attack—much more than after it.

In 1960 the American Heart Association acknowledged the evidence of several studies which showed that the death rates from heart attacks among middle-aged men are from 50 to 150 per cent higher among heavy cigarette smokers than among nonsmokers. In 1963, the AHA board asserted that while a causal relationship had not been established, the evidence was such that it was joining with other agencies in educational programs to discourage cigarette smoking, particularly by teen-agers and people with symptoms of susceptibility to heart attacks.

A few scientists of undoubted integrity and competence questioned some of the Hammond-Horn conclusions, and in some cases the validity of the statistical results. They contended, variously, that (1) the sample studied was not representative of the national population; (2) while there was no doubt about the numerical association between cigarettes and lung cancer, cause and effect had not been proved; (3) other factors—notably viruses, air pollution and industrial hazards—were not mentioned as causes of lung cancer; and (4) one scientist suggested that inherited personality traits were to blame; they either predisposed to both lung cancer and cigarette smoking, or incipient lung cancer caused a person to smoke. Some wondered that so many different diseases—lung, heart, circulatory and others, seemingly independent—could be caused by a single habit. It is to be noted that many of the skeptics themselves did not smoke cigarettes, and some of them advised people, particularly youngsters, against the habit. It is doubtful if any of them (or many in the industry itself) now would recommend smoking to a son or daughter of their own after reviewing the research findings.

Reservations by scientists against the harmful effects of cigarette smoking have dissipated gradually as research findings piled up. A growing number of carcinogens—including arsenicals, aromatic polycyclic hydrocarbons, phenols, organic acids, radioactive polonium, nickel, insecticide traces and free radicals—have been identified in cigarette smoke. Cancers have been induced in a variety of experimental animals by application of cigarette smoke condensates. Not only does cigarette smoke contain numerous identified and unidentified carcinogens but it also includes cocarcinogens—substances which, in animal experiments, multiply the effect of carcinogens by a factor of 50 or more. British scientists have produced evidence that tobacco mosaic virus might be involved, but at this point it is regarded as suggestive at best.

Meanwhile, one massive autopsy study, which was tedious and time-consuming, brilliantly conceived and meticulously objective, has built a solid bridge of evidence linking what had been considered unrelated diseases of the lung, heart, and circulatory system.

Dr. Oscar Auerbach of the East Orange (N.J.) VA Hospital and Dr. Arthur Purdy Stout of Columbia, pathologists, and Dr. Hammond and Lawrence Garfinkel, Cancer Society epidemiologists, undertook a series of double-blind studies which have correlated with remarkable precision the biological effects of cigarette smoking. In the entire series, the pathologists examined under the microscope more than 100,000 samples of tissue removed from the lungs of more than 1,500 men and women who had died of various causes. The pathologists had no way of knowing the identity of the dead donors of samples, their smoking histories, or the cause of death in each case. They graded each sample for the abnormalities they found in it—the erosion of whiplike cilia which sweep particles from the breathing tubes, benign overgrowth of tissue lining the tubes, the overgrowth or disappearance of mucus-producing cells, the walls of tiny arteries, the structure of millions of minuscule air sacs, cells which had mutated, and cancer cells.

The results of the combined pathology-epidemiology investigation were breathtaking in the mathematical fidelity with which the smoking history of each dead tissue donor came to light. The investigators found that all kinds of lung damage were in direct proportion to the amount of cigarettes smoked. In the heavier smokers, cilia and mucus-producing cells had eroded away, the lining of breathing tubes had thickened, and, quite often, precancerous cells and unsuspected cancer cells were found. Equally dramatic changes were discovered in the pulpy part of the lung—the delicate air chambers through which oxygen is drawn into the system and noxious carbon dioxide expelled were severely affected. Their fragile walls had ruptured and leathery fibers had replaced elastic tissue, forming great pockets of stale and stagnating gases. Small blood vessels had broken and dried up.

In these studies lay the key to the many evils which befall smokers—lung cancer, emphysema, bronchitis, coronary artery disease and various signs of oxygen starvation. The tissues apparently fall victim to a vicious cycle of events: (1) paralysis and eventual destruction of cilia and mucus-secreting cells leave the bronchi and lungs open to contaminants drawn in with each breath; (2) overgrowth of the breathing-tube lining restricts the intake of air; (3) the loss of lung elasticity and the formation of fibrous pockets of stale gas limit the discharge of wastes; (4) the carbon monoxide in cigarette smoke (and, of course, from other sources) saturates red blood cells, depriving them of their capacity to pick up and transport oxygen; (5) in efforts to supply oxygen to smothering cells throughout the body the heart increases its beat and pressure, and the pumping muscles enlarge; (6) the large arteries, under great pressure, tend to harden and the small arteries supplying the heart, brain, and lung thicken and clog; (7) the effect on many arteries throughout the body is atherosclerosis. Under these circumstances, the person ages rapidly and becomes subject to many of the chronic diseases of old age. Atherosclerotic diseases kill more than 500,000 Americans annually.

No responsible authority contends that cigarette smoking is the sole cause of lung cancer among men. Some estimate it is responsible for 60 per cent; others say 80 or even 90, particularly in men. (Six men die of lung cancer for every woman victim, and while cancer attacks the male bronchial lining, it favors the pulpy part of the female lung.) Almost all who have made objective studies feel that cigarettes are the principal cause and that cigarettes and other factors have combined to produce the lung-cancer epidemic which has grown rapidly and inexorably during the twentieth century, its rate doubling with each decade. The 1963 toll was estimated at 47,000 victims, with 41,000 dying during the course of the year. It is 5 per cent curable—or less—and it is an ugly disease which moves toward death too slowly to please some of its victims.

While there are several technical points over which a few scientists quibble, the sweep of research has eliminated one doubt after another that cigarette smoking is a habit with brutal consequences. The majority opinion in science, as in other areas of public affairs, does not indicate infallibility by any means, but it does seem reasonable that people who value an extra five to fifteen years of healthy life would make an effort to learn what has been accomplished in research on tobacco, be guided by the opinions of more than 95 per cent of the informed and objective scientists, and then decide whether or not to smoke.

The potentially harmful effects of cigarette smoking on health have been acknowledged—usually with recommendations that people, particularly young people, not smoke—by an impressive list of medical and scientific bodies in the United States and throughout the world. They include, in the United States, the Third National Lung Cancer Conference, Public Health Cancer Association, American Cancer Society, American Heart Association, the Surgeon General of the U.S. Public Health Service, New York State Commissioner of Health, Director of California State Department of Public Health, American Public Health Association, American College of Chest Physicians, National Tuberculosis Association, and a large and rapidly increasing number of state medical organizations. In other countries similar sentiments have been expressed by the British Minister of Health, the Swedish Ministry of Health, Danish Committee on Cancer Prevention, Medical Research Council of Great Britain, Health Council of Holland, Research Council of Sweden, National Cancer Institute of Canada, World Health Organization, International Union Against Cancer, Canadian Cancer Society, Royal College of Physicians, the Norwegian Finance Minister and numerous others.

Despite the number of learned societies which have condemned cigarette smoking, all doctors and some of their major professional organizations cannot be regarded as vigorous antismoking campaigners. The American Medical Association as late as 1964 was a conspicuous absentee from the list of medical and scientific societies which had condemned cigarette smoking; Dr. John B. Talbott, the editor of the *Journal of the American Medical Association,* in 1959 had declared editorially his belief that nothing had been proved about cigarettes one way or another in the lung-cancer matter, and he recommended that physicians advise patients in accordance with their own individual appraisal of the facts. The physicians' attitudes then were reflected in an American Cancer Society survey by Dr. Horn which showed, in response to the question of whether "cigarette smoking is definitely, probably, probably not, or definitely not a major cause of lung cancer:" definitely is, 33 per cent; probably is, 31 per cent; no opinion, 14 per cent; probably is not, 13 per cent; and definitely is not, 9 per cent. At the same time, a poll among Massachusetts physicians showed, despite a substantial drop in smoking by doctors, that 44.5 per cent smoked, and 38.5 per cent smoked cigarettes. A Cancer Society survey, involving 2,000 interviews with adult Americans, showed that only one in six patients ever discussed smoking with his physician, and of these only one-third had been told that cigarette smoking can cause lung cancer. Nevertheless, it must be said that these surveys indicated a gradual awakening of the medical profession to the problems of cigarette smoking; as compared wtih earlier studies, doctors progressively are smoking less and talking more; smoking doctors also are dying in large numbers of coronary attacks and lung cancer. A five-year study of 6,033 male physicians in Massachusetts showed cigarette-smoking doctors had about twice the mortality rate of nonsmoking doctors, and their deaths were 75 per cent in excess of the rate for men generally. No nonsmokers in this study died of lung cancer.

Dr. George E. Moore, of Roswell Park, in an article in *Medical Tribune* in 1963, pointed out that treatment of lung cancer continues without significantly greater success. "An equal amount of thought, energy and money spent on education and prevention might save 40,000 lives rather than 2,000," he wrote. He said that at Roswell Park a "Cigarette Cancer Committee" of scientists and physicians had been established, cigarette machines had been banned, tobacco withdrawal clinics had been started, cigarettes made from vegetable leaves had been tested, and many other measures were being taken to discourage cigarette smoking. Appealing to physicians to employ preventive measures to save 40,000 of the lives lost annually to lung cancer, Dr. Moore wrote: "We recommend that physicians use only a few facts in social conversations about this problem: (1) more people die of lung cancer than in auto accidents; (2) 98 per cent of all patients developing squamous-cell carcinoma of the bronchi are heavy smokers; and (3) whereas 23 per cent of nonsmoking American men aged thirty-five will die of all causes before age sixty-five, 41 per cent of smokers (about twice as many) will die. Naturally such statements will be considered more seriously if the physician himself is not smoking. We advise adults that they can reduce their chances of lung cancer by 50 per cent if they will stop smoking for at least a year. For those who are unable to stop, we suggest that they should (1) smoke less, (2) not inhale, (3) leave 1½ inches of each cigarette unsmoked, (4) use filters or filter-tip cigarettes, (5) switch to pipe or cigar smoking and not inhale, and (6) stop smoking completely if they develop 'smoker's cough,' shortness of breath, or evidence of any cardiovascular insufficiency."

A decade passed between the first Hammond-Horn report and the Surgeon General's committee report of January, 1964. In terms of cigarette sales and lung cancer deaths, little change was noted—cigarette sales continued to mount, although the line leveled off somewhat in 1962, and lung cancer deaths increased with unabated vigor. One need not go beyond his own acquaintanceship to realize that many smokers have become uneasy; about 40 million of America's 70 million smokers have shifted to filters, a few others to pipes and cigars, and some—mainly those who have reached the age when smoking effects are noted on the lungs, heart, and circulation —have quit. Their places have been taken by new volunteers, however.

Who smokes? And why?

Cigarette addicts smoke. Tests have shown that it doesn't take long to develop an actual physiological craving for regular doses of nicotine. It may be that cigarette smoke contains narcotic traces; esculetin, cotenine, and scopoletin, for example, which have been identified in cigarette smoke, have not been tested for addictive qualities.

Youngsters smoke. They smoke in ever-increasing numbers because of or despite the infantile romance and glamor appeal skillfully concocted on Madison Avenue for morons. Within a few months many are habituated; and within two years most of them are hooked for life—or for death.

Dr. Moore has said:

> Addiction to smoking is difficult to combat. The strength of it is apparent when one sees patients who have lost feet, legs and fingers from peripheral vascular disease but who still will not stop smoking. Several of our patients with laryngectomies have even devised attachments to fit their tracheotomies so that they can continue smoking. There are no easy methods for preventing withdrawal symptoms. The resurgence of appetite and weight gain following cessation of smoking is an additional deterrent and excuse for many.

There are many kinds of cigarette addicts and many degrees of addiction. A few have the blessed ability to smoke when they want and only as much as they want and to quit for long or short periods without withdrawal symptoms. Many more feel that they can take or leave cigarettes—or at least, they feel that way until they attempt to leave them. And some unfortunates can neither take nor leave them; several studies have shown that from one in five to one in three smokers and one in seven nonsmokers show markedly allergic skin reactions to extracts of tobacco. Tests at New York University have shown that 44 of 95 in one series of patients with thromboangiitis obliterans, or Buerger's disease, and 78 per cent in another series were allergic to tobacco. At Mount Sinai Hospital, New York, 56 of 106 survivors of heart attacks were found to be allergic to tobacco; the tobacco reactors developed heart disease about ten years earlier than nonallergic smokers and from thirteen to eighteen years earlier than nonallergic nonsmokers. These and other findings of serious conditions predominantly in smokers suggest that an exploration of the allergens (and carcinogens) in cigarette smoke in relation to autoimmune diseases might prove fruitful.

Even more astounding than the persistence of smoking by people allergic to tobacco contents is the failure to curb smoking among pregnant women. Several well-publicized findings have shown that premature birth, stillbirth, underweight babies, and fetal brain damage occur more often with smoking than nonsmoking mothers. (One small study at Stanford, however, showed smoking mothers bore healthier babies than did nonsmoking mothers.) Babies of alcoholic mothers have been born drunk; babies of narcotic addicts have been born addicted and suffered acute withdrawal symptoms following birth; the babies of cigarette-addicted mothers may also pay for their mother's habit in mild or severe congenital conditions.

Charles Lamb said 150 years or so ago, "For thy sake, tobacco, I would do anything but die." By the standards of many modern smokers, Mr. Lamb was a piker.

Several studies have concurred almost completely in describing the kind of person who takes up smoking and the reasons for it. Dr. Eva J. Salber at Harvard, in a study of 3,449 boys and 3,361 girls in Newton, Mass., schools, found in 1959 that, in the seventh grade, 7 per cent of boys and 1 per cent of girls smoked; by the time they became seniors, 46 per cent of boys and 55 per cent of girls were cigarette smokers. The reasons the smokers gave for their own taking up the habit usually were curiosity and enjoyment; the reasons they gave for others' taking up the habit were to emulate adults, impress others, and rebel against conventions. The facts showed that the family had great influence—when parents smoked, the children smoked (girls tended to do as Mom did, boys as Dad did); older sons and daughters also seemed to set an example; the likelihood of smoking among youngsters increased when fathers (but not mothers) came from a lower social class. Smoking students, as compared with nonsmokers, spent more time watching TV, motoring, and dancing and less time on books, sports, and clubwork. Catholic men and boys and Jewish women and girls were the most frequent and heaviest smokers; Catholic women and girls smoked least.

Dr. Brian MacMahon, who is Professor of Epidemiology at the Harvard School of Public Health, has expressed the opinion that "it is now established beyond any reasonable doubt that lung cancer would be reduced to less than 10 per cent of its present incidence if cigarette smoking were discontinued."

Another Harvard study has covered the smoking habits and basic personality traits of 252 alumni for more than twenty years. They were selected for the study as sophomores between 1938 and 1942 because of their lack of visible abnormalities at that time. Smokers, as compared with nonsmokers, were less masculine (the more they smoked the less masculine they were), had an aversion to strenuous exercise and sports, were low in physical fitness and poor in muscular coordination, were less well integrated, manifested greater nervous instability, tended to be shy, asocial, self-conscious, and inhibited; and their aptitudes were for the arts, letters, and philosophy. Another Harvard study showed that smokers were more inclined than nonsmokers to restless energy, alcohol, and coffee. By 1960, sixteen per cent of the Harvard subjects quit smoking—most of them during the "health scare" of 1954–55.

Dr. Abraham M. Lilienfeld, now of Johns Hopkins, found in earlier work at Roswell Park that, as compared with nonsmokers, men and women who smoked cigarettes married more often, moved more frequently, changed jobs more often, were hospitalized more and participated in more sports.

Dr. Maurice J. Barry, Jr., of the Mayo Clinic's Section of Psychiatry has written that, in youngsters, smoking symbolizes rebellion, defiance of authority, and setting aside of a rule that has been imposed by adults who, themselves, do not abide by it. He has said that, in folklore, smoking represented manhood, power, and virility (as indicated by proud fathers passing out cigars, or cartoons and movies in which political bosses and executives smoke cigars). His principal point is that smoking, a throwback to infant feeding, is an oral ritual, symbolic of companionship and mutual acceptance; and, he has added, "the most important dynamic force operative in perpetuating the smoking habit . . . is in the act of suckling . . . a universal and necessary gratification . . . which persists long after weaning and extends into adult life." In the same category, he has said, are thumb sucking, nail biting, pencil gnawing and gum chewing, which increase in the face of stress and frustrations.

There is a sharp contrast between smoker profiles as found in scientific studies and as pictured in television commercials.

Study after study—epidemiological, biological and chemical—have been in concurrence on the awe-inspiring damage done by cigarette smoking.

A series of three recent reports seemed to shatter, for the time being, the complaisant attitude of the industry and soften what had become obviously cynical responses to scientific evidence.

The first of these came in the form of a well-documented, sixty-page report, *Smoking and Health,* issued in 1962 by the Royal College of Physicians in England. A widely read booklet both in Europe and the United States, it asserted flatly that cigarette smoking is a cause of lung cancer and called for prompt action by the British Government "to produce beneficial changes in smoking habits." It proposed a public education campaign, especially among school children, and urged restriction of tobacco advertising, bans on smoking in public places, and wider use of filter tips. It admonished that "the doctor who smokes will find it harder to help his patients who need to stop smoking." This report was followed by a sharp decline of tobacco sales and stocks in Britain, editorial support by the leading medical journal, and approval in Parliament. The London correspondent for the American industry journal, *Tobacco,* reported under the headline, "UK Cigarette Sales Slump in Health Scare," that "Altogether it's a worrying time—but we are hoping this scare will eventually go the way of all others. But it will take longer." He was right.

The second major blow came in December, 1963, when Dr. Hammond published the results of an enormous study of more than 1,000,000 Americans. For this report, 37,000 male cigarette smokers had been paired with 37,000 male nonsmokers. Except for their smoking habits, each pair studied was matched for race, age, religion, longevity of parents and grandparents, occupation, stature, education, amount of exercise, nervous tension, marital status, previous diseases, rural or urban residence, numbers of brothers and sisters, age of mother at birth, drug use, circumcision, baldness, number of hours of sleep, and many other factors. Many of these categories showed some relationship to death rates. The stark standout, however, was cigarette smoking. Early death depended very much on the age when one started smoking, the number of cigarettes smoked, and how deeply one inhaled. Cigarettes were shown most dramatically to be coffin nails in cancers of the lung, mouth, and pharynx (or T-zone, as cigarette ads used to say), bladder, and pancreas. Coronary artery disease also claimed large excesses among cigarette smokers. Pipe and cigar smoking had relatively little bad effect.

Dr. Hammond's figures showed that some factors depressed death rates to a degree, but all of these did not compare with abstaining from smoking. The life-lengthening factors included being white, and particularly native born white, having no history of serious disease, having long-lived parents and grandparents, being born to a mother 30–34 years old, being 71–73 inches tall, having a good education, being a white-collar worker (but not a doctor, dentist, or veterinarian), having a slight-to-moderate nervous tension, being married, having brothers and sisters, eating fried foods and getting about seven hours (little more or less) sleep.

The report was given at the December meeting of the American Medical Association in 1963. Despite it and the unanimity of forty earlier reports on the ill effects of cigarette smoking, the AMA failed once again to take a stand. In effect, the AMA validated the tobacco industry's contention that the case had not been proved, by voting to conduct an extensive study of tobacco effects on health. The tobacco industry spokesmen expressed its gratification and awarded the AMA $10,000,000 to support research.

The third and most influential study was conducted over fourteen months by a ten-man Surgeon General's Advisory Committee on Smoking and Health. Members were appointed in 1962, following the Royal College of Physicians' report, to review and evaluate all the scientific evidence available. Five of the members smoked; five did not; none had ever taken a stand on the smoking issue, and all were presumed to be objective; all were respected and honored scientists or physicians. Their report, in January, 1964, was spread across the nation in eight-column headlines and with as many as six or seven solid pages of news coverage; radio and television networks carried half-hour or hour-long shows on the report and associated comment. The conclusions of the committee were the same as those reached in the objective studies they had reviewed: the committee had agreed unanimously that death rates were 70 per cent higher for cigarette smokers than for nonsmokers (120 per cent for heavy smokers), that deaths from heart disease were nearly twice as frequent among cigarette smokers, that cigarette smoking is the most important of the causes for chronic bronchitis and highly important in emphysema. The committee said the risk of death is enhanced for cigarette smokers by these ratios: generally 1.7 times (2.2 for heavy smokers), lung cancer 10.8, bronchitis and emphysema 6.1, T-zone cancers about 4 or 5, coronary artery disease 1.7, stomach and duodenal ulcer 2.8. Cigar smokers ran almost insignificant risks of any kind, and pipe smokers ran a small risk of mouth cancer. There was no evidence that filters saved the lives of the 60 per cent of cigarette smokers who now used them. If there was any surprise at all in the committee's 387-page report, it was only that ten independent scientists could agree on all conclusions; there was no dissenting or minority opinion.

By January, 1964, when the Surgeon General's committee reported, the public had become used to such reports. Some tobacco stocks actually rose, first in anticipation of an unfavorable report and again after it was made. It was known that the British people now, less than two years after the Royal College's report, were smoking 5 per cent more than before the report, and, despite the long succession of findings unfavorable to cigarettes, the American public was smoking more than ever.

There was, of course, a flurry of feature stories on antismoking clinics which had started and on the many theoretical ways to quit smoking.

But the hard facts were on the financial pages: in the decade since the first Hammond-Horn report cigarette sales had risen from $2.8 to $4.5 billion, per capita consumption had gone from 3,339 to 4,000 cigarettes a year, total consumption had risen from 368.7 to 523.3 billion, and employment, profits, and other dimensions of the industry had soared accordingly. It was now an $8 billion industry which made 14 billion more cigarettes in 1963 than in 1962 (cigars were up 115 million to a total of

7.1 billion) and paid out $3.3 billion in Federal, state, and local taxes, and tobacco was the nation's fifth largest crop.

Some quit smoking—and wondered how long they could stay off the stuff. Some were frankly worried about their health—and to quiet their nerves (the Surgeon General's committee conceded that "a source of comfort" was a principal motive for cigarette smoking) they smoked more than ever.

In reply to the Surgeon General's committee, tobacco industry spokesmen were very restrained. They could afford to be. They knew from ample experience that sales would be depressed—probably for two or three months.

Among the many now impressed with the inadvisability of smoking were physicians. A survey of doctors throughout the country by the journal, *Modern Medicine,* showed that by now only 22.5 per cent smoked cigarettes and 89 per cent of these considered the habit a health hazard. An additional 34 per cent smoked pipes and cigars. One of four who had changed their habit did so under influence by the Surgeon General committee's report.

There are any number of possible solutions to the cigarette quandary, none of them perfect, but perhaps several of them practical to a degree.

Laissez-faire seems to be good only for tobacco companies and stockholders. Since the outbreak of the controversy until 1964, per capita consumption of cigarettes (which had declined sharply between 1952 and 1954) had risen sharply.

Laws in forty-six states prohibiting sales to minors have proved futile. Prohibition of cigarettes probably would revive all the evils which came to life under the Volstead Act, a moral and social plague without precedent. High taxes are being tried, and they are no deterrent. Increased life-insurance premiums for smokers are under test. In Italy, cigarette advertising has been banned; and in Finland, the television industry has sacrificed this lucrative revenue voluntarily.

"Safe" cigarettes, so-called, have been tried, and they have won a substantial number of converts. Whereas the old-fashioned, unfiltered, "unsafe" cigarette—much milder now than it used to be and still the choice of serious smokers—spews out in its smoke 30 to 38 milligrams of tar, including 1.7 to 2.1 milligrams of nicotine, filtered cigarettes, depending on the brand, have reduced the tar content anywhere from 15 to 80 per cent and nicotine from 0 to 80 per cent. (Some filters give a mere illusion of reducing harmful substances.) It remains to be seen whether some "safe" cigarettes really save lives or whether they encourage continued smoking among a lot of people who otherwise could and would give up the habit. A few scientists have voiced the suspicion that certain cigarette tips may filter out of the smoke chemicals which neutralize the carcinogens.

Court action has been tried. A lung-cancer victim in Pittsburgh sued Liggett and Myers for $1,250,000, contending that as a result of smoking Chesterfields for more than 25 years he developed lung cancer and lost his right lung. In the first trial, the federal judge directed a verdict of not guilty; in the second trial, a jury decided that although cigarette smoking caused the cancer, the tobacco company was not financially responsible. In another damage suit brought, lost and appealed by the family of a Coral Gables man who died of lung cancer, the Florida State Supreme Court, asked by a U.S. Court of Appeals for a ruling, decided that the manufacturer is legally liable when death is traced to the use of its product. If higher courts, including the U.S. Supreme Court, were to hold similar views, disaster might soon overtake the tobacco industry.

Legislation is being sought. One bill in Congress would give the Food and Drug Administration the same authority over tobacco as it now wields over food, drugs, and cosmetics. If this bill should pass, action would be determined largely by the attitude of the agency administrator and those to whom he is responsible. It is difficult to predict what would happen.

Shortly after the report to the Surgeon General, the Federal Trade Commission proposed that each cigarette pack be labeled a health hazard and that advertising claims of mildness and reduced dangers be restricted to proved facts.

Several countries have established withdrawal clinics for addicts who would like to stop smoking. Dr. Borje Ejrup, who has worked in six such clinics in Stockholm, has reported that 1,012 of an initial 6,000 patients completed the treatment and, of these, 75.8 per cent stopped smoking during treatment, and 21.7 per cent cut their habit down to 1 to 25 per cent of previous consumption. Six months after treatment, 50 per cent (or about 380 patients) of those who had stopped reported that they still were not smoking or were smoking much less, and 95 per cent said they were satisfied with the treatment. The patients—male and female, aged 12 to 70 years—joined the clinic for a variety of serious reasons: poor physical condition, nervousness, chronic bronchitis, stomatitis, cardiovascular symptoms, digestive complaints, emotional disturbances, and a combination of economic and health motives. The ten-day treatment consisted of reading a manual on how to stop smoking, a discussion of the habit with a physician, injections of nicotine or nicotine derivatives (to satisfy the craving), other drugs and substances which, during smoking, produced a foul taste. Those who responded reported improved skin texture and color, return of senses of smell and taste, increasing work capacity, disappearance of cough, easier breathing, decreased heart rate, and a feeling of well being.

The history of most smoking-withdrawal clinics shows that all the rewards are not enough to induce smokers to stay away from cigarettes. Most resigned smokers are at it again within a year and probably fewer than 10 per cent abstain for two years. The ten-day plans and the five-day plans begun so enthusiastically on the heels of a first-class "health scare" often fold and the ex-smokers quickly or gradually become ex-ex-smokers.

The sad fact is that no substitute yet has been found for will power, and it takes plenty of that to shake a well-developed cigarette habit. This is evident from the sorry scores emerging from most withdrawal clinics. Some of the magic formulas may help a little—the little litanies of "I will not smoke," lots of liquids, and plenty of rest and fresh air, well-balanced diets, abstinence from coffee and liquor (which are said to trigger the need for a smoke), candy, gum, posthypnotic suggestion, B vitamins, drug injections, or a growing assortment of pills, pink or otherwise. Will, and will alone, does the job, almost all authorities agree.

Dr. Horn, now with the NCI, has proposed that those who are addicted physiologically or psychologically to cigarettes may find some help in this "relatively painless" routine: 1) Carefully analyze and list your reasons for wanting to quit and the situations in which you smoke; 2) select those situations in which smoking can continue and those in which it can be discontinued consciously; 3) keep the cigarettes in an unusual place (another pocket, another drawer, another room) where you cannot automatically and unthinkingly light up; 4) before you light up, ask yourself, "Do I really want this cigarette?" If you do not want it, put it back; if you do, by all means light up; 5) analyze the motions, gestures, hand movements, breathing characteristics, and other elements of your habit and then consciously try to change each component of the habit; 6) when possible, substitute a lump of sugar, chewing gum, doodling, physical exercise, or taking a drink of water; when not possible, smoke.

After a few months of classes for U. S. Public Health Service employees who wanted to quit smoking, Dr. Horn found that many of the "students" had cut down progressively until they were able to shake the habit altogether. The question, "Do I really want this cigarette?" was the key. The interval between yes's gradually became longer—and eventually, for many, the invariable answer was no—until the smoker found it no longer necessary to pose the question.

The fact that some middle-aged long-term smokers who suddenly kick the habit die within the year should be investigated carefully. Drs. Levin and Graham found the lung cancer risk 2.7 times normal during the first year as an ex-smoker. Dr. Hammond has reported that over-all mortality among those who have quit within the year is 1.41 times that of those who continue to smoke. It is 1.35 among those who reported quitting because they were sick or had a history of sickness and 1.19 among those who did not report sickness. Whether withdrawal contributed to the deaths of the 0.19 excess deaths should be looked into. If sudden withdrawal from narcotics or alcohol results in a considerable number of deaths, it is not unreasonable to suppose that some long-addicted cigarette smokers may also suffer severe, and in some cases, mortal, withdrawal symptoms.

Also worth investigating is the bare possibility that a few smokers may have adapted to the toxins and the carcinogens and have come to actually require them. This sort of adaptation—or natural selection—is noted regularly in laboratory cultures exposed to toxins; organisms deprived of their accustomed poisons fare very badly indeed. We shall see in later chapters that resistance to some carcinogens (ultraviolet and X-rays) can be built up by graded prior doses of the carcinogen and that the course of developing cancers can be terminated by large doses of the carcinogen (X rays and viruses) which initiated them. Drs. Levin and Graham found that those who started smoking at age 10–14 years had only 0.77 the lung cancer risk of those who began at 15–19 years. This is an unpopular finding and has been described by the investigators as having no statistical significance. Nevertheless, it is an extremely interesting anomaly (those who start smoking at age 15–19 years run 1.72 times the risk of the after-age-25 bracket) and should be explored carefully.

With the cigarette habit coming more and more under the guns of zealots for health and morals, its virtues, if any—sedative, stimulant, or whatever—have been lost track of almost entirely. However small any minority which may require its lifelong habit of smoking, its members should be identified and indulged. In some countries, notably England, narcotics addiction is dealt with more intelligently than is the smoking habit within some homes and offices in an aroused America.

By and large, however, it seems advisable to kick the cigarette habit. At the end of one year, ex-smokers begin dying at about the same rate as those who continue to smoke; at five years they have reduced their chances of untimely death by 25 per cent and at ten years by about 40 per cent. Dr. Levin's and Dr. Dorn's studies show that the risk of lung cancer is almost halved among those who have quit for two years and is reduced to one-quarter that of the smokers after four years of abstinence.

Lung-cancer deaths have increased from less than 3,000 in 1930 to 18,000 in 1950 and 47,000 in 1963. Today's college students will begin to contribute to the toll in the 1970s, and high school students will be paying liberally with their lives in the 1980s.

Most statistical signs point to the certainty that death will come much earlier to today's cigarette-smoking youngsters than to their smoking parents. Boys and girls are smoking much earlier and much more than their parents. Whereas today's victims survive well until their forties—and the danger actually begins to ebb slightly during the late fifties—smoking students could begin to feel the impact during their thirties.

Dr. Salber checked up on the Newton, Massachusetts, high school students more than a year after her original survey in 1959. She found that antismoking campaigns had failed. Because the Newton findings so closely resembled the situation in other localities, the results well may reflect a national trend.

Dr. Salber found on the second go-around that students were smoking at earlier ages—boys at about 11, girls at 12—and they were smoking more. In a surprisingly short time, they had become addicted. Two-thirds of the boys and more than one-half the girls who had tried to quit were smoking more than ever. She checked over a sample which a little more than a year earlier had been in the ratio of 10 smokers to 10 nonsmokers to 10 ex-smokers; within this short period these students now stood in a ratio of 30 smokers to 15 nonsmokers to 10 ex-smokers.

Two-thirds of the boys and more than one-half of the girls who had forsworn cigarettes the year before were puffing away again more than ever. Senior girls were outsmoking the boys in their class—about 55 per cent to 45 per cent respectively. They had begun smoking about ten years earlier than their mothers had, and the boys about six years earlier than their fathers. The mothers, incidentally, were now surpassing the men as cigarette smokers by 57.4 per cent to 49.9 per cent; this had come about as a result of more women taking up the habit, while 40 per cent of the men were trying to quit smoking and about 15 per cent more had taken to cigars and pipes.

The number of father ex-smokers remained fairly constant, for one reason, because as the backsliders retrogressed from ex-smoker to ex-ex-smoker, an equal number of smoking fathers decided to try to become ex-smokers.

Statistics, much less conclusive for women than for men, indicate that their sex may give women smokers some protection from lung cancer; how much protection and from what diseases should be known when they have been smoking a few more years. Present-day girl smokers will be paying health penalties at ages much younger than their mothers —if a heavy-smoking mother (who started at age 22) dies at age 60 years, for instance, her heavy-smoking daughter (starting at age 12 years) may die when she is in her early or middle forties. Women may not be as immune to lung cancer as has been thought. Dr. William Haenszel of NCI reported in 1964 that female smokers already were showing 11 times the lung cancer risk of non-smoking women.

What youngsters, parents, physicians, and scientists do not seem to realize is that for some people cigarette smoking is an addiction. The portion of the Surgeon General's report which called cigarette smoking habituating but not addictive, one suspects, must have been written by the nonsmoking members. The committee described the characteristics of addiction as (1) an overpowering desire or need to continue taking the drug and to obtain it by any means, (2) a tendency to increase the dose, (3) a psychological and generally a physical dependence on the effects of the drug, and (4) detrimental effect on the individual and on society. They mentioned morphine, alcohol, and barbiturates as addictive. Many who have tried and failed to break the cigarette habit, their wives, their children, and their colleagues could have set the committee straight. The committee obviously never heard of the man whose mouth is dirty with the residue of thousands of cigarettes, who loathes the sight of a cigarette, who hates himself for being unable even to cut down on his consumption, and yet who reaches regularly for a smoke, who will go out at five in the morning to find a shop or restaurant that sells them, who sweats as much as a cold turkey-ized morphine addict on occasions when he can *not* light up, and who will do violence to anyone who interferes with his overwhelming compulsion for the little white stick he despises. The failure to recognize or acknowledge these simple facts of life could account for the complete and utter failure of adults to behave as adults and to stave off early death for their children.

Future salvage of human life from the cigarette addiction must come primarily from parents, many of whom already have sacrificed years of their own lives to the habit. Permissive parents who tolerate dangerous experimentation by children, who know the health score but are naive enough to think they will smoke for a little while and then quit, must be made to realize what they are doing. Children should be restrained— by old-fashioned discipline, if necessary. At this point, there is no safe way of cigarette smoking—filter tips, light smoking, or any other quasi-compromise. For some people a little tobacco is like a little morphine, and no lecture on morality, health, family, or other argument is going to deter the addict.

If youngsters somehow could be made to recognize the inner torments of reluctant addicts, very few of them would test that first cigarette which makes them acutely ill, and fewer still would take the second which helps put them on the road to a variety of disastrous chronic sicknesses.

The American Public Health Association estimates that, under present trends, more than one million American children now in schools will develop lung cancer before they are seventy years old. Many more will develop and die of heart disease, emphysema, and other "diseases of old age" while still in what should be their prime years.

Unfortunately, teenagers do not have the capacity to look even a little beyond their teens. It is, as the Pennsylvania Dutchman said, "We are too soon old, and too late smart."

Everyone eventually stops smoking. Mother Nature—the most permissive of parents—sees to that. Those who smoke heaviest stop earliest.

There is one other lesson to be learned from the many and elaborate cigarette smoking studies which have been conducted. Many carcinogens —viruses, food additives, drugs, air and water pollutants, radiations, industrial chemicals, and all the rest—are now regarded as innocent as was cigarette smoking a short decade ago. Perhaps some of the skeptics will find—and prove—that these, too, contribute substantially to the cancer death rate when stern statistical tests are made.

CHAPTER 10

RADIATION
AND CANCER

Such terms as megaton range and strontium-90 have crept into the chatter at cocktail parties and the sober conversations of children. The change dates back to 1945 when it was demonstrated in Nagasaki and Hiroshima that a small equation in theoretical physics, $E = mc^2$, could be applied to practical problems.

There hovers over the earth the fear that in radiation the human mind has found something which will dwarf the natural calamities of all time —the prehistoric destruction of large organisms by the unpremeditated radiation from supernovae, the extinction of sea life by rising continents, and of land life by floods, fires, droughts, and volcanic eruptions. The succession of natural catastrophes always left some life to repopulate the earth; of the numerous vertebrate species which existed 100-odd million years ago, twenty-four have descendants in modern times. Some of the more anxious people of this age fear that in its periodic gambling fervor the human race may destroy not only itself and all the life about it but its planet as well. While the next catastrophe will not be the first to befall the earth, they feel it could be the last.

Radiation is not necessarily an evil thing. On the contrary, it is essential to life. The average human body experiences 200,000 potassium-40 atomic disintegrations every minute. Each individual exists amid an incessant and indispensable fireworks of radiation. The sources are above him, below him, around him, and inside him. Between one-fourth and one-fifth of natural radiation exposures come from our own bodies—largely from potassium and radium-type compounds.

Long before the earth formed in a flaming mass, our sun and countless suns before it filled the universe with their emanations. The first life— the molecule which first learned how to become two molecules—was made possible by intervention of solar radiation. Each pulse or breath of life today is the direct or indirect product of the sun's rays. A momentary flash of light in darkness transforms a colorless, stringy, slow-growing cellulose organism into a verdant, flourishing plant. Plants capture the sun's rays and package them into chemical compounds, which as food become the basic source of energy of animals and man. Plant-packaged sunlight is transformed by chemical processes, which rapidly are becoming understood, into the muscular energy of movement in swimming, flying, and walking creatures, into heat which warms the body in cold weather, into the stunning, 600-volt, electrical shock of eels, into the energy bats use as radar, into the cold light of fireflies, and into the sensory and brain powers of man.

Natural radiations over two billion years or so have helped mutate life forms, until by the countless trials and innumerable errors of evolution several hundred thousand strains and species have come to survive for measurable periods. Man is one of the recent products.

There are many kinds of radiant energy—light, heat, sound, electrical, magnetic, and a variety of atomic, or ionizing radiations. Most of them can be transformed into one another. Humans can sense only some of them. We are sensitive by touch to heat, by vision to light, by hearing to sound. Even here, however, human senses fail to detect vast areas of the light spectrum and powerful subsonic and supersonic waves. The fact that they are beyond detection by the senses does not mean that these forces are not powerful. The dark sides of the light spectrum, the silent sounds, the unfelt frequencies of magnetic fields, the subsensory splitting of atoms can kill when properly, or improperly, applied.

Cosmic rays shower down on us constantly, sometimes in a gentle mist and sometimes in violent storms. They comprise about 30 per cent of natural radiations to which we are exposed. No one knows their source in outer space. Some believe they are debris from explosions which many light-years ago demolished stars or produced galaxies. Traveling with the speed of light through endless space and countless eons of time, these particles pick up the magnetic charges of the universe as they bounce off stardust; pregnant with the nuclei of hydrogen, helium, and heavier elements, they attain an energy potential which makes man's megaton devices seem of firecracker force by comparison. Much of the energy is filtered out as the cosmic rays approach the earth, but what is left as they reach the earth's mountain tops still can penetrate 49 feet of lead or 700 feet of earth. When they strike metal roofs, their showers drench those beneath with radiation.

Radioactive materials whose decay is measured in millennia are sown in the ground we walk upon and settle to the bottom of the deepest seas. They and the radioactivity of the materials in houses make up 50 per cent of natural background radiation. The traces of uranium-238, with a half-life of 4.6 billion years, retain half or more the radiation that was present when the earth first formed. As rocks weather, they release their radioactive materials which combine with other chemicals to find their way into streams and distant soils. Potassium-40, which clings to clay, is taken up by plants and, when eaten by animals, becomes part of flesh; carbon-14 is expelled into the atmosphere as the carbon dioxide of smokes and expired breath; radioactive hydrogen (tritium) descends in rain and snow to combine with oxygen and form heavy water. These are some of the elements which comprise "background radiation," which can be as much as fifty or sixty times as strong in bubbling spring as in running brook and varies greatly from mountain to plain and sometimes from acre to adjacent acre.

Magnetic forces—the earth itself, with north and south poles, is a massive magnet—produce fields which orient the position of molecules and control the movement of charged and uncharged particles in the metabolism of plants, animals, and man.

Among the many rhythms of nature, from the spin of electrons in their atomic orbits and the movement of molecules to the majestic migrations of heavenly bodies, man lives by diurnal, menstrual, seasonal, annual, and many other frequencies, including sounds too soft or shrill for human hearing.

Ultrasonic waves have mutated seedlings, broken chromosomes, generated violent motion of fluids and particles within cells, turned cell solids into gels, broken large molecules into small ones, scorched cells and filled them with bubbles.

Man lives within a narrow range of thermal radiation, or heat, and this exercises considerable control on the rate at which he lives, his efficiency, and his reproductivity. A small rise or fall of body temperature can kill him.

We live by and die of radiant energy in its many forms.

Only recently has man begun to tap natural sources of radiant energy to any significant degree. This he must do to survive and to support the impressively proliferating human race. Not only is the population exploding but the power requirements per person are rocketing—for defense, industry, research, and many other purposes.

Until the beginning of the Industrial Revolution little more than a century ago, 95 per cent of the energy needs of humans were met adequately in terms of manpower (the 35-watt force which lifts 27.5 pounds one foot in one second) and horsepower, which is set at twenty times that of manpower.

By the middle of the twentieth century man and his horses supplied only 5 per cent of human energy needs; the other 95 per cent came from fuels—coal, oil, and gas—supplied by long-gone fossils. These resources enabled a locomotive engineer to command 100,000 times and jet pilots 700,000 times their own muscle power. In the 1960s, power demands still were rising sharply as man and his satellites moved into space. At this rate of expansion, fossil fuels might last out the century, but it became evident that new energy sources would have to be found.

Atomic energy offered a partial solution.

When stable matter is split asunder into charged particles, it becomes ionizing radiation. The postively and negatively charged particles exert such force in seeking to combine with particles of opposite charge or to avoid particles of like charges that they produce violent turbulence within the atomic and molecular microcosm.

From the beginning of its development as a scientific, industrial and medical tool in the 1890s, ionizing radiation from radium and X-ray tubes has been a mixed blessing. Some of the original workers died of their life-saving discoveries.

Today people still are dying from exposure to these Jekyll-Hyde materials—not only those who work with them but medical patients and other "beneficiaries" of their radiations as well. The prospect is for a continued rise in radiation usage. The exploitation of radiation as a common energy source has barely begun.

Perhaps the commonest kind of radiation death is by cancer. Some say one of radiation's principal effects is to speed up aging.

Cancer often comes insidiously many years after a critical exposure to a carcinogen or as a result of the sum of a long succession of small exposures. For this reason it is impossible to say how much cancer is due to radiation.

Many scientists feel that the cancers and other effects of radiation on body cells are of minor importance when compared with the genetic consequences to irradiated seed cells—sperm, ova, and fertilized eggs. The cancers die with their host; the hereditary effects live on in generation after generation.

Radiation can affect future generations in many ways. It sterilizes potential parents so that, for them, there are no future generations. It may maim or kill embryos; or it may alter their seed so that while they survive to live normal, healthy lives, their offspring may be cripples who beget cripples.

An appreciable part of a century may elapse before the effects of an accidental or ill-advised exposure become known. Then they may appear as a cancer in the original victim. Or, long after the irradiated parent is dead and forgotten, they may appear in a newborn physical monster or mental defective.

The commonest man-made radiation exposures are in the fields of medical diagnosis and treatment. These account for more than 90 per cent of exposure to man-made sources and about 60 per cent from all sources; other contributors include rapidly growing industrial and military operations and some commercial products.

There is no serious dispute as to the potential dangers of these sources nor as to the culpability of each in a few classical cases involving humans. In all areas, however, there are heated, self-defensive denials of blame for the generally rising incidence of cancer and protestations that exposures within each area are well within safe limits. While 100 per cent lethal doses and 50 per cent lethal doses (meaning one-half are killed) have been established for animals and humans, science doesn't have the vaguest idea of what dose would cause cancer in all people—or what would be half-safe. Observations that from 80 to 200 rem (abbreviation for "roentgen equivalent man") have caused human leukemia, and 100 to 200 have caused thyroid cancer in isolated instances have shed only a little light on the problem.

One of the many reasons for the difficulty in establishing carcinogenic doses for humans is that people are outbreeding and consequently are a heterogeneous lot. Just as some inbred mouse strains may be extremely susceptible to radiation and cancer while other inbred strains are resistant, so may humans living next door to one another vary widely in their inherited susceptibility to radiation-induced disease.

Different kinds of radiation may have an additive, synergistic or neutralizing effect on one another, depending largely on the dosage schedule and sequence in which they are applied. In some instances ionizing radiation has behaved like sunshine and tanning effects—a few small prior doses have protected against the injurious effects of later larger doses. In animals, radiation has even cured radiation-induced cancers. Most of the experimental evidence, however, shows that radiation has a cumulative effect—cancer can come as a consequence of a single large dose or an equivalent sum of small doses.

Various rays and chemicals interact in many ways, and this further complicates efforts to establish threshhold doses for humans. Radiomimetic (or radiation-imitating) chemicals may add to, multiply or prevent the carcinogenic effects of radiation. Some chemicals sensitize systems so that a tiny, and normally innocuous, radiation dose becomes carcinogenic. Other chemicals protect a system, so that a normally lethal or carcinogenic dose has only a mild, transient effect.

Back in World War I, a sixteen-year-old girl signed up for a job painting the hour and minute hands and the numerals I to XII on the dials of watches. The watches were on order by the United States Army. An older employee showed her how to do it. One dampened the end of the paint brush between one's lips; this drew the brush tip to a fine point. Then the brush was dipped into the luminous paint, and the figure was made on the watch dial. The brush again was drawn between the lips and the procedure repeated. The girl worked for eighteen months.

Thirty-nine years later, in 1956, when the former luminous dial painter was fifty-five years old, her left leg was amputated because cancer had developed in the bone. In the long interim she had been reasonably well, except for the loss of teeth early in life and a painful arthritis, which had bothered her in recent years. Boston physicians who diagnosed the cancer and traced it to mesothorium deposits in her bones, found that her expired breath still contained measurable traces of radon, which is the gaseous part of decaying radium.

Of the 1,000 or more workers who painted luminous figures on watch dials, no one knows how many eventually came down with cancer in one form or another. The elapsed time between exposure and onset of the disease was so long that many dial painters became lost to the records and no reliable figure is available. Fewer than four hundred had been traced, and, of those examined, about one-third carried measurable radiation.

The case of the luminous-dial workers was an unprecedented opportunity to determine the effect of measurable doses of radiation on human health. Radium has a half-life of 1,620 years, and its decay products would send out their hard and soft emanations for thousands of years; with counters, the source could be located and measured in the living system and even in the dust of the dead. Dr. Joseph Aub of Harvard Medical School more than three decades after the incident reviewed the reports on thirty dial painters who had been traced and found to have been exposed. Of the thirty, ten had died—eight of them of cancer of the nasal sinuses and bones of the leg, jaw, elbow, and hips. Others had developed bone and other forms of cancer, including leukemia, but were still alive; and still others presented X-ray pictures of bone areas which were becoming less dense, a possible forerunner to cancer. There was only the loosest correlation between illness and the time each victim had worked at painting dials, because different batches of the paints had contained variable amounts of mesothorium. Each worker took up a different dose and was a walking or dead record of the radiation she had retained.

Most workers who stored as much as 10 millicuries died of acute damage to their bones and marrow; between 1 and 10 millicuries usually meant death many years later of cancer or leukemia; one microcurie or less, minor changes in bone; and one-third of a microcurie no significant changes in more than 30 years. There were intriguing exceptions to these rules.

The case of the luminous-dial painters presented a relatively simplified problem in dosage, because the radiation had been retained. One curie represents the disintegration of 37 billion atoms per second; one rad is the absorption of 100 ergs of energy by one gram of matter; one roentgen produces two billion positive ions and two billion negative ions in one cubic centimeter of dry air at freezing temperature and sea level. One rem is the dose which gives the biological effect elicited by one rad of X, gamma, or beta rays or 0.1 rad of alpha rays. (Metric units are calibrated with such prefixes as mega- (1,000,000) kilo- (1,000), hecto- (100), deca- (10), deci- (0.1, centi- (0.01), milli- (0.001), myria- (0.0001) and micro- (0.000001); radiation scholars often deal in terms of micromicro-measurements and Angstrom units: the latter represent one-tenth of a millimicron, or one-ten-millionth of a millimeter.)

Studies of the dial painters proved one point which seems to have been lost sight of in current debates on the dangers of fallout and other sources of radiation exposure: there is a vast difference among individuals in their sensitivity to rays. As little as one microgram of the radium residue had rapidly produced precancerous and cancerous changes in some dial painters, whereas three others stored between 10 and 23 micrograms for a quarter of a century without apparent untoward effects on their health. In establishing "safe," "tolerance," "maximum permissible," "acceptable," "threshhold," and other dosages, agencies and individuals are inclined to lump people, like mice, into various categories of embryos, children, adults, and aged. While this principle might afford a rough estimate of mass survival in a thermonuclear attack, when all life would become extravagantly expendable, means and averages are not a fair peacetime standard for those who are most sensitive to radiation.

The fate of the dial painters had durable impact on scientific studies of human hazards but only temporary effect on commercial practices and population exposures. Books were written contending radium had nothing to do with these cancers; and courts denied claims for damages. People continued to buy "radium water," which was described as good for arthritis and virtually all that ailed man and beast. Shoe clerks continued to expose themselves, their customers, and curious children with ancient, ray-scattering shoe-fitting machines.

The misfortunes of the luminous dials were not buried with their painters. In 1956, a committee of the British National Research Council reported that wrist watches contained enough excess radiation to deliver a sizable dose to the gonads of the male bearers. Dr. J. L. Haybittle of the committee found that his own watch emitted 2.2 microcuries, almost ten times the assumed dose in the luminous dials; and he regarded this as a carcinogenic hazard to the skin beneath the watch. Three years later, in 1959, the U.S. Atomic Energy Commission sent out an urgent appeal to purchasers of GM7 Rolex wrist watches to turn the timepieces in; some of them contained excessive strontium-90. In 1962 the New York City Health Department banned the sale of pocket watches with radioactive luminous dials because of genetic dangers to reproductive organs.

Thousands of natural-water sources in the Midwest still present five or more times the maximum permissible radiation level. A New York State study which showed that childhood malformations are 50 per cent higher in areas of high background radiation, particularly in well and spring water, than in areas of lake and stream water supplies has not changed water sources for these populations. Several other populations are getting their drinking water from streams below new uranium mills; some feel that children born in these areas may pay in crippling diseases for the citizenry's oversight. Despite guards and precautions, cadavers at autopsy in these areas occasionally show a very high uptake of radioactive materials.

Dr. Eugene P. Pendergrass, the University of Pennsylvania's veteran crusader for improved medical practices, delivered a memorable lecture at the annual meeting of the American Cancer Society a decade ago. As the Society's President-elect, he struck out against many abuses which had rankled in the minds of the most qualified radiologists but remained unuttered because of the protocol governing polite medical interprofessional relationships and a desire not to alarm the public. Among his charges were:

1. Many specialists in surgery, urology, gynecology, otolaryngology, and dermatology used radium to treat cancer without adequate knowledge of screening, dosage, or radiation effects. In the absence of follow-up examinations, radium implants which often slipped out of place damaged normal tissues. The complications, preventable by proper procedures, the specialists wrongly attributed to the disease.

2. Many patients, first treated with surgery or radiation by nonradiological specialists, were referred to radiotherapists only when they reached the stage for palliative and terminal care and when they had very little money left.

3. Some radiologists had little medical status; they served virtually as technicians in carrying out surgeons' instructions.

4. The content of radon in tubes almost invariably was not of the strength certified by some commercial houses which sold them; the tubes contained anywhere from no radon at all to 300 per cent the stated strength. Failure to check the actual radon content placed the patient in peril.

5. In the light of these and other difficulties, few graduate medical students were entering the specialty of radiotherapy. And relatively few institutions supported the kind of medical team—including at least a radiation physicist, a physician, a cancer surgeon, and a tumor pathologist—which could give the cancer patient his best bet for a cure.

In thirty-seven of the fifty states there are nominal control programs governing the use of X-ray machines, some of them recently established. They range from optional compliance to mandatory registration of the machines and periodic inspection. In thirteen states even these, often toothless, regulations do not exist. Dr. James Barrett Brown, a St. Louis plastic surgeon, has said that he treats regularly many patients badly burned by X-ray machines operated by amateurs in industry and commerce. He was particularly appalled by the damage done by those who used X rays for the removal of superfluous hair. "This procedure," he said, "has caused some of the most dramatic, extensive, and useless burns, affecting the entire lower legs, outside of the thighs, the armpits, the upper arms and forearms, hands, face, front and back of the neck. The pain sometimes is so acute that sedatives have no effect and only prompt and deep surgery brings relief."

In the absence of effective governmental protection of patients, the welfare of the public is left largely up to the conscience and competence of dentists and doctors.

The radiological competence of doctors and dentists has been raised to question in a 1962 report by Dr. Hanson Blatz, Director of the New York City Health Department's Office of Radiation Control. With four years elapsed in a five-year period permitted for voluntary conversion of outmoded equipment, and with one-third of the city's 17,000 registered X-ray machines and fluoroscopes inspected, this sorry score emerged:

Ninety-two per cent of the diagnostic X-ray machines and fluoroscopes were deficient.

In 27 per cent of establishments, some of the equipment was more than twenty-five years old.

Two-thirds of the physicians and dentists dosed themselves liberally while overdosing their patients.

Most of the physicians and dentists operating the equipment were unaware of recommendations for the control of radiation, and of those who were aware of them, many didn't understand them.

While the city's radiation control program had received the backing of professional societies, not a single physician or dentist had converted his obsolete equipment voluntarily.

If New York's practices are typical of those elsewhere, the United States population is receiving an unnecessarily high dose of medical and dental radiation each year. New York State is more strict than most insofar as it inspects and licenses equipment and prohibits operation of X-ray machines by other than doctors, dentists, podiatrists, osteopaths, and licensed or supervised operators.

About 70 million Americans have an annual average of three diagnostic X-ray pictures each for special examinations, 18 million more in mass chest X-ray programs and another 18 million in dental examinations. When one considers the fact that a poorly made chest X ray can deliver to the gonads between 200 and 500 times the small amount of radiation involved in a properly made picture, there is reason for grave concern for future generations as well as the present crop of patients.

Of equal concern is the occasionally free-and-easy employment of fluoroscopy. These machines deliver 300 to 500 times the X-ray film dose to the chest and 100 times the dose to the testes in a chest examination.

An uncomfortable intermediary in the problems of medical radiation is the American College of Radiology. This is the professional association of diplomates of the American Board of Radiology—about 5,000 physicians who, after completing medical school and their internship, spent an additional three or four years of residency learning radiation diagnostic and treatment techniques at a teaching hospital. Too often these qualified experts pay in public for the radiological sins of 40,000 nonradiologist doctors and dentists whose principle qualification in the field is that they can afford to buy or rent two-thirds of the diagnostic X-ray equipment in the United States.

The American College of Radiology has set two goals for itself, and often they are not compatible. One is to persuade physicians operating radiation equipment to exercise care and intelligence to protect themselves and their patients. The other is to allay the growing apprehension of the general public toward medical radiation.

Typical of ACR's service to physicians and dentists is the publication of an attractive thirty-one page *Practical Manual on the Medical and Dental Use of X-Rays with Control of Radiation Hazards.* Profusely illustrated with line drawings and cartoons, multicolored and printed in several large typefaces, it delivers in simple terms the rudiments of practical radiology. It is distributed free and, no doubt, with a fervent prayer that it will be read. Busy physicians who take the time to read it will become acquainted with the ABC's of such radiation hazards as genetic changes, malformations, cancer, leukemia, life-shortening, and various local and lethal effects, correct dosages, over-all radiation exposures, discretions in selecting patients for X rays, cautions in using equipment, safety measures and the proper procedures for various kinds of diagnoses and treatments.

Through ACR speakers and the services of a large New York public relations concern, the public is given such messages as: "A chest film, properly taken, exacts a penalty so small one could have them taken as often as needed"; "The slight risk [of diagnostic X rays] is far outweighed by the benefits involved"; "The patient must have confidence in his doctor"; and "A survey of 5,000 college members indicates a 50 per cent improvement in medical protection during the last five years." College speakers have decried "the emotional response of the public and science" to reported radiation hazards and pointed with justifiable pride to the constant development of better and safer equipment and new techniques which reduce radiation damage.

The ACR arguments, however, are based largely on the performance of its one skilled member who has learned through long training and experience to respect radiation to almost ten untrained physicians for whom radiology is, at best, a part-time occupation.

The principle that eighteen minutes of dark adaptation enhances visual acuity 100-fold is only of academic interest if the examining physician does not practice it. New image amplifiers, films, filters, cones, diaphragms, shields, and other devices which greatly reduce or improve radiation protect only the patients whose physicians have them and use them. While conservative radiologists may use the tuberculin test on children, the inexpert still often employ chest X rays. X rays are not a substitute for a careful history and giving a thorough physical examination. It is the inexpert who most commonly is a menace to himself, his patient, and even people in the adjoining room.

Estimates cited by the ACR indicated as recently as 1958 that medical and dental radiation exceeded exposures from all other natural and man-made sources together. Medical and dental radiation was set at from 150,000 to 300,000 rems per million persons annually (or 100,000–150,000 rems to the gonads) as compared with 100,000 rems from natural background, 5,000 from occupational exposure and 5,000 from industrial fallout, 7,000–15,000 from military sources—or a total of 270,000–400,000 rems from all sources.

Some scientists view these average exposures with considerable apprehension.

The shortened life span of radiologists has been used as a yardstick of aging effects of radiation. Radiologists have an average life span of only 60.5 years, while nonradiation-using physicians live an average of 65.7 years. Several sources calculated on this basis that each roentgen of absorbed radiation curtailed longevity by as much as fifteen days; others said the cost was one day per absorbed roentgen.

Radiologists have been reported as having ten times the leukemia incidence in physicians generally, and almost 100 times that in the general population; dermatologists have four times the average for physicians. In recent years, certified radiologists have shown a three- to fivefold excess of leukemia.

Dr. Wendell Scott, a prominent St. Louis radiologist, has stated that "the patients should not hesitate to have radiographic examinations if their physicians recommend them." He added, however, that the examinations should be done by physicians with training and experience in radiology, that written reports be made, films be preserved, and both films and reports accompany the patient if he is referred elsewhere, that initial examinations should be made carefully to avoid repeated exposures, and that female pelvic examinations should be limited to the two weeks following the last menstrual period (to avoid irradiation following conception) and, when necessary, delayed until the last trimester of pregnancy "when the fetus is well established and less sensitive to radiation." He emphasized the increased protection given patients by new fast films, more effective screens and other ultramodern equipment—which seldom is found in the establishments of nonradiologist physicians.

Each year many thousands of parents look with profound dismay upon their grotesque, misshapen newborn infant and search their conscience for the sins which merited this misfortune.

Statistical studies indicate that the commonest sin was the mother's submission during the first three months of pregnancy to pelvic X rays—often for frivolous reasons. Scientists conducting independent studies in London and New Orleans have come to identical conclusions: pelvic X rays during the first trimester double the child's chances of leukemia. An assortment of other congenital conditions also are associated with early pregnancy pelvic radiation: they have been observed in prenatally irradiated humans and induced in animals.

A Harvard University survey of a 1 per cent sample of 734,243 births in thirty-seven large Northeastern maternity centers indicated a twice-normal risk of cancers of nerve and brain as well as of leukemia among children irradiated *in utero;* the victims usually developed their diseases during their first seven years—these cancer dangers seemed to subside when the child attained eight years. Another Harvard study showed an abnormally high number of leukemics among the first-born; it is not known whether this is related to an increased tendency to examine the pelvis radiologically during the first pregnancy. The procedure which measures the pelvis delivers an enormous dose of 800 mrem (millirem) to the marrow and 2,500 mrem to the ovaries, as well as liberal amounts to the sensitive embryo.

Depending on the technique, pelvic examinations may involve anywhere from 0.1 to 30 roentgens (r) delivered to the fetus. Dr. Robert Rugh, Columbia University's Associate Professor of Radiology, has expressed the opinion that a dose of 10 or more r to the human embryo during its first forty days presents sufficient medical reason to end the pregnancy.

While radiologists emphasize the dangers of radiation during the first ninety days of pregnancy, when the basic embryonic organs and structures are forming, animal studies in several research centers have shown that radiation late in pregnancy can do irreparable damage to the central nervous system. Animals irradiated during their late residence *in utero* at the National Institutes of Health were born with undersized skulls, shrunken brain hemispheres, displaced and otherwise abnormal nerves. Some of the animals which appeared almost normal during their early life developed congenital nervous defects late in life which bore a striking resemblance to conditions which develop in mature humans.

Sensitivity to X rays, of course, does not end at birth. Children are especially susceptible to cancer and other penalties of ill-advised radiation.

Dr. Lenore Simpson Englander of Roswell Park has made several studies of radiation effects in children. One investigation of 1,200 children whose upper chests had been irradiated for an enlarged thymus gland showed that this treatment was associated with an increased leukemia incidence twelve times and thyroid cancer incidence 150 times the normally expected frequency. A study of 2,400 children irradiated in Seattle, Washington, Buffalo and Rochester, New York, confirmed the findings— leukemia was ten times and thyroid cancer more than 100 times as common among the irradiated children as is expected in their age group. Dr. Englander points out, however, that in these studies there were no controls—that is, a comparable group of children with enlarged thymuses treated by means other than radiation had not been studied. Lacking control data, one must consider the possibility that it was the enlarged thymus rather than the radiation which caused leukemia and thyroid cancer. Dr. Englander, however, considers radiation during childhood especially hazardous because of the cumulative effects of radiation during the child's long life span ahead, the fact that the entire reproductive period is in the future, radiation's interference with growth and hormonal balance and the special sensitivity of young tissues. "Nowadays," she reported, "the physician is adding an average of 50 per cent or more to the usual amount of radiation an individual would receive from other sources."

One of the most questionable practices in medicine is the dermatologist's use of radiation for acne and other skin conditions, like eczema, plantar warts (on the soles of the feet), anal and genital itch, dermatitis caused by local irritants, fungus infections, psoriasis, and shingles. One study showed that dermatologists use X rays to treat 23.1 per cent of all skin conditions, and of these the most commonly treated is acne. Acne occurs at one time or another in about 80 per cent of all youngsters as a consequence of their changing hormonal status; and with reasonable care and cleanliness it passes without durable damage to the skin. Scars, when they occur, usually can be erased quickly and easily with medical abrasive techniques— the wire brush, for instance.

X rays usually have only temporary effect on acne—the lesions return after two or three months. But the X rays used to treat acne can do lasting damage to other tissues and to the patient. Occasionally, radiation treatment of acne calls for radical surgery to remove the superficial and deep tissues destroyed by the rays. And in an appreciable number of cases, radiation for acne and other skin conditions leads to cancer. A study of patients in three hospitals in Pittsburgh turned up 105 patients with skin cancers following irradiation for benign skin conditions, including acne; the cancers developed from fourteen to forty-five years after treatment.

Radiation treatment for benign uterine fibroids also appears to bring occasional unwanted sequelae many years later. A Buffalo check-up on 746 patients so treated showed that 71 had developed cancers, whereas only eighteen normally would. There were six times the normal number of uterine cancers, 2.5 times that of cancer of the cervix and three or four times the normal rate of cancer of the ovary, bladder, and rectum.

A spinal arthritic condition called ankylosing spondylitis, or poker back, sometimes is treated with a shower of X rays over the rigid backbone. British investigators found that the leukemia incidence among 1,627 patients so treated was twenty-one times the expected figure; among 399 treated by other means, no leukemia developed. British scientists reported that in these cases radiation showers produced immediate blood-cell changes in many patients which resembled those of leukemia.

Dr. Bradford E. Cannon of Massachusetts General Hospital has reported that, of forty-four patients with severe sequelae from radiation for acne and other benign conditions, nineteen had developed cancer, eighteen of them skin cancer. The cancers developed, on an average, twenty-six years after X-ray treatment.

Thorotrast, a radioactive material which makes the digestive tract, blood vessels, spleen, liver and other structures stand out in X-ray pictures or under the fluoroscope, has induced tumors in experimental animals; now, after three or four decades, physicians are finding cancers in human bone, liver, kidneys and other organs which suggest its long-latent effects.

Scientists at the National Cancer Institute found that when they turned on a beam of radiation of as little as 50 r, all mice got out of the way; perhaps the smell of ozone warned them. A poll of the nation's dermatologists, conducted by the University of North Carolina School of Public Health, showed that only 3.9 per cent of all their patients with skin conditions refused X rays because they feared them.

Ten per cent of human cancers are caused by the ultraviolet rays of sunlight. They are mostly of the skin, and between 75 and 95 per cent of skin cancers are curable, depending in part on who treats them and how. The evidence indicates that in the ordinary light spectrum there are small areas which mutate and kill cells, which cause cancer and which prevent mutations, cancer and other damage. Ultraviolet rays even in ordinary fluorescent lights occasionally cause dry, itchy skin inflammation.

Light waves, like sea waves or sound waves, are measurable. The light waves are measured in Angstrom units (abbreviated A). An Angstrom unit is one-ten-millionth of a millimeter long, and a millimeter is 0.039 inch. Light waves reaching the earth range from 2,900 A (in the ultraviolet) to 18,500 A (in infrared). Many know the light spectrum as ranging from invisible ultraviolet through violet, indigo, blue, green, yellow, orange, and red into the invisible reaches of infrared. In these colors, visible and invisible, are powers, largely unexplored, of healing and killing, of stimulating and preventing growth, of aging tissues and possibly of rejuvenating them.

Leo C. Massopust, a veteran medical photographer at Marquette University, has spent much of his long career exploring slender areas of the spectrum. He has found narrow bands in the 9,500–10,000 A range which appear to have variously mutagenic, lethal and antimutagenic effects. Mice irradiated with one part of the spectrum, which he calls M rays, developed rough coats and their exposed offspring were hairless. When deprived of M rays, tadpoles hatched dead from frog eggs, and monster fruit flies emerged from their eggs.

Dr. Alvin Rieck, also of Marquette, exposed white mice to powerful, burning ultraviolet rays. He then kept one-half of them in darkness and the rest in visible light or under fluorescent light. Two weeks later, the mice kept in darkness showed great injury—their skins were ten times normal thickness. Light-treated mice, on the other hand, were in good shape—their skins were only twice their normal thickness.

Dr. Albert Kelner, then at Brandeis University, once played ultraviolet light of 2537 A on immature fruit flies. He then placed one-half of them in the dark, and they developed as monsters. (Inasmuch as the new traits were not transmitted to offspring, they were phenocopies, rather than mutations.) The other half were placed in ordinary light, and they became normal.

Dr. Charles Breedis of the University of Pennsylvania has shown that light in the 2,000–3,100 A range makes amputated salamanders grow extra limbs. Chemical carcinogens have similar effects.

The sunburning wavelengths are in the 2,900–3,150 A range and strongest at 2,970. (Another, at 2,537 A, is emitted by germ-killing lamps, but does not reach the earth naturally.) Dr. A. Clark Griffin of the University of Texas has kept white mice under lamps at 3,660 A twenty-four hours a day for ten months without a sign of sunburn or tumors. When he placed the exposed animals for a very short time under sunburning wavelengths, however, he activated the seemingly innocuous prior exposure and produced acute sunburn and tumors.

The rays in sunshine which age tissues are identical with or very close to the sunburning part of the spectrum. And they are also identical with or very close to the carcinogenic part of the spectrum. The aging effects are obvious to the ordinary observer: the Venuses and Adonises who acquire Florida, Arizona, and sunlamp tans too often eventually look old before their time. Those who make a career of exposing themselves too long to the sun run the same high risks as weather-beaten farmers and sailors of developing not only a prematurely old, tough, and leathery skin but skin cancer as well.

One group of scientists nipped small tissues from the face, lower arms, and buttocks of chronically overexposed sunworshippers and examined the cells under the microscope. In fair-skinned but overtanned people, cells from the face and arms resembled cells from the skin of very old men and women; cells from the unexposed buttocks, however, retained their youth. The skin which had aged prematurely proved to be particularly susceptible to cancer.

The natural chemicals inside the skin and circulating in the blood have a pronounced effect on the person's response to sunlight. One class which sensitizes tissues to ultraviolet (and X) rays is porphyrins. Porphyrins, free and in hemoglobin, supply the coloring matter and fluorescent material in red blood cells. In a bizarre disease called porphyria—characterized by having excessive porphyrin in the blood—the victims cannot stand sunlight. A brief exposure (in the range, specifically, of 3,000–4,100 and 5,060–6,020 A) may bring on a fantastically severe sunburn. Several other diseases (like pellagra, due to niacin deficiency) are marked by abnormal discoloration of face and hands. These signs are common among aging drunks, widows, and recluses who pay little attention to diet. Children with certain hereditary skin diseases almost invariably die of cancer.

Some of the new and common drugs sensitize the skin to the sun's rays. They include many of the tranquilizers, antidiabetic preparations, some antibiotics and most sulfas.

With new energy sources being brought into industrial use, radiation dangers to workers and the public are beginning to increase. A half-million workers are now exposed on their jobs to ionizing radiation.

A half-dozen or more nuclear reactor accidents are known to have occurred; but the reports indicate that the casualties were few. The formidable feats of submarines which already have traversed, submerged, the oceans and icecaps of the world are the first step to land, sea, surface, and air craft powered by splitting or fusing atoms.

Dr. Wright Langham of the University of California's Los Alamos Scientific Laboratory has worked on three nuclear propulsion reactors, the nuclear-rocket engine prototypes for future passenger-carrying space vehicles. He has said that these craft will present some slight safety hazards —they will be carrying more uranium-235 than an atomic bomb—and should they remain in orbit for ten years, this radioactive load would diminish only a little. However, the risks lie almost exclusively in the possibility of an accident on the ground which would be contaminated by spilled fuels. Even this cannot produce a significant explosion under the most drastic conditions, Dr. Langham states. All the conceivable dangers attending one of these vehicles are small compared to those involved in the explosion of even a nominal nuclear weapon fired in anger.

One of the fundamental forces—the Van Allen radiation belt which forms an electronic girdle around and several hundred miles above the earth—was greatly distorted on July 9, 1962, when the United States exploded a large hydrogen bomb 200 miles above the Pacific. The distortion, expected to be mild and transient, turned out to be severe and long-lasting—much to the surprise of the scientists who engineered the experiment. The biological effects may never be known.

Of increasing concern, so far as health hazards go, is the swelling usage of electromagnetic radiation, or microwaves. They are most familiar to the average person as the source of television energy and the radar curtains which, one hopes, protect from sneak attacks. These are different from the massive north-south magnetic d-c currents which nature has woven around the earth. Natural or man-made, they hold considerable sway over life, whether it be life within the cell or within man.

Two decades ago scientists at the State University of Iowa discovered a dramatic effect of currents on growth. They amputated the tail of a worm which readily regrows a new tail. Then they wrapped the worm in an agar leaf and passed a very small battery current through the leaf. If they placed the amputated end near the anode, the worm grew, as it normally did, a new tail. But if they put the amputated end next to the cathode, the worm grew another head—it became a tailless, two-headed worm. When they placed chick embryos with their heads toward the anode (under 0.88 to 168 microamperes per square millimeter for from 13 to 68 hours) the hatched chicks showed gross distortions of the brain, displaced heart, malformed tail, and a general shuffling of other organs. The scientists felt their experiments indicated that in normal growth and development there is an electrical flow of ions from several axes and that these natural currents were disturbed by the battery.

Dr. John H. Heller of the New England Institute for Medical Research has explored electromagnetic radiation. With megacycle force (million-cycles-per-second, rather than standard broadcast radio's kilocycle, or thousand-cycle-per-second frequency), he has observed tiny plastic balls align themselves obediently along the lines of force created. In the lower frequencies motile microorganisms march with the precision of parading Marines along the lines laid out for them in the electromagnetic field; when the frequency is turned high, they pivot 90 degrees and march in that direction. Cultures of *Euglena* were made to swim with the precision of shells in a regatta, changing course with a change in fields and field strengths.

The effect of these fields in Dr. Heller's experiments resembled the action of ionizing radiations, poisons, and carcinogens. The rays altered the gene nucleic acid of garlic root tips and fruit flies; chromosomes stuck together when these cells tried to divide, or they clumped or were shattered. On the molecular level, specific enzymes were inactivated and their chemical bonds were broken with a frequency of 14.46 megacycles.

This kind of radiation too has shown its Jekyll-Hyde nature. When workers at the National Institutes of Health exposed the brain "arousal centers" of monkeys and apes to 290 and 388 megacycles, the animals went into convulsions and died. That was the Hyde side. Several investigators hope to bring out the Dr. Jekyll characteristics: implanted cancers are being 'buzzed" with various frequencies and doses to establish cancer-killing frequencies.

Dr. Carl B. Braestrup and Dr. Richard Mooney of Columbia University's Francis Delafield Hospital wondered whether the additional radiation from such household appliances as television and laboratory equipment such as electron microscopes and oscillographs might affect viewers and contribute to human mutations. They made several checks of radiation emitted by these devices. The radiation was such a small fraction of the current maximum permissible dose (10 r from birth to age thirty) for medical radiation that the scientists concluded that "the possibility of radiation injuries to TV viewers is very remote."

Workers around radar and other microwave installations are exposed to considerable radiation. And so are workers in dozens of old industries now using radioactive materials and new industries whose primary purpose is the production of radioactive material. Exposure may be the lot of the janitor who sweeps the floor of a biochemistry laboratory, inspectors who check for flaws and foreign bodies in steel products, those engaged in sterilizing food and drugs, engineers who use isotopes to test the fidelity of pipelines, luminous instrument makers, atomic energy plant workers, the numerous people who work in hospitals and other buildings housing betatrons, cyclotrons, and other massive radiation machines.

In 1928 Federal law set the maximum permissible level of occupational exposure at 100 milliroentgens (mr) a year. As understanding of and respect for radiation increased, permissible levels decreased—to 60 mr in 1934, to 30 mr in 1936, to 15 mr in 1950. Still lower levels are set for younger workers.

Some hospitals, too, have set limits of exposure to patients who have been treated with radioactive isotopes. For nurses and attendants the permissible exposure from all sources is 230 milliroentgens for not more than thirteen consecutive weeks, or a yearly dose of not over 5,000 milliroentgens. Visitors are forbidden to be exposed to more than 500 mr a year; and any hospital exposure is forbidden people younger than eighteen years. The beds of patients given radiogold are kept at least 4 feet apart, and in the case of radium and cobalt, 6 feet.

These days may well prove to be the Model T era of radiation usage and exposure. A new age now is being proclaimed by those studying optical masers, which are an abbreviation of the term *microwave amplification by stimulated emission of radiation*. Masers may bring about a revolution in man's command of vast natural forces. By passing a microwave of a specific frequency through a crystal or gas, the affected molecules are stimulated to produce a vibration peculiar to their natural resonance; and atoms, in their excited state, emit their waves. On this principle, it becomes possible to produce very narrow beams. Enthusiasts contend that masers make it possible for 100 million different television programs to be carried simultaneously over the optical area of the spectrum; large antennae no longer will be needed; space satellites can be powered from the ground; all the old methods of metalworking, welding, and melting will become obsolete; a new day is dawning in many fields, including photography, ophthalmology, communications, spectroscopy and perhaps medicine. Whether these unlimited possibilities turn out to be a blessing or curse depends on the uses to which man applies this newly discovered principle.

Lasers are the amplified light counterpart of masers. They too herald a new era in radiation. The fantastic forces in the spectrum of light include death rays and possibly a means of curing superficial cancers. In preliminary tests, a laser beam exploded animal cancers with an exposure of only one-one-thousandth of a second. A few human tumors, including melanoma, have disappeared under laser treatment. The regressions are considered temporary.

The fears of fallout from military testing may be out of all proportion to the reported dosage of ionizing radiation so far delivered. Average exposure to medical radiation is about thirty times that so far experienced from fallout. Some confound fallout with the tragic toll of lives lost at Nagasaki and Hiroshima. Almost all of these 152,000 Japanese deaths were due to the close-up effects of the first four minutes following the explosion—blast, burn, and radiation flash. There are no precise estimates of untimely deaths caused by fallout from these bombings or subsequent testing of weapons; fallout is distributed randomly over much of the world and during long periods, and the diseases caused by it take years to develop.

When an atomic or hydrogen bomb bursts, it releases many kinds of radiation. Some of the radioactive particles have only a momentary existence; others throw out strong emanations for millenia. Some of the radiation is so soft it affects only nearby molecules; other radiation permeates the air for considerable distances and penetrates dense materials. Some debris falls at once to contaminate the immediate vicinity for a few days or weeks; other particles are borne aloft to travel with the stratospheric currents for months or years and gradually to settle whenever and wherever the weather brings them down.

Surviving victims of the Nagasaki and Hiroshima bombings showed radiation effects which varied with the distance between themselves and the bomb blast. Some who had escaped the lethal shock waves, which traveled at 720 miles a second, and the flash and heat, which moved almost with the speed of light, died within hours or days of massive hemorrhages caused by one minute of radiation. These were near enough to be irradiated by gamma rays and neutrons from the burst itself. In others, a little less exposed, the "radiation syndrome" was more gradual—they suffered from nausea and vomiting for a few days, they soon were overcome by a profound weariness and lassitude, and, between five and ten days later they began bleeding from the gums and nose, their hair started falling out, and they went into a state of general intoxication. They aged years with the passing months—if they lived that long.

Five years after the bombings, investigators were able to assess the increased incidence of leukemia among Hiroshima citizens and correlate its frequency with distance from the epicenter of the bomb blast and with radiation dosage. The leukemia rate dissipated rapidly over a single mile (1,609 meters) radius: the rate was 1,790 per million inhabitants at a distance of 700–900 meters (which gave a radiation dosage of 2,620 rads, the rad being the unit of absorbed dose, equal to 100 ergs per gram), 950 at 900–1,000 meters (1,060 rads), 355 at 1,100–1,300 meters (430 rads), 230 at 1,300–1,500 meters (177 rads), 69 at 1,500–1,700 meters (77 rads) and zero at 1,700 meters and farther (less than 34 rads).

Dr. Jacob Furth, now of Columbia University, and Dr. Arthur C. Upton of Oak Ridge have described experiments in which animals were staked out at various distances from the burst of bombs tested on Pacific Islands. Autopsy studies indicated what various doses of atomic radiation do to humans. These are their principal observations: (1) radiation shortened the life span; (2) leukemia and tumors of the thymus gland were among the earliest and commonest lethal diseases to appear; (3) in some strains there was a great increase in cancers of the pituitary, breast, glandular tissue, adrenals, Harderian glands, liver, and ovaries; (4) in other strains, normally susceptible to cancer, there was a decrease in cancers of the lung, breast, connective tissue, and nonthymic leukemia (cancer inhibition often was produced by an enormous radiation dose); (5) hair turned white and cataracts appeared within ninety days; (6) with increasing dosage, the iris of the eye atrophied; (7) nephritis and nephrosclerosis were induced with more than 40 rads; (8) teeth dropped out (this was ten times as common in males as females); (9) ovaries were sterilized, and (10) neutrons appeared more responsible than gamma rays for these effects.

The effects of these weapons on mice closely mimicked the havoc noted in humans at Hiroshima. Fifteen years after the bombing, Hiroshima had had more than ten times its normal number of leukemics. Also, significantly higher than normal were rates for cancer of the lung, stomach, breast, and ovary; these tumors began to appear after the leukemia rate had plateaued and begun to drop.

Human beings exposed to 400 to 600 r of whole-body radiation over a period of hours soon will begin to hemorrhage, and they will die within weeks. The same amount of radiation given over months or years permits recovery, although death may come many years later from one form of cancer or another. As much as 5,000 r may be delivered safely to limited areas of the body. The health effects of low doses are hard to trace.

Even more difficult to trace are the genetic effects. A gonadal dose of about 30 r, on an average, increases the mutation rate 10 per cent in some animals—that is, it enhances the risk of producing mutant children and grandchildren.

The average person is exposed to "safe" doses of background radiation.

He is limited to "safe" doses of occupational radiation. He receives "safe" doses of medical radiation. Fallout radiation usually is well within "safe" limits. The radiationlike effects of each of hundreds of chemicals in food, drugs, air, cigarette smoke and other areas of environment, individually, may be "safe."

Are all of them together "safe?"

This disturbing question hovers over the problem of atomic testing, ordinarily offering only 3 or 4 per cent the exposure of medical and dental diagnostic X rays. Among the several important differences, however, are two that must be considered: (1) The patient can accept or reject medical radiation; and (2) After a diagnostic film is made, the X-ray machine is shut off and the exposure ends, whereas in fallout some long-lived particles salt the ground and water and seed the body.

The radioactive elements, or isotopes, considered most hazardous to health and heredity in fallout are strontium-90 and cesium-137. Some feel that iodine-131 and carbon-14 have serious effects. Minor attention is paid to other fallout isotopes because they occur in small amounts or their radiations are weak, short-lived or not known to affect human systems.

Strontium takes the place of calcium in living systems. About 20 per cent of ingested strontium settles in bone or is excreted in milk. It emits beta rays which irradiate nearby tissues. The half-life of strontium-90 is about 27 years; that is, one-half its radiation is dissipated in 27 years. It effectively irradiates bones for more than 40 years. (Another isotope, strontium-89, has a half-life of only 53 days; by the time it falls out of the atmosphere it is usually too weak to do much damage.) Strontium-90 is particularly dangerous to children because (1) it is concentrated in milk (cows gets it from the grass they eat), (2) it is incorporated in growing, newly forming bone, and (3) children have much time ahead of them in which to suffer the consequences of cumulative and long-lived radiation. Because of the gradual accumulation of strontium-90 in bones and the possibility that both the atmosphere and the earth and its products will be contaminated with it more and more with each passing year (should testing continue or increase) any present "safe" doses are questionable. Animal experiments leave little doubt about carcinogenic properties of strontium-90; the isotope readily induces bone cancer.

Cesium in many respects takes the place of potassium in normal body chemistry. Cesium-137, which emits both the local radiation of beta rays and far-reaching gamma rays, has a half-life of about 27 years; it can be dangerous to living systems for more than a half-century. Cesium is distributed uniformly throughout the body; like potassium, it accumulates in muscle, marrow, ovaries, and testes. Its concentration in gonads makes cesium a potent mutation threat.

Iodine-131 has a half life of only 8.05 days, but it is readily measurable in such fallout targets as iodine-containing seafood, crops, grass, and the thyroid glands of cattle and humans. About 90 per cent of the iodine which enters the system goes promptly to the thyroid, where it is incorporated into hormones which pervade the entire system. Children's thyroids are small and active and, according to one estimate, their cells received 18 times the iodine-131 dose delivered to adult thyroid cells. Children's thyroids are considered generally much more susceptible to carcinogens than adult thyroids are; damaged thyroids contribute to a hundred distinct and vague nonmalignant miseries. During the 1961 atomic tests, children in some milk areas received three times the maximum permissible dose of iodine-131.

Some scientists view carbon-14—formed in fallout by the uniting of nitrogen nuclei with neutrons expelled from exploding atoms—as a potentially great, but unappreciated menace. With a half-life of 5,600 years, carbon-14 is a durable danger. In 1959, scientists estimated that the carbon-14 content of the atmosphere and the earth had been increased about 1 per cent by atomic weapons. The carbon-14 of living systems may have increased 10 per cent.

Other radioactive isotopes in fallout include zinc, cobalt, and zirconium, but they are not considered important.

When concentrations of fallout radiation crept higher and higher during the early 1960s, countermeasures were considered. Temporarily, unpredictably and randomly, concentrations have at times exceeded the limits considered safe. Areas favored by negligible fallout one week are hit the next with levels well beyond those considered safe.

Perhaps the simplest and most practical protective measures in an emergency would include putting children and lactating and pregnant mothers on previously prepared uncontaminated milk—powdered, refrigerated, and stored or canned sterile whole milk. Another step considered is to remove the radioactive iodine and strontium from milk with ion-exchange resins. Cattle feed can be stored in fallout-proof containers and fed when fallout reaches dangerous concentrations.

In seasons and areas of high fallout, cattle and people might be fed stable iodine and thyroid-gland extracts to speed the elimination of radioactive iodine from their systems.

Also under consideration as measures to eliminate long-lived strontium-90 are (1) removing contaminated grass and crops; (2) using leaching solvents to wash contaminants deep into the soil; (3) adding calcium (lime) to the earth to reduce strontium's competition for a place in growing plants; (4) deep plowing, and (5) adding stable calcium to the diet.

In the event that the worst should come to pass, the biochemists might offer solutions to the problems of those fortunate enough to be beyond the weapons' blast, heat, and immediate radiation effects but in areas of massive fallout. Relief measures would have to be started at once. Of theoretical help in reducing the menace of strontium-90 are (1) adding calcium to the diet, (2) intravenous injections of calcium, (3) eating agents which bind strontium in the digestive tract, block its passage through the intestinal wall and into the bloodstream, and lead to its rapid elimination through the bowel, (4) the intravenous injection of binding agents to prevent strontium's settling in bone and speed its excretion in urine. Magnesium salts, which appear to attach only to the surface of bone and which may displace calcium and strontium, might also prove helpful.

Theoretically, cesium damage might be reduced by giving acetazolamide, maleate or any of several other drugs which, in animal experiments, increased the excretion of cesium (and potassium). Dietary potassium might also help prevent cesium from concentrating in the body.

And then, of course, there is the much-debated problem of whether it is prudent and practical to build fallout shelters. All measures so far considered offer puny prevention against the atomic forces now on leash. If it is true that potential combatants have stored sufficient energy to burn, blast, and irradiate all life into extinction, the question may become not so much one of saving samples of the human race as of preserving some kind —any kind—of animal, plant, or microbial life and enough nonvitreous earth surface for it to survive, reproduce and, perhaps in a few billion years, repopulate this sorry planet. Any gamble to this end is worthwhile.

It goes without saying that a highly acceptable substitute for all that science now has to offer is a measure of intelligence and decency in human relations.

CHAPTER 11

EMOTIONS
AND CANCER

Often confounded with the function of the mind, emotions are the basis of psychosomatic (mind over body) ailments. Some physicians feel that almost all illnesses are of a psychosomatic nature. Others believe that some mental troubles may be somatopsychic—a body illness adversely affects the mind and the emotions.

Some have attributed to psychosomatic stimuli, acting in concert with genetic and other factors, the symptoms of such assorted conditions as bronchial asthma, peptic ulcer, ulcerative colitis, essential hypertension, Raynaud's disease, obesity, diabetes mellitus, arthritis, some skin problems, many hormonal disturbances, and a host of other diseases.

Now that the chemistry of various emotions is coming to light, it begins to appear that stress is a factor in cancer. This is best shown in animal experiments. Scientists at the Squibb Institute and elsewhere have studied the chemical changes which occur in various organs as mice are subjected to such nonspecific stresses as transplants of normal mouse skin or subcutaneous injections of turpentine. Under these stresses, the nucleic acids (RNA and DNA) are altered in several hormone-producing and other organs; when cancer was transplanted, and as it grew, similar changes, and with a specific pattern, took place in the organs.

While the evidence, as it is accumulating, indicates that stress is associated with cancer, it remains to be determined whether the stress is a contributing cause or the effect, or both, of the disease.

Much of what has been reported on emotional aspects of cancer seems fuzzy and fanciful, particularly to sound psychologists and psychiatrists.

Dr. George M. Perrin and Dr. Irene R. Pierce, psychologists of McLean Hospital, Waverly, Massachusetts, have reviewed twentieth-century literature on psychosomatic aspects of cancer. Their report cautioned readers often against accepting the "findings" of many of the seventy-five sources they cited; they were critical of the number, and selection of cancer patients and kind of controls (when controls were used) in many studies; they found fault with measuring instruments—when investigators made any pretense at measurements; they noted a serious lack of statistical tests in most studies; and they complained of the "loose and arbitrary terms demonstrated throughout these studies." They disapproved the approaches and experimental designs and questioned the conclusions drawn.

Another review by Dr. L. L. LeShan also cited seventy-five references —only fourteen of them shared by Drs. Perrin and Pierce. He was less critical.

Dr. Daniel Horn, co-author of the classical study which showed the statistical association between cigarette smoking and lung cancer, and himself a psychologist, has stated that, amid the welter of contradiction and equivocation on the relationship of emotions and cancer, one frequently reported finding is relatively undisputed: the loss of a personal emotional relationship (usually the death of or separation from a loved one) prior to the appearance of cancer symptoms. He feels that this may be of significance. He believes that a large-scale prospective, or forward-looking, study (in which the mental health of living people is studied until death) might yield much valuable knowledge on the influence of psychological factors of many illnesses, mental and physical—including cancer.

For what it is worth, here is a cross section of the reports cited but not necessarily endorsed in the Perrin-Pierce review:

• Eleven patients with breast cancer and an equal number with uterine cervical cancer showed, on the basis of Rorschach and Draw-A-Person tests, that they had "negative feelings toward heterosexual relations." Of the two groups, the breast-cancer patients were better adapted to their sexual maladjustment, primarily through denial of their sexuality. The responses of both represented rejection of the female role; and both had problems of mother dominance.

• One could hypothesize a relationship between body image and cancer site. The "interior" cancer type might visualize his body as very permeable and easily penetrated; the "exterior" type could conceive of his body as surrounded and protected by a sheath.

• "Dull" cancer patients do better than "bright" ones; and patients in whom the disease does not proceed rapidly tend to be "worthless rascals and totally irresponsible fanatics," according to one group. The profiles of fifteen rapid cancer patients showed two or more of these characteristics: (1) high defensiveness or strong tendency to present the appearance of serenity in the presence of deeper inner distress; (2) anxiety and depression unrelieved through neurotic or normal channels of discharge; and (3) an abnormal lack of ability to decrease anxiety through usual outward corrective action.

• Various reports are contradictory; psychotics are said to have more than, less than or about the same amount of cancers as normal people.

• One investigation noted that 4 per cent of schizoid patients and 13.6 per cent of paranoid patients developed cancer. A possible explanation is that schizoids die relatively young, while many paranoids live long enough to attain the "cancer age." Average ages at death are: for normals, about seventy years; schizophrenics depart their make-believe world at forty-one; paranoiacs evade their persecutors at sixty-six years, manic-depressives disembark from the roller coaster at fifty-seven years, and for melancholics sadness ends at sixty-seven years. The percentage of deaths due to cancer for each group was: schizophrenia, 2.5; paranoia, 15; manic-depression, 7; and melancholia, 6.

• Cancer rates in psychotics should be lower than normal, because they die earlier than nonpsychotics. The principal causes of early death in mentally deranged people, one report suggests, are syphilis and tuberculosis. Among the reasons advanced for excess cancers in psychotic populations (most of them were of the digestive system, particularly the stomach and the pancreas) were "nervous disturbances" and "overstimulation." Investigators who found fewer cancers in psychotics attributed this variously to early death from other causes, simple life and fewer stimuli.

• Some psychiatrists and psychologists, the Perrin-Pierce report showed, don't need a large series of patients on which to draw sweeping generalizations. One group studied only four patients and came up with such conclusions as: all showed "an amazing degree of psychological repression and denial of their own impulses and feelings" . . . they were oblivious to their own attitudes and traumatic events in their lives . . . they often took refuge in an infantile, Pollyannalike outlook on life . . . they were unable to express pressing and hidden emotions . . . they depended on the social code and norms in determining which affects and emotions they ought to express . . . their relationship with other people was stereotyped and shallow . . . all earlier had had an extremely dependent and immature relationship to either parent, the relationship abruptly terminated by separation or death. One author cited two patients in whom cancer regressed under psychotherapy.

• "Personality profiles" of cancer patients have been drawn. Various investigators have stated that cancer patients show shame, blame (themselves or others), anxiety, dependency, inferiority, overconscientiousness, guilt, severe depression, rejection, withdrawal, isolation, dissociation, identification, denial, avoidance, sublimation, and so forth. Some have said that women with leukemia showed prior shame, sadness, helplessnesses, and hopelessness or self-dislike and distrust, while leukemic men were said to have a history of the loss of a near relative, loss of a chum, change of a school, or an operation for a herniated intervertebral disc.

• Patients with cancer of the uterine cervix have been described as subject to a dislike for sexual intercourse, failure to attain an orgasm, frequent divorces, a history of leukorrhea, and a tendency to marry men who drink.

• Breast-cancer patients, one report solemnly states, have these characteristics: masochism, inhibited sexuality, inhibited motherhood feelings, inability to deal appropriately with anger, aggressiveness and hostility covered with a facade of pleasantness, unresolved conflicts with mothers and the use of denial as a psychological defense, usually against guilt.

• Men with lung cancer, one source has it, often suffer from serious marital problems, venereal disease, and alcoholism—suggesting "deviant psychological attitudes;" men with prostatic cancer, on the other hand, were reported in another study as tractable, easy to please, and remarkably unaggressive.

• People with skin cancer, according to one evaluation, tend to become depressed easily.

• A French study showed that cancer frequency in Paris paralleled the ebb and flow of national tensions—cancer rates rose during the Dreyfus case, for instance; this was not true in Lyon, however.

• One investigator who hypnotized twelve cancer patients to relieve them of pain concluded that these people were either "inhibited, with repressed anger, hate and jealousy," or "good people," stoical, yet laden with self-pity. Another observed that male cancer patients had excessive female hormones and females had excessive male hormones.

• The speed with which cancer progresses has been correlated by various investigators with many personality factors. One suggested that "the higher the investment in ego" the faster the cancer. Another said that fast cases are characterized by greater defensiveness, more anxiety, less ability to release tensions through "acting out," exaggerated bodily preoccupation, self-deprecatory attitudes, and less distortion of reality.

• One associate professor of psychiatry recounted instances of patients having had dreams anticipating future disease, and he commented, "actually, there is experimental evidence to indicate a possible mechanism for such seeming precognition without taking recourse to the supernatural." He cited cases in which waking subjects reported only vague impressions immediately after viewing pictures flashed momentarily on a screen, but after sleeping and dreaming were able to fill in considerable detail.

In this wonderland of words, two definitions of cancer stand out.

One called cancer "passive suicide."

Another described it as "paranoia at the cell level."

The gap between animal instinct and basic human emotions may be enormous. Nevertheless, in contrast to most of the psychological and psychiatric "penetration-of-the-body-boundary scores" and similar antics in semantics in connection with human cancer, animal studies seem to carry substantial significance for humans.

Experimental animals can be matched genetically, with twinlike quality, for age and physical condition. They can share precisely the same environment. They and control animals can be paired or separated into groups with true mathematical randomness. They can be subjected to similar experimental conditions and yield measurable results, the significance of which can be computed against the mathematics of chance. And while the terminology may be derived from Greek and Latin words, the jargon of biologists usually involves substance rather than shadow.

At the University of Illinois Medical School, for example, scientists found that some stresses—surgery or heat (110°F) but not cold (32°F)— increase rats' susceptibility to injected cancer. The experimental and control rats were carefully matched; the stresses, and the animals' ability to survive them, were measured; the results were tabulated and averaged, and the likelihood of coincidence or chance computed. The investigators were frank in saying that their results, by themselves, might or might not hold significance for humans. Should these results confirm those obtained by other investigators using other species, other stresses, other procedures and spontaneous rather than transplanted tumors, however, one might then suspect that they hold some implications for humans.

The burden of evidence generally in animal experiments is that stresses do speed the course of cancer, although there is only the most tenuous indication that stress by itself will help initiate the development of cancer.

In Amsterdam, Holland, scientists have tested the effects of isolation on mice with a strong tendency toward spontaneous breast cancer. They felt that by caging these gregarious little animals alone, or in pairs, or in small groups, they might produce a kind of emotional stress. In repeated experiments, the results were always the same—the greater the isolation, the earlier and the more frequent the breast cancers. Of fifty mice crowded into a single cage, only fifteen developed breast cancer during seventeen months of supertogetherness; five or six of every group of ten caged together and almost four of every group of five developed cancer. That hormones play a role is indicated by the fact that when castrated mice were used, 53 per cent of the isolated and only 11 per cent of the crowded mice showed breast cancer.

Other animal tumors also were stimulated by stresses. Baby mice which were removed from the nest for three minutes each day for their first twenty-four days died much more quickly from implanted leukemia than did mice not removed from the nest.

In other experiments, mice subjected to the trauma of a surgical operation and the application of chemicals which cause cancer showed substantially more and earlier cancers than mice given the carcinogens only.

Soviet scientists in Kiev, using Pavlovian techniques, trained mice to come for food at the sound of a bell and then made the mice neurotic by shocking instead of feeding them; neurotic mice developed breast cancer at eight months—instead of at ten months, as nonneurotic animals did.

Many authorities feel that emotions well may be related to cancer; but they deplore most of the present-day clinical approaches to the problem— approaches which are unscientific or pseudoscientific or even supernatural. One of the exponents of the scientific approach is Dr. Eugene Pendergrass of the University of Pennsylvania and former president of the American Cancer Society. He has said:

> There are great differences among cancer patients—in some a tumor will smolder and grow slowly; in another, it will grow steadily; and in a third, it will grow rapidly and spread throughout the body. Some tumors may stop growing and in rare instances disappear completely.
>
> I personally have observed cancer patients who had undergone successful treatment and were living and well for years. Then an emotional stress such as the death of a son in battle, the infidelity of a daughter-in-law or the burden of long employment seems to have been the precipitating factor in reactivating the disease which resulted in death.
>
> The opposite may obtain. I have patients with extensive malignant disease spread throughout the body who are living with their disease and living in comfort. The disease has been controlled by radiation, surgery, hormones and supportive care. These patients live in happy homes.

Even if psychological factors have no influence on the course of the disease, they have a great deal to do with the well-being of the patient. We as doctors must begin to emphasize treatment of the patient as a whole, as well as the disease.

It is my sincere hope that we can widen the investigation of cancer to explore—with the best instruments now available to science—whatever influence the mind and emotions may exercise over the disease.

CHAPTER 12

HORMONES AND CANCER

Cancers—possibly all of them—are associated with disturbances of glands and the hormones manufactured by the glands. Some animal cancers can be caused by giving hormones or by depriving the host of hormones. Humans with certain kinds of cancers often can be helped greatly, but not cured, by removing glands or giving hormones.

The relationships of hormones to various cancers are among the most fascinating and at the same time most confusing facets of the quest for the cause and control of the disease. Very few reliable rules are involved. The principles which apply to mice may not apply to men; and sometimes among inbred strains of mice the response to hormones is variable. Some scientists in the past have proclaimed that most or all cancers are due to a "hormonal imbalance," and their statements usually are not disputed, because they are as hard to disprove as to prove.

The question of whether hormones cause cancers is a profound one. If they do, then cancer may be a consequence not only of outside influences such as accidental exposure to carcinogens, but also of one's thoughts, emotions, and personality. Just as hormones influence human behavior, so does behavior influence the kind and quantity of hormones produced. Thus, cancer might represent the fruit of an unbridled free will or of uncurbed emotions; and one's way of life might predetermine his manner of death.

Reproduction is regulated by hormones. The potential for paternity is based upon sufficient male hormone to permit the reproductive act and for the production and release of sufficient sperm. Maternity requires ovarian estrogen for the development of female structures which would accommodate offspring, pituitary hormones for the normal release of the egg, or ovum, progesterone to build the uterine nest for the fertilized egg and the embryo, (at least in rodents) relaxin to soften the pubic tissues to permit birth, and prolactin to provide nourishment for the baby. Male hormone, and probably only male hormone, stimulates the female libido. Many other ponderable and imponderable factors are involved, including emotional, psychological, moral, esthetic, spiritual, and even financial; but basically and physiologically, reproduction and the sex urge are an endocrine, or hormonal, matter.

Natural sex activity, free of fear, is medically approved. Its abuse—by unrelenting restraint or by unregulated license—presents problems. The question has arisen as to whether cancer is one of the problems.

Two of the most common sites of female cancer, the breast and uterus, are sensitive to hormones. Epidemiological studies show a striking contrast between the personality types of those prone to breast cancer on the one hand and uterine cancers on the other.

The extremes of these two types are found in convents and in brothels. Nuns have very little uterine cancer but an inordinate share of breast cancer. Prostitutes are highly susceptible to cancer of the uterine cervix and not to breast cancer. Various gradations are found in the large area between these two groups, and destiny is meted out not so much as to saint and sinner but rather according to sexual behavior, if not to the reproductive urge.

A life of celibacy, abstinence from tobacco and alcohol, balanced diet, good housing, and communal living apparently pays off in health benefits. Dr. James T. Nix of New Orleans has reported these figures in a study of 1,116 deaths among 116,173 nuns in the United States during 1963: average age of death, 77.5 years; average age of cancer death, 67.2 years; percentage of deaths due to cardiovascular disease, 46 per cent and, to cancer, 25. Death from cancer of the uterine cervix was virtually nonexistent; cancer of the breast was unusually common.

Dr. Fabien Gagnon of Quebec has made a close study of the illnesses of 3,280 nuns in four orders for over twenty years. There were 130 deaths from cancer—none from cancer of the uterine cervix, only two from cancer of the body of the uterus, and the amazingly high total of 53 from cancer of the breast. Nine cancers of the ovary cropped up in this series, and this was much higher than the rate for the general population. Additional studies of the illness records of 13,000 nuns in Quebec and others in Verona, Würzburg, and Chicago and a preliminary survey of all nuns in the United States showed a similar rarity of cervical cancers. Dr. Gagnon reported that nuns had a lower than normal incidence of cancer generally until age fifty-nine years, normal incidence then until age sixty-nine, and higher than normal after that. The residents of convents and cloisters were more free from lethal diseases generally than the rest of the population and lived longer than the average person, although their tuberculosis rate during the decade 20–29 years was substantially higher than for the general population. Dr. Gagnon concluded that cervical cancers stemmed from chronic cervicitis and that this malignancy could be prevented by systematic treatment of the infections and inflammations of the cervix.

Prostitutes in Copenhagen showed a high incidence of cervical cancer, a condition which numerous studies throughout the world have indicated is related conversely to socioeconomic status—the lower the status, the higher the cervical cancer rate. The Danish investigator, however, found that prostitutes have four times as much cervical cancer as do women on a similar socioeconomic level. Numerous surveys, on the other hand, show that breast cancer is directly related to socioeconomic status—the higher the status, the higher the breast cancer rate. In these cancers, sex activity and hormones may be involved; poor people usually marry early and rich people late.

Dr. Lester Breslow of the California Department of Public Health has reported that in cancer generally, late diagnosis, inadequate treatment, and early death are proportional inversely to socioeconomic status—or, to paraphrase an old song: "the rich get rich, and the poor get cancer." One prominent exception to this was breast cancer, which affects better-off women much more than needy women. One California study showed that the only abundance poor people have is what they would be happy to reject—more divorce, more hospitalization, more days lost from work, and more chronic diseases than their prosperous neighbors.

Several studies relate cancers of the breast and of the cervix to non-commercial sexual experience and physical condition. Investigations show, with numerous exceptions, of course, that the more children a woman has and the worse her medical care, the greater her risk of uterine cancer. These tumors sometimes are attributed to unrepaired uterine injuries incurred in childbirth. Not so easily explained, however, are the results of several surveys which indicate that cervical cancer is most common in women who start their sexual experience early in life, finish childbearing in their mid-twenties, are divorced, separated, or widowed, and have had multiple sexual partners. A Kaiser Foundation study showed that the biggest single factor among cervical cancer patients in the San Francisco Bay Area was adolescent intercourse. From fifteen to twenty years of age is the susceptible period, and a single coitus can initiate the cancer process, the investigator, Dr. I. D. Rotkin, has concluded.

Drs. Alfred I. Sherman and Ralph B. Woolf of Washington University closely studied 133 women over a ten-year period who were diagnosed as having endometrial adenocarcinoma, cancer of the lining of the uterus. About 15,000 women develop this disease annually in the United States, and about one-half of them are cured by competent surgery or radiation. Most of the patients were obese, sterile, hypertensive, diabetic, and bothered by excessive facial and body hair. The key to their condition lay in their ovaries; these organs had atrophied in the normal manner with the menopause except for one surprising feature—large clusters of Leydig cells had developed, and they were producing prodigious amounts of progesterone, the female "pregnancy" hormone. The progesterone, produced under stimulation by the pituitary gland, was causing the uterine lining to grow, and it or an associated male hormone was masculinizing the patients. The investigators discovered that by giving the patients progesterone, they were able to halt pituitary stimulation of the ovaries and inhibit the glands' production of hormone. They began treating precancerous conditions with progesterone in hope of preventing adenocarcinoma of the endometrium. Dr. B. J. Kennedy of the University of Minnesota later used artificial progesterone preparations to treat endometrial cancers, and he reported achieving control of the disease for varying periods in about one-quarter of the patients, with metastases in the lungs responding even better than the pelvic tumors.

The Washington University scientists felt that the wayward ovaries which produced endometrial cancers might have been abnormal from the time they formed in the embryo. Until the human embryo is more than one month old and two-thirds of an inch long, male and female sex glands are alike. At this time, either the inner core of the gland or its outer covering begins to develop. If it is the inner core, the gland will be a testis; if it is the outer covering, it will be an ovary. A few cells of the other sex may survive, but as a rule almost all atrophy and leave the gland with very male or very female structure and function. In the ovary, Leydig cells produce progesterone; in the testis, they make a few alterations in the progesterone molecule which then becomes the male hormone. Meanwhile, other cells in ovaries, testes, and adrenal glands produce hormones of the opposite sex, and still other ovarian and testicular cells produce the seed of the new generation—eggs and sperm.

An investigation at Columbia University's College of Physicians and Surgeons also indicated that heavy, stocky women are most subject to endometrial cancer. In this series, patients with cancers of the breast, cervix, and ovary were morphologically highly feminine. Stature and figure, fundamentally, are due to the glands one inherits and the hormones they produce—sometimes in response to external and internal stimuli.

Dr. Ernest Wynder of Memorial Cancer Center, New York, in a study of 1,200 breast-cancer patients in the United States, Japan, England and India found that the women patients had married later than an equal number of controls, became pregnant later, had fewer children, and nursed later and less. He discovered as not significant in breast cancer such factors as breast size, trauma, and hormone therapy. He cited a Kinsey-type study by Japanese investigators who discovered that breast-cancer patients experienced "breast massage and caresses" during love-making only about one-half as often as other women. Earlier diseases reported most often by breast cancer patients included hypothyroidism, diabetes, and chronic cystic mastitis. Dr. Wynder reported that at Memorial Cancer Center the left breast becomes cancerous 8 or 9 per cent more than the right, that the upper half of the breast is involved more than three times as often as the lower half, and that cancer occurs in fully 41 per cent of the cases in the outer-upper quadrants of the breasts. He believed that hormonal factors—more than the tendency toward long nursing—were most responsible for the very low breast-cancer rate in Japan.

The number of menstrual periods during a woman's life is correlated with her risks of breast cancer, Drs. Levin, Saxon Graham, and others at Roswell Park have decided. Japanese women, with low breast cancer rates, menstruate for an average of 21 years and lactate for 6 or 7 years; American women, one study showed, menstruate 30.2 years and lactate 1.2 years. American breast cancer patients attained their menopause at an age of 49.7 years; matched controls without cancer had their menopause at an average age of 47.2 years. In Japan, the menopause comes several years earlier than in the United States.

The Roswell Park studies showed that, with the ordinary woman having a risk of 1.00 for breast cancer, the risk goes up or down according to these factors: artificial menopause, 0.50; nursed 36 months or more, 0.46; never married, 1.07; married, never pregnant, 1.08; married more than once, never pregnant, 1.42; married after age 25, one or more live births, 1.47; first pregnancy after age 25, 1.36; married, pregnant, live births, never nursed, 1.24; nursed less than 36 months, 1.21.

A hormone is a chemical produced by a gland; it migrates to specific or general areas of the body and there does its work. It speeds up or slows down certain chemical processes in cells, making the cell manufacture certain substances, grow, divide, or die. Scientists have come to recognize only some of the hundreds of hormones produced by humans.

The absence, deficiency, or excess of various hormones can, and regularly does, result in a strange assortment of defects. Among the products of abnormal glands and defective hormones are dwarfs or giants, jumping jitters or statuesque apathy, emaciation or rolypoly plumpness, licentious libido or the sex urge of a vegetable. Hormones—countless combinations and constantly changing levels of them—induce the great and gradual changes as man develops from a single cell through embryo, fetus, infancy, adolescence and maturity to the decline and decay of old age. A remarkable feedback system, under pituitary control, increases and decreases hormone production and release to meet the body's needs.

The pituitary, a pea-size structure midway between the temples and at the base of the brain, is called the master gland of the body. Shaped like a miniature boxing glove with the posterior part resembling the thumb, it produces a variety of protein hormones, most of which stimulate other glands throughout the body to manufacture and release their hormones. The posterior "thumb" of the pituitary makes hormones which control blood pressure (vasopressin), the body's retention and kidneys' uptake and release of water (antidiuretic hormone) and the contraction of the uterus (oxytocin). The front (anterior) part of the pituitary produces hormones which induce body growth (somatotropin, or growth hormone) and stimulate the adrenal membrane (adrenocorticotropin, or ACTH), thyroid (thyrotropin), breast (prolactin), ovaries and testes (gonadotropins), and probably other glands as well. An intermediate part— between the boxing-glove thumb and fingers—produces a hormone (melanocyte-stimulating hormone) which acts upon the cells which manufacture pigment and give the skin and other tissues their coloration.

While the pituitary exercises sensitive control over many other glands and tissues, it, in turn, is controlled by a small bit of the bottom of the brain, the hypothalamus, which fits over the pituitary top like a beret. The hypothalamus is the switchboard which connects the brain, and the many miles of nerves strung from it to all parts of the body, with the pituitary and the glands under pituitary control. The hypothalamus sends to the pituitary an assortment of chemicals representing information on and remedies for situations in the distant reaches of the body. The pituitary responds with gland-stimulating hormones for the defense, efficient operation, and comfort of the body. The hypothalamus, by its action on the pituitary, makes it possible to satisfy sundry appetites for food, sleep, fight, flight, sexual gratification, water, body warmth, and other essentials; and it helps translate nerve-communicated thoughts, emotions, urges, and various stresses into hormone-stimulated body response.

The adrenal glands, atop the kidneys, are called the glands of stress and their hormones, "stress hormones." The hormones enable one to cope with the stresses of everyday living and the strains of unusual situations. The adrenal core (medulla) produces adrenalin and noradrenalin, which rouse the system to a state of alarm, and acetylcholine, which lubricates nerve joints to speed transmission of impulses. When the adrenals are removed from experimental animals, the animals die gradually of wear and tear—they become, literally, tired to death—or quickly from strains induced by a loud noise, hunger, thirst, cold, heat, a minor infection, or a slightly toxic substance. When the outer part of the glands (the cortex) is under functioning, the victim suffers from loss of strength, profound fatigue, wasting, nausea, vomiting, diarrhea, stomachache, blood-sugar deficiency, irritability, nervousness, depression, pigmentation over joints, black freckles, and sparse pubic and armpit hair; the blood's sodium and chloride (from salt) are low and potassium high. In overfunction (hyperfunction) of the adrenal cortex, the victim is weak, susceptible to infection and bruise marks, fat of face, neck and trunk, hypertensive, water-logged, blood-sugar-rich, of unstable mood, and sometimes psychotic.

The overproduction of hormones of one's own sex by ovaries, testes, or adrenals results in exaggerated sexual characteristics, often accompanied by some physical difficulties. Underproduction deprives the victim of some of the normal sex characteristics. Overproduction of hormones of the other sex—hormonally, everyone is part-male, part-female—feminizes males and virilizes females.

Overactivity of the thyroid, low in the throat, is reflected in usually thin and always nervous, easily-perspiring people; underproduction of thyroid hormones leaves the person fat, apathetic, and subject to a great many vague complaints.

The parathyroids, tucked into or behind the thyroid, regulate the distribution of calcium and metabolism of phosphorous in the body. Too much of the hormone fills the blood with calcium, robs it of phosphorous, and the calcium, instead of strengthening bone, calcifies kidneys and forms kidney stones. Underfunction of the gland raises blood phosphorous, lowers blood calcium, plays hob with the autonomic nervous system and brings on the numerous ugly symptoms of tetany.

The pineal gland in the brain, soberly described for centuries as "the seat of the soul," has functions which are poorly understood. Various scientists have reported that it secretes melatonin, which suppresses ovarian function and lightens dark skin, and four common hormones which facilitate the transmission of stimuli in nerves. Others have found evidence that the pineal makes gonads and adrenals respond to light stimuli and regulates some diurnal rhythms of the body. The gland slowed the growth of transplanted rat cancers; when it was removed, the cancer grew and killed rapidly.

The thymus, a gland which usually shrinks up in humans at about the thirteenth birthday, has been reported to produce hormones which turn fertility cycles on and off. Composed largely of lymphatic cells, it also sows the body early in life with either antibody-producing, disease-fighting cell clusters or a hormone which stimulates these (lymphocytes) cells throughout the body.

Other organs also produce hormones. The pancreas turns out sugar-burning insulin and a sugar-producing hormone called glucagon; several organs, like the stomach and intestines, produce hormones which regulate their own function. Many important hormones are yet to be discovered.

For many years, observing physicians have detected signs of overactive adrenal glands in their far-advanced cancer patients. The cancers were varied, and most of them had no known relationship to hormones. In some instances, the effect was that of Cushing's syndrome—moon face, bull neck, buffalo hump, protruding belly and edema; and on at least forty-four occasions scientists saw fit to comment in journals, casually for the most part, on the fact that one or more of their cancer patients had a second condition caused by excess secretion of cortisone or cortisol. Recently, researchers at the University of Cincinnati reported on several such associations of Cushing's disease and lung cancer. And workers at Stanford and Vanderbilt Universities teamed up to explore the phenomenon; they discovered that a substantial percentage of cancers produced a substance closely resembling ACTH and that these patients had overgrown and over-functioning adrenals.

That hormones do play a prominent part in several cancers there can be no doubt. Dr. William U. Gardner of Yale for many years has been causing, accelerating, preventing, arresting and in a few cases curing cancer in experimental animals. It was all done with hormones and the imbalance they caused. He points out that hormone administration has induced cancer in such animal organs as breast, uterus, uterine cervix, kidney, lymphoid tissue, liver, bladder, prostate, bone, and connective tissue. To these he has added cancers of the pituitary, testis, ovary, adrenal cortex, adrenal medulla, and thyroid—hormone-produced cancers of hormone-producing glands. Over the years, this scholar has considered and tested many possibilities in attempting to ascertain the fundamental role hormones play in cancer: (1) they induce the original cell change toward cancer; (2) the hormones themselves are changed into something which incites the cell to cancer; (3) they activate or act in concert with another agent like a virus or gene; or (4) they merely increase the cell population which becomes an enlarging target for a carcinogen.

Dr. Gardner also has studied the possibility that hormones are not by themselves carcinogenic and do not trigger the cancer process. In this case, they might stimulate the growth of cancer cells during a phase of their development requiring hormonal stimulation, knock out the body's defenses or accelerate the tissue aging process which brings cancer.

The Yale investigator concluded that the potential for cancer exists, at least in some cases, in the target organ itself. When he transplanted still-normal tissues from animals destined by heredity to develop cancers in them to cancer-resistant strains, the tissues became cancerous in the cancer-resistant hosts. Similar tissues from cancer-resistant strains re-

mained healthy when grafted to highly cancer-susceptible hosts. Hereditarily cancer-susceptible vaginas and ovaries became cancerous under
prolonged stimulation by the female hormone, estrogen, even when they
had been transplanted to castrated male animals. Moreover, they developed cancer very rapidly when the estrogen was applied directly to
them, indicating that the hormones acted directly on the target rather
than through some systemic effect.

Dr. Gardner has pointed out that in some cases estrogens acted upon
the pituitary gland, causing it to turn out hormones (lactogenic) which
made breasts grow and excrete milk, and other hormones (luteinizing)
which produced testicular tumors. He felt, however, that the carcinogenic
action of estrogen may well have been on the target tissues themselves.
When he transplanted pituitary glands from one mouse to another of
either the same or another strain, the pituitary often became cancerous,
and sometimes the hormones produced by the grafted gland made the
new host's breasts grow and become cancerous. Estrogen injections also
induced leukemia in mice, and estrogen plus radiation had an additive
effect. Male hormone often offset the carcinogenic action of estrogen up
to the time when the tumor became irreversibly malignant; its action is one
of prevention rather than cure.

Many other scientists have built upon Dr. Gardner's observations and
come up with new clues—often confusing ones—to the role of hormones
in cancer. Dr. Otto Muhlbach of the Netherlands Cancer Institute, Amsterdam, and Drs. Erhard Haus and Franz Halberg of the University of Minnesota found that if they implanted extra pituitaries in mice, the animals
developed breast cancer. When, however, the Minnesota scientists implanted both pituitary and hypothalamic glands together, little if any
cancer developed. Something in the hypothalamus neutralized the cancer
agent in the pituitary. The cancer-causing agent may have been the adrenal
hormone, corticosterone, which was produced in large quantities under
stimulus of the additional transplanted pituitary.

There is one striking difference between mice and humans in breast
cancer: the disease is most common among women with no or few
children, whereas in certain strains of mice breast cancer is absent in
virgins and appears only after they have been bred, caused to have a
pseudopregnancy or given estrogens. Dr. Muhlbach attempts to reconcile
this fundamental discrepancy. He contends that the human menstrual
cycle, from a hormonal standpoint, is the equivalent of a monthly pseudopregnancy during the phase when women produce progesterone (mice
make progesterone only when pregnant or pseudopregnant). Mouse pregnancy lasts twenty days, whereas mouse pseudopregnancy lasts only ten
days—it ends at the stage when prolactin fails to be produced and to start
milk production in the mouse breasts. In this respect, the breast cancer-

susceptible mouse and menstruating human have one thing in common: both undergo a hormonal "pseudopregnancy." One possible conclusion is that a hormone produced by mouse and woman prior to the prolactin stage—probably progesterone—fulfills the hormonal requirements for breast cancer. Progesterone suppresses pituitary production of gonadotropins, which stimulate ovaries to pour out their hormones. A variety of natural and artificial progestins in recent years have been used to control pseudopregnancylike overgrowth and cancer of the uterine lining, as well as menstrual irregularities, early puberty, habitual abortion and premature birth, and, in males and females, to suppress fertility. As in the case of injudicious use of any hormone, hazards attach to progestins— digestive and nervous disturbances, tender breasts, reduced sex urge, fat, edema, menstrual delays, and masculinization of the female fetus. Whether the rapidly expanding use of progestins will increase or decrease the incidence of various cancers will not be known for some time.

Dr. Jacob Furth over many years has studied the development of various tumors under the influence of a malfunctioning pituitary. He feels that most of these cancers initially are dependent upon and responsive to hormones but eventually become autonomous. Some of the tumors occurred in mice staked out at various distances from exploded atomic bombs; the pituitary hormone-producing cancer cells grew to the point where they occupied most of the brain space. One of the tumors was comprised by cells which produce thyrotropin, the thyroid-stimulating hormone; another was made up of cells which produce ACTH, the adrenal-stimulating hormone. Both of these may represent impairment of the target glands, crippling them so that they do not produce enough thyroid and adrenal hormones to satisfy the system and shut down the desperate and futile pituitary cell production. A third tumor was of the pituitary cells which make prolactin, and Dr. Furth has speculated that this may have been caused by runaway estrogen secretion. When the target glands—thyroid, adrenals, or breasts—are capable of responding to pituitary prodding they enlarge and may also become tumorous.

A somewhat similar situation in humans has been noted by Dr. Sheldon C. Sommers, a pathologist formerly of Boston University and now at the University of California in La Jolla. For more than a decade he has studied at autopsy the pituitary cells of more than 3,000 victims of cancer and other diseases. He has concluded that various cancers come about in three ways: (1) gland malfunction—excess estrogen causes overgrowth of the breast, prostate, uterine lining and female lung, and then pituitary or adrenal hormones make the overgrown tissues cancerous; (2) irritants— chemicals act upon the cervix, ultraviolet rays on the skin and lip, and chemicals and hot food and drink on the esophagus (the pituitary and adrenals develop abnormalities after these cancers have started); and (3) heavy cigarette smoking and industrial inhalants—the common and rapidly increasing cancers of the bronchial lining are found in men with abundant male hormone production, the less common cancers of the glandular part of the lung in men with excess female hormones and cancers of the unspecialized lung cells in men with too much adrenal "stress" hormones.

The late Dr. Arthur Kirschbaum, successively at the Universities of Minnesota, Illinois and Texas, had adduced persuasive evidence that much of the age factor in cancer can be explained in terms of hormones. In discovering and proving his point, he and his several associates turned the clock both forward and back. One form of leukemia which could be induced only in young mice by painting the skin with the potent carcinogen, 3-methylcholanthrene, Dr. Kirschbaum succeeded in developing in mature mice; he merely removed the ovaries or testes of the older mice, and they became susceptible to leukemia when painted. Other cancers which ordinarily appear in mature animals Dr. Kirschbaum induced in young animals —he "aged" them rapidly with sex hormones. Mice whose ovaries were irradiated developed ovarian cancer seventeen months later; Dr. Kirschbaum prevented these cancers by transplanting new ovaries under the skin of the mouse ears anytime within six months following radiation; this showed that the cancers were due to the radiation-damaged ovary's inability to respond to the pituitary's prodigious production of ovary-stimulating hormone.

The discovery by Dr. Lew Engel at Harvard that the ovary of a woman with cervical cancer transformed male hormone into female hormone has helped explain one complication of the disease and its treatment. In this particular case, it became clear, male hormone administered to inhibit cancer became cancer-stimulating estrogen.

Many thousands of people dying of incurable cancers have left their beds of pain to live extra months and years in comfort and service because of the brilliant impatience of Charles B. Huggins of the University of Chicago and the scholars he has trained. More than two decades ago, Dr. Huggins was presented with a patient who had an inoperable and painful cancer of the prostate. His own studies on animals and the work of other scientists had convinced Dr. Huggins that something in the testis-pituitary axis—a chain of chemical events probably triggered by male hormone— was responsible for malignant prostatic growth. He removed the patient's testes and, in a further effort to suppress male hormone, administered estrogen. The patient recovered and, with his cancer still under complete control, died fifteen years later of other causes. A large series of prostatic cancer patients similarly treated yielded remissions in about 80 per cent of the cases. Hormonal treatment began to show promise. Until this time, the only endocrine procedure of help had been ovarectomy for breast-cancer patients which an Englishman first used in 1896. Dr. Huggins was criticized as being impetuous in applying his laboratory observations to the treatment of human cancer. His critics, however, soon came to use his technique, vindicating his passionate conviction that laboratory experiments on animals should be designed to help humans.

Dr. Huggins' achievement turned out to be not only a boon to prostatic cancer patients—in itself a giant therapeutic step forward, inasmuch as about one-third to one-half of all aged American men harbor cancer of the prostate (although in most cases it remains quiescent)—but it stimulated considerable basic and clinical research into endocrine influences on other forms of cancer. Others learned that some inoperable breast-cancer patients could be helped with sex hormones; but the vagaries of response to treatment lessened their effectiveness. When cortisone became available, Dr. Huggins showed that the adrenal glands could be removed safely, thus cutting off another source of sex hormones. Adrenalectomy helped between one-quarter and one-half of patients with breast cancer—giving some of them four or five comfortable years. Adrenalectomy was effective most often in those who had responded well to castration; it gave them still another renewal of their lease on life.

When the history of hormonal investigation finally is written, Dr. Huggins' major role may not be so much his considerable contributions to cancer therapy but work done more or less in collaboration with others— with those who inspired him and those over whom he wielded a profound influence. Among the former is Dr. Albert Szent-Gyorgi, the Nobelist of the Institute for Muscle Research, Woods Hole, Massachusetts, who introduced Dr. Huggins to paired and unpaired electrons; in these microcosmic clouds the Huggins group searched for and may have found some basic causes of cancer. Dr. Paul Talalay, a Huggins scholar now of Johns Hopkins University, has offered a classical concept of how a steroid hormone works: the hormone acts as a sort of co-coenzyme in transporting a hydrogen atom between pyridine nucleotides, producing the exquisite, dynamic imbalance which activates enzymes and thus provides life's basic spark for growth and energy production. Dr. H. G. Williams-Ashman also has made considerable contributions in this area.

Dr. Albert L. Lehninger, of Johns Hopkins, began his career in Dr. Huggins' laboratory exploring the mysterious mechanism by which a phosphate-splitting enzyme relates to the disintegrating bones of prostatic and breast-cancer victims and now is celebrated for his work on mitochondria, the cell structures which store phosphates as the principal source of power.

Dr. Choh Hao Li of the University of California, whose magnificent work in producing prolific rat cancers with growth hormone and in isolating pituitary hormones, taking them apart, and determining their amino acid sequence, benefits mutually with Dr. Huggins by a cross-fertilization of ideas. Dr. Thomas L. Dao of Roswell Park Memorial Institute has repeated much of Dr. Huggins' recent highly imaginative work, confirmed his findings and embellished them with independent advances of his own; in science it is almost as important to be confirmed by competent workers as to do original work—startling discoveries often incite savage attack which delays the introduction of life-saving clinical measures.

Perhaps the most notable work of Dr. Huggins' career is in progress at this writing. With Dr. N. C. Yang, he has found that some of the most powerful carcinogens—polynuclear aromatic hydrocarbons—in size and molecular configuration closely resemble steroid hormones of the adrenals and sex glands. In length and breadth the carcinogenic hydrocarbons are identical with the steroids; in the third dimension, depth, they are a little larger. But both molecules fit snugly into a frame formed by paired segments of the long coiled DNA (deoxyribonucleic acid) molecules which comprise genes. On this basis and the additional fact that the carcinogenic molecules contain an unpaired electron which makes them unstable and avid to join with other molecules, Drs. Yang and Huggins have postulated a basic principle of cancer causation. They believe that the carcinogenic steroid counterfeit slips into the DNA segment (inside nucleotide base pairs), takes the place of a natural steroid, alters the DNA molecule, or gene, and thus effects the malignant transformation of the cell. The theory—independently proposed also by Dr. Leonard Lerman of the University of Colorado—has far-reaching hints to the cause, prevention, and, possibly, cure of cancer. Some of the implications already seem to have been realized. Dr. Huggins has (1) induced extremely rapid and malignant breast cancers in albino rats by giving them a single dose of an overweight, overcharged, steroidlike compound called 7,12-DMBA; (2) prevented the cancers by simultaneously giving the animals natural steroids; (3) temporarily arrested the cancer's development with the female hormone, estradiol 17B, and (4) completely extinguished the growing cancers and permitted normal breast development with a combination of two ovarian hormones, estràdiol 17B plus progesterone. DMBA's action on the adrenal glands was dramatic; it reduced the cortex to a necrotic mess. Drs. Huggins and Elizabeth Ford discovered that DMBA has a strange dichotomous effect on the ovaries and testes of the rats. The ovaries are undamaged by the chemical; the dividing cells of the testes are killed and the testes themselves, after two weeks of increased growth, atrophy. Most recently, Drs. Huggins and Ford have prevented cancers by feeding animals anticarcinogenic hydrocarbons along with the carcinogens.

Dr. Dao and his Roswell Park associates showed that DMBA and 3-MC acted by completely different hormonal mechanisms. With DMBA, the adrenals appeared to play a critical role; their cortex was destroyed.

With 3-MC, the ovaries took a prominent part in the carcinogenic process: (1) pregnancy and the ovarian hormones which usually accelerate rat breast cancer, nullified the carcinogenic effect of 3-MC; and (2) males, which were almost completely resistant to 3-MC, became susceptible when they were castrated and bore grafted ovaries—more than one-half the altered rats came down with breast cancer.

A long list of scientists and research groups have contributed valuable information on hormones in health and in disease. Only a few, however, have exploited the information to the advantage of the cancer patient.

The feeling is inescapable that if the hundreds or thousands of isolated findings and observations were evaluated for their soundness and the valid ones were put together in some logical composite picture, one would obtain a much clearer understanding of the cause and course of cancer; almost necessarily this would lead to improved methods of treating the disease in humans.

One may regard hormones from many angles—their structure, genesis, synthesis, release, transport, activation, kinetics, metabolism, ultimate destiny. One can contemplate them in their relationships to Mendelian and molecular genetics, various cell structures, enzymes, tissue states, diet, reproduction, aging processes, physical and mental functions, illnesses, emotions, and effects on various metabolic systems. Endocrinology has many distant horizons, and the complete endocrinologist has an enormous demand on his intellectual potential. Compatible teams of scientists with tangential interests often do fine work.

The late Dr. John J. Bittner of the University of Minnesota and his group managed to explore many of the facets of hormones (or genetics, or viruses—one could never be quite certain which was the central theme). Each of the gifted group was an individualist: Drs. Carlos Martinez, who devised new transplantation techniques and who helped uncover the role of the thymus in immunity; Cyrus P. Barnum, who explored nucleic acid synthesis and enzymes; Herbert Hirsch, whose interests ranged through immunology and polymerization processes; Robert Huseby, who investigated the interrelationships of hormones; Halberg, the authority on biological rhythms; Haus, who transplanted pituitaries and hypothalami, and many others of widely diverse interests and skills. Because each was a strong and competent investigator in his own right, there was no general concurrence within the groups as a whole or even with Dr. Bittner whose principal interests lay in trying to make sense out of the contradictions and snarls in the interplay of genes, virus and hormones. In this organization there was no element of master-minding or "mass-think"; rather, it was a matter of intellectual team play with each man being his own quarterback.

On all levels—molecule, cell, mouse, and man—a vast endocrine literature has accumulated. All of it may have direct or indirect application to cancer.

Charles D. Kochakian, now of the University of Alabama Medical Center, showed many years ago that growth and development depend upon hormone and enzyme interactions—in this case the effect of male hormone and certain enzymes on the building of muscle and masculine structures. That hormones also destroy cells has been shown; when they were at Yale in the early 1940s, Dr. Thomas F. Dougherty, now of the University of Utah, and Abraham White, now at Yeshiva University, found that adrenal stress hormones rapidly aged and dismantled lymphocytes, which are a powerful natural mechanism of immunity.

Dr. Leo Samuels and the succession of brilliant students he trained at the Universities of Minnesota and Utah have traced many of the chemical processes by which the adrenal glands produce their hormones, and he has devised methods of measuring several of the estimated 80 blood-borne products of these glands. More than a decade ago he determined that in the normal course of events, stress hormone levels in the blood rise and fall in a diurnal rhythm—a rapid rise between 2 and 8 A.M. to a peak and a gradual fall to the trough (from one-third to one-half the peak levels) at midnight. Cortisol levels, he found, rise gently with the aging process—due to the system's failure to dispose of the hormone rather than to increased production. In mental illness, rhythms are distorted. From two to seven days before death due to cancer or other illness, Dr. Samuels discovered, the cortisol level rises to five or ten times normal and remains there; this portent has turned out to be more reliable by far than the patient's physical condition or the doctor's judgement.

Dr. George Sayers of Western Reserve University has devised ways of measuring adrenal-stimulating ACTH in the blood, and he has regarded this level as a measure of "uncompensated stress"—it falls when a physical or emotional crisis has been met with and overcome. ACTH, Dr. Sayers has found, has an explosive activity. Its half-life in the blood is only one minute, but a single stressful incident elevates the ACTH level fivefold, and sustained stress can increase it to as much as twenty-five or thirty times normal. Dr. Curt P. Richter of Johns Hopkins Hospital found that fierce wild rats had much larger adrenals than do tame laboratory rats.

Man inherits many of his hormonal characteristics. Others he acquires before birth or during his lifetime. Dr. Emil Witschi of the University of Iowa has shown that various doses of estrogen can so alter the maternal uterine environment that offspring will be born with a topsy-turvy endocrine system. He gave estrogen to female frogs and noted the effect on their offspring. Moderate doses feminized male offspring; high doses masculinized females. The administered estrogens appeared to act upon the embryonic pituitaries which then prevented development of testes, enhanced the growth of male hormone-producing cells of the ovaries and enlarged the adrenals. Some overhormonized offspring developed benign tumors or cancers.

It is obvious that something like this occurs naturally in humans. The instances in which parents change their offspring's name months after birth from Harry to Harriet or from Charlotte to Charles are by no means uncommon.

Dr. William H. Fishman of Tufts Medical School has shown that enzymes which activate and deactivate hormones can be as important as the hormones themselves in cancer. In his work with an enzyme system which attaches glucuronides to steroid hormones and detaches them at their site of action, Dr. Fishman demonstrated a decisive influence on some cancers. The capacity to produce the enzymes is largely inherited, and the enzymes may represent a powerful genetic factor in hormone-related cancers.

Cholesterol is the raw material from which steroid hormones are made. Known to the public largely as the fatty material which thickens the blood and piles up in the bore of aging arteries to set the stage for strokes and heart attacks, it actually is a valuable substance; without it, people would have no stress or sex hormones. Dr. Gregory Pincus of the Worcester Foundation for Experimental Biology, who has made many remarkable biological discoveries during a long and distinguished career, has explored the chemical processes by which cholesterol becomes various hormones. With Dr. Erwin Schwenk, he found that as laboratory animals develop cancer something at first depresses the liver's manufacture of cholesterol and then, under stress of the growing cancer and the influence of increased adrenal activity, the liver produces cholesterol prolifically. Other stresses have had a similar effect in raising the blood content of cholesterol. Preliminary observations indicate that many cancer patients have similar cholesterol patterns. The findings raise the question as to whether stress and cholesterol contribute to the cause of cancer, whether cancer sets up a stress, or both.

During the course of testing many hormonal and antihormonal compounds for their role in cancer and other conditions, the Pincus group discovered that small amounts of estrogen and a weak progestin block ovulation and abolish fertility in women for as long as the drugs are taken. In trials of the preparations in more than 800 women over four or five years, it is beginning to appear that the combination also prevents cancer of the uterine cervix. More time and more extensive studies are needed to determine the ultimate effect of the drugs.

Among the factors which enter into the picture of hormones and cancer is dietary restriction. The incidence of many kinds of cancer dropped during World War II on rations issued by conquering Axis armies in occupied countries. Wartime semistarvation also brought about remarkable endocrine changes. A great many soldier-survivors of the Bataan death march, for instance, developed gynecomastia—their breasts became comparable to those of young women and many actually lactated. The ill-nourished livers simply could not destroy the men's normal female hormones. (The condition cleared up after the war when the diet again became sufficient.) Of a group of 450 Western women taken prisoner by the Japanese in Hong Kong, 250 failed to menstruate for about three months.

That there is no common role for hormones in cancer has been made clear by the work of Dr. A. Clark Griffin, now at M. D. Anderson Hospital, Houston, Texas. Dr. Howard Richardson of Little Rock, and Dr. Henry Moon at the University of California. They and their associates gave animals several kinds of chemical carcinogens. If they removed the animals' pituitaries before or shortly after giving certain carcinogens, the cancers failed to appear. Other carcinogens, however, produced cancers as readily in animals without pituitaries as with them.

In the absence of more definitive evidence of the part played by hormones in the genesis of cancer, two guesses are consistent with the known facts: (1) Some hormones, particularly steroids, may be changed by a metabolic fault into a carcinogen—such a change has been wrought in test tubes in experiments at Clark University: Drs. William R. Nes and D. L. Ford have changed pregnenalone in eight chemical stages into 4′, 10-dimethyl-1,2-benzanthracene—and (2) by overstimulating metabolism in specific organs and tissues, hormones enhance the organs' exposure to all blood-borne substances, including carcinogens (the increased metabolic activity of sex hormone stimulate breasts and uteri, for instance, and increase their mathematical chance of taking up carcinogens).

The list of hormones used to treat cancer is not long. The catalogue of cancers so far found responsive to hormonal treatment also is short. Hormones do not cure cancer. With many exceptions, the additional time given patients by hormones is brief—less than one year on an average, although some will benefit for three or four years and a few for more than a decade.

Despite all the magnificent work by large numbers of biochemists, despite the interesting observations and achievements of an army of biologists on vast numbers of mice and rats, and despite successful attacks launched by some investigators against a few human cancers, the endocrine treatment of human cancer at this point leaves much to be desired. If hormones could be used in other than hopeless cancer patients, however, the results might be more impressive.

The usefulness of endocrine measures in cancers which have advanced beyond cure by surgery and/or radiation is easily summarized. Castration and estrogen helps up to 80 per cent of prostatic cancer patients and often for five or more years. In advanced breast cancer, various combinations of removal of the ovaries, adrenals, and pituitary, estrogens and androgens aid almost one-half the patients for a few months and some for many years. (In one study of less than 400 hopelessly advanced breast-cancer patients, those given hormonal therapy survived an average of 20.2 months after cancer's recurrence, while those without hormonal treatment lasted only 14.5 months.) ACTH and cortisol-type preparations are helpful to some patients with lymphatic cancers—to 50 to 70 per cent of children and about 25 per cent of adults with acute lymphatic leukemia and a few with chronic lymphatic leukemia. Recently, progestins have been reported as giving remissions to some patients with breast and uterine cancers. Cortisone has been used for years as "supportive therapy" in several kinds of solid cancer; careful investigation into its effects, however, has shown that it sometimes riddles the body with cancer colonies, alters the electrolyte balance, and sends the patient into a fatal tailspin.

It is argued, and with considerable merit, that while endocrine therapy in most cases adds little if any time to the short life span of the advanced cancer patient, it often brings dramatic relief from pain and, in some cases, makes the patient feel normal for varying periods. Some assert that to the person whose days are numbered, it is better to live a few weeks with a sense of well-being than to survive, sick and in pain, for a few months.

Modest as the published statistical successes in experimental treatment of cancer seem, they nevertheless represent a substantial cut above the results achieved by physicians whose idea of chemotherapy is to put the inoperable patient promptly on morphine. The most impressive statistics reflect the effects of treatment by teams of specialists in leading cancer centers, equipped with the most modern equipment and drugs, staffed by competent consultants and with a well-used library of current medical and scientific journals. The patients are followed carefully with an eye to the numerous or occasional unwanted side effects of treatment—the possibility of surgical shock in organ-removal procedures, the high blood levels of calcium with physical distress, mental aberrations, and coma. Most patients do not receive this quality of care.

Administered hormones have their unwanted side effects. In men, testicular lesions may be caused by estrogens. Women run the risk of virilization (including baldness, hirsutism, acne, and increased libido) when treated with androgens. There are the possibilities of Cushing's syndrome on adrenal hormones and adrenal failure when the hormones are withdrawn, the jitters of hyperthyroidism and sluggishness of hypothyroidism and, on most steroids, the tendency to retain sodium with consequent threat of congestive heart failure. With adrenalectomy, an important source of male hormone is cut off, because in both men and women, male hormone (and apparently only male hormone) increases libido, whereas adrenalectomy usually depresses the desire for sexual activity.

Constant efforts are being made to overcome the defects, dangers, and discomforts of hormonal treatments. In some instances a measure of success has been achieved. Scientists at the University of Chicago some years ago devised a system of implanting radioactive yttrium beads in the pituitary, and they reported that this seems to have achieved more complete hormone-suppressing effects than surgical removal of the gland. The method, which calls for considerable skill, has been adopted and perhaps improved at the University of California at Los Angeles, but it is little used elsewhere.

Drs. Nylene Eckles and Mary E. Sears of M. D. Anderson Hospital, Houston, have severed the stalk which connects the hypothalamus with the pituitary and blocked the flow of materials between the two organs. They felt that in patients with metastatic breast cancer they might achieve the good therapeutic results and none of the side effects of pituitary removal. The operation suppressed the function of pituitary-dependent ovaries, adrenals, and thyroid, granted remissions to a few patients and, surprisingly, caused lactation in those who had the procedure. When the pituitary was removed and cut up and slices of it implanted in the abdominal wall of the patient, similar results were achieved—and without lactation.

Many artificial androgens and progestins have been synthesized, and some of them have much milder side effects than the natural hormones; whether they retain comparable therapeutic value, however, is debatable. Dr. Albert Segaloff of the Ochaner Clinic found in trials of scores of these preparations that very few artificial hormones are better than the natural ones.

An imaginative approach to endocrine tumors has been made by Dr. Walter Burdette of the University of Utah. His studies of tumor-susceptible fruit flies and other insects showed that metamorphosis from the worm to fly form is governed by three hormones: (1) brain hormone, which stimulates the prothoracic gland to secrete, (2) ecdysone, which makes immature tissues grow and mature, and (3) juvenile hormone (also produced by humans as an intermediate product in the formation of cholesterol), which suppresses or balances the effect of ecdysone. The hormones —derived from tons of silkworms—have been tested on transplanted cancers in mice. Ecdysone, which stimulates nucleic acid and protein synthesis, arrested or regressed the cancers. So did juvenile hormone in toxic doses. Brain hormone had no effect.

While a great deal of ingenuity has gone into test-tube and mouse work with hormones, and while basic endocrine studies have advanced at a dizzying pace, very little of the progress has filtered down to the treatment of human cancer. The most effective treatments now used were introduced from ten years to a generation or so ago, and a few reported successful long ago are ignored or forgotten today.

Dr. Paul Starr of the University of Southern California, for instance, is highly critical of the modern practice of surgery for most benign and malignant growths of the thyroid. The gland often is removed for goiter or because of the existence of a single lump, or nodule, which in about 10 per cent of the cases indicates cancer. Thyroid cancer is *not* very common—about 1,200 Americans die of it each year; and while it does not have a high cure rate, its victims often live normal lives with the disease for ten or twenty years. Dr. Starr points out that surgical thyroidectomy involves an inevitable small mortality from the operation and considerable permanent disease due to damage to the voice-box cords and inadvertent removal of parathyroid glands governing calcium metabolism. He charges that surgeons sometimes don't realize that in removing the thyroid they are producing a hypothyroidism which, untreated with thyroid hormone, can have grave consequences to the health of the patient.

Treatment of goiter with thyroid hormone was initiated in Germany in 1895. This simple and cheap therapy was highly effective. Goiters and thyroid cancers are caused to grow by thyroid-stimulating hormone produced by the pituitary. Dr. Starr says that thyroid hormone halts the pituitary's stimulatory action, shrinks up 75 per cent of the goiters and controls thyroid cancer and its metastases in patients whose cancers are sensitive to hormones. Treatment of hyperthyroidism with radioactive iodine, he states, will destroy 90 per cent of the toxic part of the thyroid —at a cost of about $100 in medical expenses. Fears that radioiodine may have late carcinogenic effects, he says, are proved groundless by statistics.

Despite these obvious advantages of simple, safe and cheap therapy, potentially disabling surgery remains the common treatment for these thyroid conditions.

Cancer researchers seldom use more than one or, at most, two hormones or other drugs simultaneously against various kinds of cancer. This uncomplicated pattern of treatment has been employed in both mouse and man. The simplicity of this approach is in contrast to the fact that the endocrine is a complicated system and cancer seems to be a complicated disease.

Hormones, as scores of scientists have demonstrated, do not function in a vacuum. They are completely dependent upon the availability of the substances from which they are formed, a long list of enzymes which catalyze each step in their synthesis, the dietary amino acids, vitamins and trace metals which comprise various enzymes, substances like glucuronides which bind to the hormones to activate or inactivate them and the enzymes responsible for binding and releasing them, the reactions which establish the ion-charged environment in which they perform, the substances which make the cell permeable to them and others which create their target compounds.

Beyond all this, hormones act together in concert, concurrently or in sequence. One hormone is essential to the health of the gland which produces another hormone; one is necessary to produce the environment in which another is effective; one hormone may act directly upon another hormone to activate or degrade it or itself. The complicated hormonal feedback system can be distorted in several ways.

These considerations—well established in the test tube, experimental animal, and man—suggest that an entire sequence of drugs may be advisable or necessary to restore the hormonal balance of the cancer patient. A shotgun approach might call for the use of combinations of hormones, enzymes, vitamins, trace metals, energy-yielding phosphates, ion-transport systems, and perhaps other chemicals known to be involved in the endocrine system one wishes to influence.

Generally ignored are implications of the work of Drs. Halberg, Samuels, and others who have shown that endocrine glands function in rhythmic cycles as faithful as those of the tides. The ebb and flow of hormones throughout the system proceed in diurnal, circadien (roughly, 24 hours), monthly, seasonal, annual, age, and other cycles. Under the influence of hormones, various types of cells and systems throughout the body observe periodicities in their growth and function. Radiation or alcohol given a mouse at 9 A.M. will have no untoward effect; the same dose at 9 P.M. will kill the animal. It is of major importance to determine in human patients the most effective times to take hormones.

Some clues to improved treatment of cancer may be obvious. For several years a few scientists reported that, in its physical and biochemical effects, cancer resembled starvation. A few scientists tried forced feeding in an effort to overcome the emaciation of advanced cancer patients; it didn't work very well. Dr. Oscar Neufeld found similarities between the cachexia of cancer and the wasting in diabetes, and he decided to give insulin to seven patients (three who had cancers of the lung, two of the esophagus, and one each of the liver and stomach). His aim was to stimulate their appetite. In all but one (the stomach-cancer patient), appetite returned; and all of them gained weight and felt better; some experienced a feeling of euphoria. The gradually increased insulin doses were generally well tolerated. These experiments are being continued on an expanded scale.

Back in 1958, British, Canadian, and American scientists found that insulin had no therapeutic effect on mouse and rat transplanted tumors, although a combination of insulin and glucagon (a sugar-synthesizing hormone) in toxic doses slowed down many of these cancers. Glucagon alone, which changes store sugar into blood sugar, also arrested these cancers.

One of the strangest oversights of all may be in the role played by thyroid hormone in many or all kinds of cancer. Some estimate that there may be as many as 30-odd different thyroid hormones. A large literature has been compiled on their synthesis, metabolism, degradation, mechanism of action, effect on various cell structures, cells, organs, and tissues, and interdependence with other hormones and hormone-producing systems. So far as cancer is concerned, this treasury of information represents unconnected academic islands of no practical application. Both the medical and scientific journals have been almost barren of articles on thyroid influences on non-thyroidal cancer. And yet, thyroid hormone has the physiological and biochemical properties of a very helpful drug for some cancers.

One investigator has given adequate testing of the effect of thyroid hormone in human cancers other than cancer of the thyroid gland itself. Dr. Alfred A. Loeser of London reported that following surgical and radiation treatment for breast cancers which had spread beyond the breast, he had put eighteen patients on thyroid hormone. At the time of his report in the British Medical Journal in 1954, all eighteen were still alive from four to more than five years, and only one had had a recurrence. A few London hospitals have recently begun long-term studies with thyroid hormone in breast cancer.

Dr. Henry Lemon at Boston University treated a series of breast-cancer patients with a combination of thyroid hormone and cortisone on the theory that these two drugs would suppress the pituitary and its cancer-stimulating hormones. The treatment, he reported, did as well as adrenalectomy or pituitary removal—about 65 per cent benefited. His observations have been confirmed in part by a group at the University of California Medical Center; 24 per cent of breast-cancer patients who had become resistant to male and female hormones, had regressions averaging six months with the Lemon-type treatment. Dr. Nicholas Petrakis, also at the University of California Medical Center, gave various thyroid hormone analogues to thirteen patients, a majority with leukemia, and found that only one benefited. Most were treated for only one, two or three weeks, however, and the longest for seven weeks.

For some reason—perhaps because thyroid hormones are so common, so cheap and have ben used clinically for more than ninety years—the great majority of laboratory and clinical endocrinologists in cancer research have completely neglected them. Enough basic work has been done, however, to indicate that the thyroid may play an important role in many cancers.

The scientific literature, while it contains occasional contradictory findings, shows that in various experimental animals, thyroid hormone

Reduces the potency of carcinogens;

Regresses transplanted tumors;

Prevents ovarian cancers caused by transplanting normal ovaries to the mouse spleen;

Regresses spontaneous thyroid cancers in fish;

Counteracts carcinogenic and other ill effects of radiation.

Thyroid-suppressing drugs and thyroid removal have been shown to increase the virulence of all categories of cancers—carcinogen-induced, transplanted and spontaneous.

A few observations indicate that the anticancer effects of thyroid hormone in mice, rats, and other animals apply also to humans. Statistics relate cancer inversely to thyroid function, with the disease being most common among hypothyroid people and least frequent in hyperthyroids. In one study, breast cancer was nine times as common among myxedematous (extremely hypothyroid) and sixteen times as common among thyroidectomized women as among hyperthyroid women. Thyroid atrophy was found at autopsy in 59 per cent of breast-cancer patients, and other thyroid disease existed in another 27 per cent. Among prostatic-cancer patients, thyroid disease was found at autopsy twice as frequently as among men who had died of noncancerous diseases. It may be more than coincidence that general cancer rates are highest in the goiter belts of the modern world and lowest in areas where dietary iodine is abundant. And it may be significant that thyroid hormone tends to reduce excess weight and blood cholesterol levels, both of which have been reported associated with animal and human cancers.

Some consider cancer essentially a failure of oxidative metabolism. Thyroid hormone stimulates oxidative metabolism.

Some consider the cancer cell an embryonic-type, unspecialized (undifferentiated) cell; thyroid hormone promotes morphogenesis of animals (like tadpoles) into their adult form.

Some consider cancer due to lack of immunity. Thyroid hormone stimulates immune mechanisms.

Cancer invades neighboring tissues and, via larger vessels and capillaries, its seeds colonize distant areas and sometimes decalcify bone. Thyroid hormones help maintain the integrity of connective tissue and prevent capillary fragility; one thyroid extract prevents the escape of calcium into the blood.

Cancer is considered by some a consequence of aging. Thyroid hormone production is depressed progressively during the aging process, and hypo-thyroid people (there are an estimated 9,000,000 Americans with hidden hypothyroidism) are rejuvenated to a large degree with thyroid hormone.

Some associate the onset of cancer with long-sustained stress or a sud-den catastrophic emotional crisis. The healthy thyroid—called the *globus hystericus* by Aristotle—helps mediate the response to emotional trauma.

Physicians often are reluctant to administer the drug in the absence of measurable hypothyroidism. This feeling prevails despite the demonstra-tion that almost all the tests of thyroid function are notoriously inaccurate and misleading; the most reliable of them—the PBI or protein-bound iodine test—indicates the amount of iodine (presumably incorporated in hormone) which is bound to blood proteins. One molecule of free (and active) hormone exists for every 1,000 molecules of bound hormone (believed to be inactive until released from the protein); so even the PBI may be an artifact so far as hormonal activity is concerned. A very few physicians feel that where there is doubt, the best course is to give gradually increasing doses of the hormone, keeping close check on the patient's response to it.

While thyroid—and all other—hormones are of limited practical value in controlling human cancer at this time, their potential has not been tapped.

CHAPTER 13

PRENATAL DANGERS

Occasionally the hand of The Potter slips. The product becomes a bizarre body or an empty mind. Or, in some cases, cancer.

A few scientists feel that many cancers may originate sometime between conception and birth, lie latent for years, and break out later in life when triggered by certain rays, chemicals, or viruses. Some have produced evidence that cancer cells chemically and in behavior are essentially embryonic; and they speculate that the malignant cells have been arrested in this state since before birth. Others have shown that many of the agents known to cause cancer produce deformed babies when pregnant women are exposed to them.

The relationship of the cancer patient to his tumor has been compared often to the association between the mother and her fetus. The big difference is that the fetal structures develop, or differentiate, into specialized tissues, while the tumor remains a formless mass of useless and predatory cells. The secret of embryonic development and differentiation may hold the answer to cancer.

The fetus in some respects resembles grafted or transplanted tissue. The fetus, genetically, is only 50 per cent its maternal host; the other 50 per cent is paternal and unrelated to the mother. Nevertheless, it lives inside the mother in a state of peaceful coexistence. Research into the mysteries of transplantation has theoretical, and possibly practical, implications for the understanding and control of cancer, which also coexists with the host but eventually becomes parasitical.

What permits the mother and fetus to survive in this symbiotic, live-and-let-live state?

For one thing, the placenta forms a *cordon sanitaire* which to a degree isolates mother and the "grafted" fetus one from another. The mother will produce antibodies against the "foreign" fetus and destroy its cells only if antigenic (large, antagonistic, immunity-stimulating) molecules pass from the fetus, through the placenta and into the mother's bloodstream; and this is prevented by the fine filtration system and probably by chemicals in the placenta. Perhaps something in the placenta neutralizes or "naturalizes" the alien particles from the fetus before they enter the maternal system.

The placenta, possibly the part produced by the fetus, manufactures pituitarylike hormones which stimulate the mother's ovaries and adrenals. The maternal glands, under this prodding, pour out female hormones, which build up the uterine nest, and cortisone-type hormones, which suppress her immune reaction against the foreign fetus in it.

The fetus—like infectious bacteria or successfully grafted tissue—may also produce other immunity-suppressing chemicals. The best guess is that these are polysaccharides, or molecules made up by a mixture of sugars.

The fetus itself is incapable of producing antibodies against the mother. Humans, sheep, and cattle cannot produce antibodies until birth or later; rabbits and mice, which are born at a relatively earlier stage of development, don't produce antibodies until some time after birth.

Sometimes grafted tissues prove more viable than the host. In these cases, the grafts produce antibodies and other substances which destroy the host's cells. Foreign cells injected into newborn animals, for instance, cause runting; the injected cells stunt the host's growth, feed on his vital tissues, and destroy him.

Many feel that something like this happens in cancer. The malignant tumor, they believe, is like a malignant fetus or a malignant graft. It somehow escapes or subverts the host's antibodies, waits possibly for years until the host's defenses (immunity) are down and then devours the host.

Congenital disasters have been attributed in times past to a variety of causes—among them evil spirits, maternal emotions, payment for parental sin, or God's will.

Animal experiments and clinical observations have suggested a variety of ways in which diseases are caused in the 600,000 or so cerebral palsy patients, the 2,158,000 youngsters with neurological and sensory disorders (the third leading cause of death among children), the victims of epilepsy, some kinds of multiple sclerosis and muscular distrophy and kidney ailments. And, in some cases, cancer, which some regard as a long-latent congenital disease.

Congenital disorders can be produced in chicks by merely cracking, warming, shaking, or varnishing the egg, or pricking the embryo. The same can be done by altering the alkalinity and acidity of natural environments of other eggs—like those of the sea urchin. And it can be done by exposing pregnant mammals—mice, rats, rabbits, and guinea pigs—to the diet, drugs, rays, and other environmental factors of humans.

Dr. Joseph Warkany of the Children's Hospital Research Foundation and Department of Pediatrics, University of Cincinnati, is one of the most active workers in the field of congenital anomalies. While acknowledging the great risks of extrapolating animal experimental results to human events, he tries to reproduce in animals the grotesque structures he finds in monstrous children. He wants to know when in gestation they originate, what causes them, how they can be prevented or controlled.

From their own and others' results, Dr. Warkany and Dr. Harold Kalter have drawn up this list of defects produced in experimental animals and their causes:

Complete vitamin A deficiency entirely destroys pig litters. With cod liver oil supplementing the vitamin A-less diet, pig litters are born but have small or no eyes, harelip, cleft palate, extra ears, closed ears, malformed hind legs, unascended kidneys and undescended testicles, misplaced ovaries, and cysts under the skin. Every single offspring of A-deficient pigs have abnormalities; but the same mothers and even the abnormal female offspring on a regular diet bear healthy pigs. Rats respond to vitamin A deficiency with young that show diaphragmatic hernia, heart and artery abnormalities, and prematurely aged skin. Excessive vitamin A also produces monsters; 52 per cent of the offspring of overdosed rats show undeveloped eyes, brains, spines, and bones.

Deficiency of the vitamin riboflavin in rats produces an "Andy Gump" type lower jaw (which is a common and very serious malformation in humans—the victims often die because they can't breathe, nurse, or eat properly), cleft palate, digits welded together, short tail and hind legs, absent ribs and leg bones. Folic acid deficiency produces water on the brain—a dome-shaped head, greatly enlarged, with the brain ventricles filled with fluid. These offspring turn out to be fairly sterile, and they show stomach and other abnormalities.

Deficiency of the vitamin pantothenic acid results in young with the brain outside the head or no brain at all and deformed digits. If the deficient diet is begun ten days before breeding, nearly all the young are absorbed by the mother's uterine tissues.

Vitamin E deficiency yields young with water on the brain, no thyroid glands, and with deformed hearts, lungs, and kidneys.

Deficiency of vitamin D produces young with skeletal defects; of thiamin, extruded brains; of C, broken and ill-formed bones, hemmorrhage in bone marrow, and retarded growth, particularly of the skin and muscle;

of E, thyroidless cretins, with imperfect heart, lungs and kidneys; of niacin, cleft palate and skeletal defects.

Other monstrosities have been produced by fasting animals at certain times during pregnancy, by withholding from their diet some of the essential amino acids needed to form protein, or essential fatty acids, and with large doses or deficiencies of such hormones as insulin, progesterone (in late pregnancy), cortisone, ACTH, and estrogen. Pregnant women needing thyroid hormone should take it, doctors have found.

Drs. Kalter and Warkany list an impressive number of drugs which, when administered to pregnant animals, usually in large doses and at certain times, produced various types of monster offspring. The drugs include phenyl mercuric acid, nicotine, caffeine, sulfonamides, and anti-biotics like penicillin, streptomycin, terramycin, and particularly chloram-phenicol, or chloromycetin. Such anticancer preparations as azaserine, 6-mercaptopurine, urethane, nitrogen mustard, myleran, antifolic acids, radiation-imitating compounds and (by exposing sperm to it) colchicine produced headless, rumpless, brainless, and other defective animals. Many of the compounds used to treat cancer also cause cancer.

The embryo lives in a rarefied atmosphere, rarer than that of the high Himalayas. If the atmosphere becomes too rare, however, as happens when the mother does not send the fetus enough oxygen (as in hypothyroidism) or maternal circulation is interfered with, monstrosities develop. The fetal environment must be kept at a fairly constant temperature—about blood temperature; when the temperature rises too high (by inducing a prolonged fever) or goes too low (as in making hamsters hibernate), the offspring show severe deformities, or the embryos may be resorbed.

Dr. Alfred M. Bongiovanni, University of Pennsylvania Professor of Pediatrics, constantly reviews the circumstances of children born with congenital malformations and referred to Philadelphia's Children's Hospital. He searches for clues to the causes of these tragic cases. And, occasionally, he finds them.

In one instance he found that the mothers of six babies born with enormous and dangerous goiters had been taking thyroid-suppressing drugs—iodides for allergy and thiouracil for overactive thyroid glands. He discovered another anomalous situation: diethylstilbesterol, a synthetic estrogen, which feminizes animals, actually masculinized the female fetuses of a few pregnant women; the girls were born with boylike genital organs. In his work in Philadelphia and earlier at Johns Hopkins Hospital in Baltimore as one of the scholars under the late Dr. Lawson W. Wilkins, Dr. Bongiovanni had investigated instances in which male hormone (androgens) given to pregnant women had masculinized girl babies' genitalia. He found that synthetic progestins, the so-called pregnancy hormones (of dubious value in preventing abortion) also had yielded pseudohermaphrodites and vitamin K in massive doses, sulfonamides and anti-folic acids had produced a variety of abnormalities.

Dr. Wilkins discovered that one kind of congenital virilism, caused by a tumor of the adrenal glands, could be controlled by regular doses of the adrenal hormone, cortisone. This finding enabled some congenitally angular, muscular, bearded, deep-voiced, small breasted women to become feminized and have babies; and it resulted in the control of "Infant Hercules" in boys—the precocious manhood that comes to some youngsters barely out of diapers. Dr. Bongiovanni traced the basic chemical cause of these disorders: something had destroyed an enzyme system which forms in the fifth month of embryonic life and enables the fetal adrenal gland to change pregnanetriol into cortisone. Pregnanetriol, which has the effect of a male hormone, thus piles up in the system and virilizes the subject. When cortisone is given regularly to the patient, the adrenal stops producing the mischief-making male hormone.

The Johns Hopkins group, which has encountered almost every conceivable sex mix-up, recognizes and uses four standards to determine maleness and femaleness: (1) Chromosomes—every normal female cell has two X chromosomes and every male cell has one X and one Y; (2) glands—ovaries, which produce more female than male hormones, and testes, which produce more male than female hormones; (3) genitalia—vagina, womb, and penis; and (4) the feeling of maleness or femaleness, which is irreversibly developed at three years of age and cannot be changed after that without profound psychic trauma. Homosexuality, the group feels, is strictly a psychiatric problem with no physiological basis. A large population of children will have among them some with every combination of sexual mix-ups—children with the sex glands and organs of both sexes, fantastic mixtures of sex chromosomes, a melange of physical structures which sometimes make it difficult to determine sex. Some of the difficulties arise from tumorous hormone-producing glands.

Dr. Emil Witschi in his laboratory at the State University of Iowa has feminized male tadpoles and embryonic birds, salamanders and opossum with moderate doses of estrogen and masculinized females with high doses. He feels that these and other animal experiments support his theory that the mother's hormone production during pregnancy or hormones produced by the placenta can influence fetal sex, often reversing it, and may predispose the unborn infant to ultimate hormone-dependent cancers of such organs as the breast, uterus, and prostate.

Investigators over many years have commented on the increased risk of congenital malformations in children born to older women. Dr. John J. Clark of Howard University studied fifty women who bore their first babies after thirty-five years of age and found that the ratio of male to female babies was 2:3. Seven women showed uterine bleeding on admission to the hospital; in four the placenta was broken. Eight were edematous (water-logged); five showed the epileptiform or convulsive signs of eclampsia. Of the fifty babies, forty-three were in good condition, three in poor condition, and four were stillborn. The only malformation was in one child—it was born without a brain and soon died. Others have reported that many geniuses were born late in their mothers' lives.

Several other surveys have indicated that older women are somewhat more prone than younger women to give birth to mongoloid idiots, who are uncommonly prone to leukemia. An investigation of the background of fifty-five mongoloid infants born at Maudsley Hospital, London, indicated that age was not the only factor—mothers twenty-seven years old or younger who bore mongoloid children were of mannish build. They had, as the British scientists say, a high androgeny (maleness) score, meaning narrow hips, broad shoulders, and generally angular build. These young women also were found to be prone to miscarriage.

Perhaps the aging and androgeny factors can be reduced to hormone problems. Dr. Witschi is persuaded that age "castrates" people—it reduces their output of sex hormones. He feels that imperfect ova in aging women and calamitous congenital consequences may be fundamentally a matter of hormones.

The moment of birth brings a critical need for oxygen. A few feel that some semisuffocated cells may become malignant. They base their belief on observations that tissues grown in culture media containing insufficient oxygen have assumed a tumorous appearance, and fetal and newborn animals deprived of oxygen have developed malformations and cancers early in life. Cancers in these cases may be an irreversible tissue adaptation to life on limited oxygen. Whether such congenital or neonatal episodes also predispose humans to a destiny of cancer, no one knows for sure.

Do the emotions, or the state of mind, of the mother produce intra-uterine chemical disturbances which can affect the unborn child? Years ago, folk tales had it that the fetus could be "marked" by a fright, a vision, an experience of the pregnant woman. This has been written off in the scientific age as superstition. Recently, however, with new knowledge of the hormonal mechanisms involved in emotions, some candid scientists have stated they are not so sure.

Dr. George W. Corner of Rockefeller Institute had this to say at the London Conference on Congenital Malformations:

Once I would not even have raised such a question before fellow scientists; indeed, in my book of 1944, *Ourselves Unborn,* I attacked with all the irony I could command the ancient superstition that makes maternal impressions during pregnancy a cause of fetal malformation. The placenta, I said, completely shuts off the infant *in utero* from it's mother's state of mind. Put in this dogmatic way, my statement was correct; but, after all, the mother's state of mind can affect her body's chemistry and alter her nutritional state. Adrenalin and adrenocortical steroids can pass the placenta; the posterior pituitary may well contribute to abnormal behavior of the myometrium [womb muscle]. Whether the human mother's emotional upsets and alarms can disturb the environment of the embryo *in utero* sufficiently to produce physical anomalies I would on the whole still doubt. Yet the question cannot at present be excluded from wide-ranging inquiries.

Dr. Bongiovanni feels that mothers-to-be can best protect their unborn children by living intelligently for nine months. Their babies can be damaged by attempted abortion, physically or by drugs, and sometimes with unnecessary and high doses of progestins which are supposed to prevent abortion, certain other drugs (her physician should be told what drugs the pregnant woman takes), dietary fads, and excesses and unbridled habits (possibly including smoking and drinking). He suggests they eschew all drugs—including vitamins—unless they are recommended by physicians.

CHAPTER 14

CANCER IN CHILDREN

Cancer, properly considered a disease of aging people, nevertheless kills more American children between the ages of one and fourteen than any other disease. Moreover, rapidly and relentlessly, it is increasing its claim on young life with each passing year.

There are many reasons for this unhappy situation. One is that the public and the medical profession long have seemed unaware of the gigantic status of cancer among the causes of childhood death, although recent improvement has been noted. Parents and physicians usually consider any of a score of conditions which cancer mimics, rather than the true cause, when a youngster complains vaguely of recurrent dizziness, partial loss of vision, bone or joint pains, headache, loss of appetite, or other seemingly minor ills. They seldom believe that the lump can be an extremely grave symptom—after all, it doesn't even hurt. And too often they "wait and see" about the unremitting symptoms which could be those of either a curable or controllable forerunner of leukemia or of incurable leukemia itself—pallor, loss of weight, sore mouth, bleeding gums, joint and bone pains, and tiny patches of hemorrhage in or under the skin.

A second cause of childhood cancer death also lies with parents and physicians—once they know it's cancer, they give up too easily. They have heard too often and believe too well the statement that children's cancers are rapidly fatal and medicine can do nothing about them. In the right hands, many children's cancers are curable; and even incurable cases can be granted a considerable extension of comfortable life. The

150

average family physician, who may see only two or three undiagnosed cases of childhood cancer during his entire career, sees little need to familiarize himself with the natural course of the disease or the best ways of altering it.

Cancer cannot be reasonably considered outside the context of childhood diseases generally. Some of the more thoughtful authorities say many cancers are congenital—that is, the disease starts in the embryo or fetus but expresses itself later in life. In support of this contention is such evidence as: (1) viruses and carcinogens in animals often cause *acute* diseases and death presumably unrelated to cancer, and, in *chronic* form, cancer; and (2) a few congenital conditions, conspicuously mongolism, often coexist with cancer in the child patient. Among cancers suggested as originating in the fetus are malignant neuroblastoma, embryonal rhabdomyosarcoma and Wilms's embryoma of the kidney.

Cancer is gaining great prominence as a childhood disease, not only because of its increasing frequency and lethal nature, but also because its rise is in stark contrast to the disappearance of most of the causes of childhood death. Since the turn of the century, immunization, sanitation, hygiene and medicine have been eliminating the classical wholesale killers. The human lifespan has been stretched phenomenally—there has been an unprecedented pile-up of oldsters at one end of the population and an equally impressive rescue of crippled and sick infants at the other end.

The great salvage of human life has been effected mainly by the brilliant observations of a few men, not by a rise in the general IQ of a generation of scientists nor the enhanced abilities of a generation of physicians. On the contrary, persuasive arguments could be advanced that with the recent great growth of science and its importance, the suddenly swollen ranks of researchers have become more conformist and less creative, and with the increased social security of the physician (thanks to the protectiveness and privilege of his profession, the essential nature of his services and the recruitment of students of diminishing academic stature) the doctor's individual contribution to public health has not kept pace with the knowledge, the techniques, the instruments, and other advantages made available to him.

One critical drop in death rates came when Sir Alexander Fleming made a commonplace observation, shared by thousands of scientists before him, and was struck by what in retrospect is an almost unavoidable idea. The observation was that organisms contaminating the air of his laboratory produced something which destroyed his bacterial cultures. His idea was: might that pest-produced something also destroy the organisms infecting man? That something—now called antibiotics—did; and in the next fifteen years infant death rates for tuberculosis, syphilis, dysentery, and whooping cough shrank to 2, or 10, or 20 per cent of the former figures. These findings, and a few others, depressed infant mortality from many causes—influenza, pneumonia, hernia, and gastritis conspicuously among them.

Congenital malformations, always a prominent cause of the death of newborn babies and a ubiquitous and cruel crippler, became a leading killer of children of all ages as science and medicine learned to rescue the malformed at birth and defer death for a few years. And cancer made its meteoric rise as the other diseases fell; in 1940 it was not among the ten most frequent causes of child death, whereas in 1960 it was second only to accidents.

The great shift in causes of childhood death during a human generation is set forth by the National Office of Vital Statistics in two mortality tables, one for 1934 and the other for 1959. In 1934 children between one and fourteen years old in the United States died at this rate (per 100,000 population) and of these causes: accidents 40.3; pneumonia 35.1; diarrhea and enteritis 18.7; measles 13.5; appendicitis 12.2; tuberculosis 10.9; diphtheria 10.5; whooping cough 8.9; heart diseases 8.1; influenza 8.0; scarlet fever 5.7, and cancer 5.2. Twenty-five years later, in 1959, these were the rates for the dozen leading death dealers: accidents 22.3, cancer 8.1; congenital malformations 6.4; pneumonia 6.0; gastritis 1.3; meningitis 1.1; heart diseases 0.9; nephritis 0.8; cerebral spastic infantile paralysis 0.8; bronchitis 0.8; vascular lesions 0.8; and anemias 0.7.

National Office of Vital Statistics reports indicate that between 1940 and 1954 death from birth injuries had dropped 58 per cent and from prematurity 47 per cent. The Chicago Lying-In Hospital records show that the advances in obstetrics made possible even more spectacular gains. In this hospital, properly administered and staffed, deaths from birth injuries were reduced over a quarter-century to almost one-eightieth what they had been; deaths from lack of oxygen were halved. A few rules helped create the record—the intelligent termination of overly long labors, anticipation of anoxia late in pregnancy and decisive measures at its first signs (often painless bleeding), abdominal delivery where forceps would create a hazardous situation, careful extraction of the breech baby, extreme care in the use of instruments. To these precautions many hundreds owe not only their lives but their sound bodies and undamaged brains. Refusal to "push the panic button" and end pregnancy very early, running the high risk of irreversible damage to the premature body and brain, close observation of maternal blood pressure and oxygen, rigid precautions against hospital infectious agents, prophylactic antibiotics where indicated—all these are factors in ushering sound babies into the world.

The United States has not made perceptible gains since 1955 in the management of birth problems. The salvage of life and healthy bodies and minds generally has plateaued or dipped. The United States, once sixth in world infant mortality rates among countries, ranked eleventh in 1962. Some of this loss of prestige can be laid to unnecessary birth injuries; many palsied and otherwise irreparably injured youngsters are a living monument to poor obstetrical practices.

The question has been asked—but not answered—as to whether some cancers may not be a consequence of oxygen deprivation during the crucial period before, during and immediately after delivery.

There is a curious difference between cancers in children and cancers in adults: the disease shows a striking predilection for different sites in the two age groups. In adults, 80 per cent of the serious cancers are of the digestive, genital and respiratory systems, whereas only 6 per cent of children's cancers are of these areas. In children, on the other hand, 80 per cent of the cancers arise in the nervous, lymphatic, blood-forming and urinary systems, but only 7 per cent of cancers in adults originate here. No one knows why cancer selects its sites in this manner. It could be due to the order in which organs form in the developing embryo, the order in which they mature and age during postnatal life, or the vulnerability to carcinogens of specific tissues at various stages of growth and aging. Or it could be due to some other factor entirely.

Almost 5,000 children are said to have died of cancer in 1963 in the United States, with leukemia accounting for almost one-half of the deaths. The commonest targets, other than blood-forming organs, were brain and nerve, bone, and the genitourinary system.

Cancer rarely is found in a newborn child. In one notable case, a mother's "black cancer" (melanoma) penetrated the placenta and appeared in her newborn baby. The cancer death curve, however, runs highest between ages one and five years, when it tapers off until age ten and then rises somewhat until age fourteen. Then it is depressed until late in the teens. Drastic changes in hormone activity accompanying male and female puberty may be associated with some teen-age cancers.

Children are prone to have many tumors (meaning growths). Somewhere between one-fourth and one-fifth of the more prominent ones are potentially malignant. The benign tumors may be located almost anywhere on the skin, or they may involve blood vessels, nerves, fat, bone, cartilage, or lymphatic tissue. They may be in the nose or throat, rectum or colon, near the eye, or in the ear. Some glands occasionally become tumorous. Moles are classified as tumors. Almost everybody has some.

Most benign tumors never cause any serious difficulty. Some of them, however, later in life may become a cancer—familial bowel polyps, or the innocent-appearing junction nevus, or blue-black mole, for instance.

Some which give parents considerable concern—like the strawberry birth-mark—spontaneously disappear in five or six years in 80 per cent of the cases.

Increasing numbers of the more common cancers are cured, if the doctor sees them early enough and treats them promptly and correctly. The best physicians go on the theory that all bumps are bad and behave accordingly.

Specialists in childhood cancers feel that cures are possible in a sur-prisingly high percentage of cases if prompt action is taken. They insist that soft-tissue tumors—of fat, muscle, nerve, and connective tissue—should be removed surgically without delay. One type of brain tumor, the medullablastoma, can be taken out if it is attacked during its early stages, when the child first begins to stumble, vomit and begin to com-plain of headaches. It is still curable in some cases when vision is affected, providing it has not damaged vital brain areas.

Bone cancers in children have an unfortunate prognosis, but still some are cured by radical amputation and X rays if treatment is begun at the first sign of abnormal growth. Not all bone tumors are cancerous, how-ever.

Experimental treatment—a combination of drugs perfused into the eye area and the administration of X rays following surgical removal of the cancerous eye—seems to be curing about 90 per cent of the inherited eye cancer, retinoblastoma, which once was considered incurable; and a combination of drugs, X rays and surgery have considerably brightened the gloomy outlook for children over two years old with cancer of the kidney.

Dr. Harold W. Dargeon reported that of 75 children treated at Memorial Cancer Center, New York, for lymphosarcoma, sometimes a forerunner of leukemia, between 1926 and 1959, twenty-one were still surviving, fifteen for more than five years. They were treated with Coley's toxins, anti-cancer drugs, surgery, and radiation.

The message that childhood cancers are curable is not easy to get across, although early referral of cases has improved recently. The cure rates can be gratifying. Drs. George T. Pack and Irving M. Ariel at Memorial Cancer Center have reported five-year cure rates of 42.5 per cent for sarcoma of the soft tissues, 19–27 per cent for bone cancer, 30–42 per cent for Wilms's (kidney) cancer, 70 per cent for retinoblastoma and 10–20 per cent for neuroblastoma, a highly malignant cancer which originates in the sympa-thetic nervous system and spreads to the skull, liver, lungs, and bones. Other cancer specialists have had equally impressive results.

Hodgkin's disease is closely related to leukemia. It is commonly be-lieved that Hodgkin's is invariably and rapidly fatal in children. This is not always so. Dr. James A. Pitcock of Washington University traced forty-six children with a diagnosis of Hodgkin's. Sixty per cent of those in whom the condition was diagnosed before generalized spread of the disease and who were treated vigorously with X rays lived five years; 35 per cent lived ten years; eight of the 46 were still alive, from five to thirty-three years following treatment, at the time of the survey. No child with generalized Hodgkin's disease lived three years; the average survival for them was about one year.

Medical literature cites instances of "spontaneous regression"—the remarkable disappearance of cancer for no reason known to medicine—in several kinds of childhood cancer. These miracles are extremely rare, but there are enough documented cases to support the contention that some incurable childhood cancers are curable if the secret of spontaneous regression can be found.

In the light of these facts, leaders in the field sometimes express impatience with the hopelessness which dominates the attitudes of parents and physicians toward childhood cancers.

Drs. Ariel and Pack have called the professional mood "abject pessimism." "This pessimistic attitude permeated the profession to the extent that some physicians refrained from giving any form of treatment to the child with cancer," they reported in the *New York State Journal of Medicine:*

> The attitude infiltrated to the parents, who would not bring the child with a tumor to the physician, feeling that the situation was hopeless. The results of treatment of cancer in children should dispel this pessimistic attitude. They should encourage every effort to treat successfully each case, for cures can be obtained. Infants and children tolerate radical operative procedures remarkably well. So-called inoperability because of "frailty" of the infant usually reflects a frailty of the surgeon.

The average surgeon is not without emotions; he sometimes is revolted by the gamble involved in the amputations and other operations which will mutilate a child for all its long or short life span. Instead, he performs a simple operation, which may not cure but also does not maim or deform the youngster. Of this human weakness, Drs. Ariel and Pack said:

> Fear of mutilation and thoughts of reconstruction must be secondary to the extensive excision necessary to cure the patient. Failure to perform radical resection will doom the patient or will necessitate repeated resections with the result that a more radical resection will be necessary for the treatment of recurrences than was indicated for the primary neoplasm [the original cancer]. The surgeon can, for

the most part, be most conservative by being radical at the onset, if a radical approach is indicated.

In the case of hopelessly ill children, the impulse to give up is difficult to resist. To the child, the hospital may be a terrifying environment—a pesthouse of sickness, pain, and death, a limbo devoid of love, a timelessness measured by the eternities between visits. The sick child wants his parents; he doesn't want to die.

To the parents, their child's hospital, like the child's illness, may be a punishment for their sins, a product of mistakes they may not remember making, a disciplinary measure by a harsh God, an event of overwhelming injustice and unreality. It also is often an occasion for complete dissembling, with tired jokes and cheerful lies that do not for a moment deceive the intuitively perceptive child but can make him lose faith in his parents.

To the skilled pediatrician, the hospital is where one restores a badly shaken faith in man and reconciles a tired young spirit to the performance of this world and perhaps to the promise of the next.

Some hospitals have undertaken an interesting experiment; they permit the parents to stay with children. After careful briefing, the parents undertake some of the nursing duties, bathe their babies, hand feed them, force fluids into them, read to them, instruct them, and amuse them. Under this system, only a few parents have been found emotionally incapable of the responsibilities to and final companionship of their children. The children seem to appreciate the privileges.

While basic research holds promise of many new and imaginative ways of controlling or curing the cancers of children, at this time the most efficacious measures lie in the field of cancer detection and prevention. The simplest way to prevent cancer is to eliminate or avoid the known causes. In the case of childhood cancer, the burden of prevention lies largely with the mother; much of her child's future depends upon the environment she provides for it during nine-months residence within her womb and for many years while the youngster is under her control.

Avoidance of unnecessary and excessive radiation is a case in point.

Drs. Theodore Winship and Randi V. Rosvoll, pathologists in the Washington, D.C., Hospital Center, have reviewed the facts on 562 children with thyroid cancer in North and Central America, Western Europe, the Middle East, and Asia. They found that in all these areas there was a definite increase in the disease, most markedly between 1945 and 1957. Eighty per cent of the cancerous children and 11 per cent of adolescents had received earlier X rays for enlarged thymus glands, adenoids, tonsils, birthmarks, eczema, acne and even warts and moles. Ten of the young cancer patients showed such coincidental conditions as mental retardation, hare lip, asthma, brain tumor, lymphoma, or retinoblastoma, as well as their thyroid cancers. The average age at diagnosis was nine years. Adults were not affected.

Drs. Edith Quimby and John H. Hanford of Columbia University College of Physicians and Surgeons, compiled similar data for 456 patients X-rayed in childhood for benign lesions of the neck. Of these, 212 irradiated for tuberculous adenitis developed thyroid cancers eleven to twenty-seven years later.

Dr. Glenn E. Sheline of the University of Colorado Medical School concluded from his study of 258 youngsters treated with radioactive iodine for toxic goiter between 1945 and 1953—eight had developed thyroid lumps—that this is a risky treatment for children.

Despite these and many other studies, children today still are treated with X rays for throat troubles, acne, and other ailments. They are also given dental X rays, often unnecessarily, and in some localities, even X-ray shoe fittings—always unnecessary. Many dentists and others do not seem to realize that radiation doses are cumulative; successive small ones can add up to cancer.

To be sure, tragedy sometimes can be averted by detecting with X rays a dangerous situation besetting the fetus before delivery. In these instances, the child's life may be saved and grave congenital conditions prevented by prompt action. Nevertheless, the use of X rays as a routine procedure in pregnancy or merely to satisfy the idle curiosity of the physician or parents (will there be twins? for example) may produce a monster, imbecile, or infant with a destiny of childhood cancer.

Many drugs and chemicals taken by the mother can endanger the fetus and, in the light of the results of animal experiments, may even lay the groundwork for future cancers. Dr. Dao of Roswell Park has offered a theoretical blueprint for this latter situation in his experiments with mice. Pregnant mice given a potent carcinogen, 3-methylcholanthrene, bore young with a strong tendency for breast cancer; 20 per cent of the offspring had breast cancer in their "middle age." The offspring of mothers not given the chemical and the offspring of mothers given the chemical only after pregnancy and during lactation did not develop breast cancer. Apparently, the carcinogen could be transmitted to the embryo through the placental barrier but not to the infant mice in strong doses via mother's milk.

Several precautions are taken by the alert pediatrician. The dangerous junction nevi, which sometimes flare up in cancer after puberty, are removed early in childhood. Nerve tumors, called neurofibromas, are excised. Any indication of one of the strangest, but not rarest, of cancers, teratoma, calls for immediate surgery. Teratomas, sometimes called "ghost twins," are tumors of the testicle, ovary, or other tissue, and often contain teeth, nails, and other tissues of a vestigal individual.

Parents have ample worries in the normal course of events without being burdened by the fear of cancer every time their child sniffles. The odds are very great indeed against a child's minor symptoms representing cancer. If the signs persist, however, the sensible thing to do is to have the case diagnosed. If it turns out to be cancer, early diagnosis and treatment well may render it curable.

CHAPTER 15

HEREDITY
AND CANCER

Studies of twins often show whether certain diseases are inherited or due to environment. If a disease is directly inherited, it should show itself with great fidelity in both identical twins at about the same time, because identical twins develop from the same egg, or ovum, and share the same genes. Nonidentical twins, which arise from two different cells, have a looser relationship—approximating that of brothers or sisters. In true genetic or hereditary conditions, identical twins, bearing identical genes, will also tend to share the same experiences much more than do nonidentical twins.

The sternest test of the inheritability of human cancers lies in comparison of its frequency in identical twins, nonidentical twins, family members and the general population. Because cancer essentially is a disease of older people, the most reliable tests would be in older groups.

Drs. Lissy F. Jarvik and Arthur Falek of the New York State Psychiatric Institute have studied a sample of 1,603 sets of twins, more than sixty years old, whose histories have been followed for more than twelve years in long-range geriatric investigation. Among these, 68 individuals had cancer. From other sources, the scientists added 26 individual twins with cancer, for a total of 94.

The studies turned up only three cases of coincidence among identical twins; (1) One twin, aged sixty-two years, was operated on for adenocarcinoma of the uterus and, three months later, her sister was operated on for adenocarcinoma of the breast—both were alive and well fifteen years later; (2) twins developed adenocarcinoma of the uterus and were operated upon at the same time—one (nonpsychotic) died of the disease three years later, and the psychotic twin was alive and physically well eighteen years later; and (3) one twin developed breast cancer twelve years after the other had died of it.

Two impressive cases were noted in nonidentical twins: (1) a female pair developed carcinoma of the breast six months apart; and (2) one man showed lymphosarcoma at fifty-eight years of age, and his twin brother developed reticulum cell sarcoma thirteen years later.

There were other cases in this series which showed unrelated kinds of cancer occurring at different ages among twins. But, as compared with the high coincidence rate for schizophrenia and for tuberculosis among identical twins (respectively, seven and six times the coincidence of cancer) hereditary influences in cancer would have to be deemed feeble.

Several other twin studies have been made, but perhaps all of them together have not covered enough people over enough time to yield definitive statistical data. Generally, the most striking results have been the same as for the New York data—of borderline significance at best.

Either as randomly as Russian roulette or for cause, cancer comes to one of four people. If any system is involved in its lethal selection of victims, science so far has failed to fathom it.

When cancer strikes one member of the family, it is only natural for other members to ask: "Is it inherited? Will it come to me too?"

The most common answer—the textbook answer—to this anxious query is: Humans don't inherit cancer; some, however, may inherit a susceptibility or predisposition, to certain tumors.

In "cancer families" it often is difficult to tell to what degree heredity is responsible for the malignancies which claim so many members of the household. The victims have shared not only seed from the same sources but also the same environment. And environment is a most impelling influence in cancer.

Scientists at the National Cancer Institute have investigated cancer families. They compared various pairs—two dead members of each family —for the frequency of various kinds of cancer. The study—which included 51 husband-wife pairs, 60 brother-sister pairs, 76 sister-sister pairs and 44 brother-brother pairs—showed that only the brother-sister pairs failed to show a significant similarity of the kinds of cancer which had killed them. The similarity of cancers which had killed husband-wife pairs indicated that environment could be as culpable as heredity, probably more so.

Nevertheless, laboratory experiments indicate that there can be many and powerful elements of heredity in cancer. They may influence only hormone production, resistance to infections or any of a score of other body functions, but under a given set of conditions, they can lead to cancer.

Cancer is inherited by many laboratory mice, sometimes with 90 per cent predictability. This happens when the disease is bred into the strain by ten, twenty, or fifty generations of mating cancerous brother with cancerous sister. Inheritance alone still usually is not enough; the animals often must also be exposed to a virus, a ray, a chemical, hormonal stimulation (by sex hormone injection, pregnancy or removal of glands), a dietary factor or deficiency, or the body chemical changes which come with maturity or old age.

And even then—with all the requirements presumably met—a few animals almost invariably escape the disease.

Nevertheless, inbred strains do respond with amazing fidelity under cancer-inducing stimuli. In experiments at East Lansing, Michigan, five different lines of white leghorn chickens reacted in five distinct ways to the administration of a virus which causes several forms of chicken cancer.

One—and perhaps only one—form of human cancer is inherited directly, although a few other diseases which strongly predispose to cancer also are inherited. This is an infrequent kind of eye cancer called retinoblastoma. It appears, in the Mendelian ratio for dominant genes, anywhere from within a few months to three years after birth. It occurs to one baby in every 20,000; only 49 of the 1,054,985 children born in Michigan during a decade developed retinoblastoma.

If retinoblastoma is untreated, it almost always kills before the victim can reproduce and sow the seeds of future disease.

Retinoblastoma is not "self-eliminating," as the geneticists say, for several reasons. One is that the Mendelian ratio permits some of its victims to survive and perpetuate the gene. And, more and more, so do modern medical techniques; in the right hands, retinoblastoma now is about 90 per cent curable. Occasionally too, retinoblastoma clears up spontaneously, leaving only a scar—and a destiny of the disease for most of the survivor's offspring. One source states that males who survive and become fathers have children with a 75 per cent risk of developing retinoblastoma; children of surviving women, 50 per cent. Others feel male and female run identical risks.

People with a personal or family history of retinoblastoma often do not have children, however; one study of 190 retinoblastoma patients showed that only six had offspring—ten in all, and nine of them developed the disease.

Retinoblastoma also develops spontaneously and sporadically in the absence of family history of the disease. In these cases, each brother and sister of the patient has a 1 to 4 per cent risk of also showing retino-blastoma.

The only other cancer so far recognized as having a probable hereditary basis is breast cancer, the commonest cause of cancer death among women, and this appears to be one of susceptibility rather than direct inheritance. Any one of several factors may present this risk. Scattered studies in the United States indicate that daughters of women with breast cancer run about two or three times the breast cancer risk of women in the general population. Nongenetic factors appear to exercise greater influence than heredity on the appearance of breast cancer.

The lifetime risk of the average woman's developing breast cancer in the United States ranges from one chance in 15 to one in 23. Dr. Sheldon C. Reed of the University of Minnesota studied the family history of 660 breast cancer patients and, as controls, the families of the patients' husbands. He found that 8.2 per cent of the patients' sisters and 4.3 per cent of the husbands' sisters developed breast cancer. The patients' sisters ran double the unrelated women's risk.

Dr. C. P. Oliver of the University of Texas, in exploring the families of 312 breast-cancer patients, found that nineteen of the patients' mothers also had had breast cancer. Only three mothers of comparable healthy control women had breast cancer.

Dr. Madge T. Macklin, then at Ohio State University, discovered in a long-term study of human breast cancer that, while sisters of patients ran two or three times the normal risk of the disease, marital status was also an important factor—breast cancer in this study was 60 per cent more frequent among spinsters than among married women. If one identical twin had breast cancer, so did the other in 60 per cent of the cases; this double disaster occurred in only 20 per cent of nonidentical twins when one developed the disease.

Several conditions which often progress into cancer appear to have a hereditary basis. These include tylosis, a sort of callous skin thickening which may lead to cancer of the esophagus; xeroderma pigmentosum, a "fish skin" scaliness, dryness, pigmentation and ulceration, which usually becomes basal cell carcinoma of the skin following excessive exposure to ultraviolet rays; and neurofibromatosis marked by multiple café-au-lait patches of the skin and mucous membrane and accompanied by tumors of the nerves which sometimes developed into sarcomas; and multiple exostoses, abnormal growths which can become bone cancer.

The former Mormon custom of plural wives and the church's keen interest in science have given geneticists a rare opportunity to study human heredity. Dr. Eldon J. Gardner, then of the University of Utah, concluded from his study of Kindred 107—the descendants of an English couple who came to Utah in 1857—that men as well as women carry a diffuse inheritance of susceptibility to breast cancer, although as a rule much less than one per cent of all breast-cancer patients are male. Breast cancer in four of the eight "Kindred 107" family lines could be traced to the fathers more readily than the mothers.

The Utah studies have yielded valuable data confirming earlier observations that a special kind of multiple bowel polyps runs in families and that it sometimes gives rise to cancers. They also showed that, when the polyps are removed in early life, the cancer hazard is reduced. About 5 per cent of all people over thirty-five years old in the United States are believed to have common polyps of the rectum or lower bowel; these are not precancerous.

The Gardner group reported such startling statistics as: one woman had bowel polyps, and so did three of her children and five grandchildren; prompt surgery saved most of them.

The progenitor of another family—a Dane who went to Utah, joined the Church of the Latter-Day Saints and had four wives and twenty-four children—left a record of this pathology: he himself died of melanoma, or black cancer; six children from his first wife died of various cancers of the digestive tract; three children from his second wife died of kidney, breast, and colon cancers, and a fourth survived removal of a cancer from his lower bowel; wives III and IV, sisters, had no cancers, and neither did their children. If these cancers were inherited who supplied the cancer gene—or, more likely, genes? The father, who himself died of cancer? Wives I and II? Or did Wives III and IV carry anticancer genes which offset the effects of the father's gene?

Another hard-luck Utah family, designated as Kindred 109, has experienced a combination of bowel polyps, cancers of bones and soft tissues, sebaceous cysts, and malformed teeth. Of thirty-six offspring of one parent over four generations, twenty were affected—the approximate Mendelian ratio for a dominant gene. The average age at death was thirty-five years.

A few authorities contend there is a genetic influence in stomach cancer. One of their arguments centers around the Bonaparte family—Napoleon, his father, brother and three sisters are said to have died of cancer of the stomach.

For every statistic which supports an inheritable influence in stomach cancer, however, there are two to contradict it.

One study of 34,000 cases of stomach cancer showed that there was a 22 per cent excess of victims with blood group A over patients with blood group O; blood groups, of course, are inherited. The evidence, if indeed it is indicative of a special proneness of people with blood group A, is not strong enough to give concern to anyone. Other studies have shown no predilection for cancer in any blood group.

A Utah study based on death certificates has indicated that prostatic cancer is three times as common among the relatives of prostatic cancer patients as among men generally. There is little other data to support this suggestion of heredity, however.

Several studies indicate that leukemia "runs in some families." Far more convincing figures indicate that common environmental factors, like radiation and viruses, are implicated.

As a matter of fact, many environmental diseases "run in families." Offspring share the same uterine environment before their birth; they are subject to the diet, drugs, blood composition and other elements of internal environment within the mother. To a high degree, the family also share the same environment during their formative years.

It is not easy to distinguish hereditary from environmental influences.

At this stage, any worry about inheriting cancer is needless. The only human cancer generally and directly inherited is that rare malignancy of the eye, retinoblastoma. Beyond this, all evidence points to other than hereditary factors as causes of human cancer. The known exceptions to this—like the Utah families—are few.

CHAPTER 16

THE CHEMICAL CODE
OF LIFE

Life is a four-letter word.

It is spelled ATGC.

Wordsmiths of science with a genius for complicating the uncomplicated thought up the spelling. A stands of adenine, T for thymine, G for guanine, and C for cytosine.

Add a molecule of sugar to each of the letters, stick them all together on a phosphate string and they become nucleic acid, or NA.

The names are as pointless as ATGC is unpronounceable. Nevertheless, such is addiction to common usage that one must abide by tradition and use the terms. They are the cryptographic code of life. In them lie the precise definitions of health and of various diseases—inherited, congenital, infectious.

The code holds the secret of youth and of aging.

It also contains the answer to cancer.

This is one version of how life—or ATGC—began.

In an infinity of space, anything is possible. In an eternity of time, everything is probable.

Perhaps it was inevitable that on one of the estimated 100 quadrillion (100,000,000,000,000,000) potentially inhabitable planets in the known universe, ATGC—life—at some time would form.

Each of the letters A, T, G, and C is a simple substance composed of a few atoms of carbon, nitrogen, oxygen, and hydrogen. About three billion years ago these elements came together under the right conditions of temperature, pressure, and acidity or alkalinity: carbon from the cooling land, nitrogen from the air and hydrogen, oxygen, and salts from the sea. A flash of lightning could have fixed the atoms in the first molecule able to reproduce—the first strange stirring called life in a dead world and perhaps in a dead universe.

A bright high school chemistry student today can reproduce in the laboratory some of the key reactions involved in the creation of life. A (or adenine) is produced readily by heating hydrogen cyanide and ammonia together. Combined with ribose sugar and phosphates, A presumably will produce T, or thymine.

A, T, G and C—combined with sugar and phosphate—are called nucleotides; that is, they are segments of nucleic acid molecules.

There was only one characteristic which marked nucleotides as unique and awesome among all the chemicals which ever existed: they could reproduce. Reproduction is the single basic attribute of life.

For convenience, we will call the nucleotides male and female, or, as the scientists say, purine and pyrimidine.

A and G are male. Each of these molecules is shaped like a pictograph—a sort of Chinese character—representing the male genitalia.

T and C are female; these six-sided ring molecules resemble the vaginal opening, the Chinese character for woman.

The nucleotides were and are monotonously monogamous. A is always mated to T; and G is always mated to C. In form, function and electrostatic charge, A is as complementary to T, and G to C, as a key is to a lock. Each pair is as complete as Yin and Yang, the Chinese divided circle representing male and female togetherness—the complementariness of light and dark, dryness and dampness, activity and passivity.

A and G, the males, have 15 and 16 atoms, respectively. They are formed of two rings of carbon and nitrogen atoms. A has one powerful hydrogen arm and G has two with which to hold their respective female mates.

T, 15 atoms in size, and C, 13 atoms, each have a hydrogen arm to bind their male mates.

Like people, nucleotides do more than reproduce. They work as individuals, rather than as pairs.

An A product with three phosphate groups is called adenosine triphosphate, or ATP. ATP is a storehouse of explosive energy. The phosphate groups can be burned like matches to release energy. When one phosphate is burned, the chemical becomes ADP, or adenosine diphosphate; and when two are burned, it becomes AMP, or adenosine monophosphate.

The energy released by the burning of phosphates in ATP, TTP, GTP, and CTP stimulates many essential chemical reactions which move a muscle, transmit an impulse along nerves, or spark many other physical and mental functions. Only a bare beginning has been made in exploring the medical uses of these nucleotides; but it seems safe to predict that as drugs—and particularly in concert with hormones and other drugs—they will prove effective against a host of diseases, possibly including cancer.

There are two kinds of NA, or nucleic acids.

One is called deoxyribonucleic acid, or DNA. De-oxyribose means that an oxygen atom is missing from the ribose sugar in NA. In DNA, the nucleotides are almost always paired as A-T and G-C (or T-A and C-G), so the molecule is two-stranded.

The other form of NA is called ribonucleic acid, or RNA. In RNA, the ribose has all its oxygen. And in RNA, the T is slightly altered (it loses one carbon and three hydrogen atoms—a methyl group); so instead of having a T, RNA contains U, or uracil. The nucleotides in RNA —A, U, G, and C with their sugar and phosphate—are regarded generally as unpaired, unsexed, and unreproductive. RNA, in its several forms, is extremely productive, however; it assembles countless specific protein molecules which, next to nucleic acids, are the most important and versatile chemicals in living matter.

DNA is the stuff that genes are made of. The DNA molecule is a long, stringy, two-stranded, spiraling stack of A-T and G-C nucleotide pairs. There are thousands of A-T and G-C nucleotide pairs in a single DNA molecule. And there are many thousands of DNA molecules in a single cell.

The number of A-T and G-C (and, of course T-A and C-G) pairs in a molecule, the order of the pairs and the position of the molecules with regard to one another determine whether the DNA is a virus, a bacterium, a plant, an animal or a man. These specifications also give the form of life all its inherited traits, its potential and its limitations.

DNA reproduces in this way, according to the theory most generally accepted at this writing: the two spiraling strands of the DNA molecule unwind and come apart, thus splitting asunder all the A-T and G-C (and T-A and C-G) nucleotide pairs. Each individual nucleotide thereupon manufactures its complementary mate—A makes T, T makes A, G makes C, and C makes G.

In this manner, the DNA in one cell makes a complete and identical new set of DNA molecules, so that when the cell divides, both daughter cells will be equipped with a full complement of genes. This manufacture, or synthesis, of new DNA is the essence of reproduction.

A current concept of how DNA, as genes, controls the chemical and physical character of the cell (and of the individual) goes like this:

DNA not only makes more identical DNA but it also makes RNA.

In making RNA, the two strands of DNA do not unwind or pull apart; each weaves its RNA mirror image minus an oxygen atom in the sugar and minus the carbon and three hydrogen atoms—transforming T (thymine) to U (uracil).

The long, single-stranded RNA molecules migrate from the core, or nucleus, of the cell through a tortuous maze of highways, called the endoplasmic reticulum, in the cytoplasm which surrounds the nucleus; and at various points the RNA settles in helical clumps called ribosomes. The ribosomes become assembly lines for the production of thousands of proteins.

According to a simplified theory, this is how protein is made:

The long, spiraling RNA molecules in the ribosomes serve as a pattern, or template, for the assembling of amino acids into the protein molecule.

Short RNA molecules—each composed of only three nucleotides—transport single amino acids to their proper positions on the long RNA template. In this they serve as switch engines making up a freight train.

While there are only four nucleotides in RNA—A, U, G and C—there are twenty different kinds of amino acids which comprise protein. Each amino acid is a tiny chemical battery, containing a carbon atom core, an alkaline positive pole, a negative pole, a hydrogen hook on top and, depending on which amino acid it is, an assortment of atoms as its foundation.

An RNA switch engine composed of the three nucleotides, UUU, hauls the amino acid, phenylalanine, to the long RNA molecule and deposits it alongside complementary nucleotides, which in the case of UUU would be AAA. UCG hauls alanine and deposits it alongside AGC, and UGG deposits glycine alongside ACC. Amino acids are added to the growing protein molecule at the rate of about two per second. When all the amino acids are in their proper places, they are joined positive pole to negative pole, and the protein molecule is ready to break away from the long RNA molecule and do its job.

Protein molecules are composed of a string of anywhere from a few to more than 3,000 amino acids. They become thousands of different enzymes which catalyze thousands of different chemical reactions involved in the building up and tearing down of fats, sugars, alcohols—and more nucleic acids and more proteins. Other proteins become antibodies in resisting infection, molecules which transport oxygen and other substances through the blood, hormones, pigment, skin covering, connective tissue containers for organs and many other substances.

Biochemistry is a science in which textbook truth is transient; with ever-increasing laboratory techniques of the past two decades, many fundamental axioms have proved to be fragile; philosophies in rapid succession have waxed and waned, and concepts which have become the style one year have died the next.

During the last decade, the scientific literature has filled to overflowing with nucleic acids. In the last few years, the wonders of these compounds have been extolled more and more in magazines and the daily public press. They are the rage in science and the darling of intellectual conversation.

Nucleic acids are not new, however; they are as old as life—they are the essence of life.

DNA was discovered in 1869 by the Swiss biochemist Friedrich Miescher, who called it nuclein. The discovery aroused little interest. With Gregor Mendel's contemporary classical findings, nuclein reposed in the limbo of literature. In 1882, DNA was rediscovered—this time by the German Walther Flemming, who detected its existence with a stain and called it chromatin. Almost thirty years later, the German Nobelist, Albrecht Kossel, defined the four bases which go into DNA, and the American, Phoebus Aaron Theodore Levene, pointed out the five-carbon sugars, ribose and deoxyribose, in RNA and DNA. Decades later, Torbjorn Caspersson, a Swede, linked DNA with genes. And in the early 1940s English and American scientists saw for the first time DNA's awe-inspiring potential; they transformed genes and life by introducing DNA from one type of bacterium into another.

At this time the nucleic acids still hold a vast number of secrets, and, despite the remarkable rate of discoveries of facts and artifacts in this area, it seems safe to predict that, for many decades hence, new and important information on nucleic acid chemistry will continue to come to light. Current concepts may have to be revised completely; until they are, however, they serve a useful purpose as a working hypothesis.

Dr. Seymour S. Cohen of the University of Pennsylvania, in a brilliant critique in 1962, charged that many of his contemporaries, in embracing the doctrine of the "unity of biochemistry," which holds that all cells share the same biochemical processes, were ignoring evolutionary changes in life, much of the recent progress in biochemistry and many of the problems in the field. He pointed out that at least eighty amino acids exist in nature, instead of the twenty cited by biochemists. The concept of four nucleotides—built on bases of A, T, (or U), G, and C—he raised to question, inasmuch as at least seven natural analogues of A alone have been identified. He outlined evidence of several pathways for the biosynthesis of various amino acids and the formation of RNA and DNA strings; and he challenged the invariability of A-T and G-C pairs by citing a mechanism which replaces A with G. With regard to the dogma that adenine is essential to cell life both as an indispensable part of DNA and RNA and as an energy-storing compound, he said, "We must ask if this is the only form, as well as the best, of all biochemical worlds."

At this stage, the layman as well as the biochemist will find both comfort and convenience in assuming any of several rough ideas of the basic chemistry of life. The prospects are for a constant change in concepts for many years to come, and an attitude of mixed tolerance and skepticism will prove helpful in following the exciting developments ahead. The literature at this writing contains faint suggestions which, if true, tend to shatter still more tenets of biochemistry. There have been reports, for instance, that DNA exists outside the chromosomes and nucleus of cells, American workers in Sweden saying they have sighted it in small cytoplasmic particles called mitochondria. RNA (in polio viruses) has been found in double-stranded form. There also is circumstantial evidence, that, contrary to all the textbooks and all the authorities in the field, viruses may reproduce outside cells. And some DNA (in a bacterial virus) has been reported to contain U instead of T.

It may turn out that the basic chemistry of life is a good deal more simple than now is supposed, that it hinges on two principles: (1) Nucleic acid manufactures protein, and (2) in manufacturing protein, RNA becomes DNA and DNA becomes RNA. Under this system, these steps might take place: (1) DNA synthesizes proteins (called histones) and in welding the protein molecules together (a process which requires the expenditure of 3,000 calories of energy and a molecule of water at each amino acid coupling) becomes RNA; (2) RNA, possibly bound, manufactures its protein and, in so doing becomes DNA, which returns to the chromosomes in the nucleus.

Or, if wild guesses and oversimplification really are in order, one might say that, when the male and female segments of DNA mate, they produce a baby, RNA. RNA migrates to the cytoplasm, produces protein, and, in so doing, matures into DNA, which then migrates back to the chromosomes, where it starts the reproductive process (producing baby RNA) all over again.

Bit by bit, trial by trial, error by error, biochemists now are tracing the beginnings of all life. By nucleic acid and enzyme analysis, they are seeking to establish the mutations which have occurred down through three billion years to produce all the forms of life in evidence today.

Perhaps someday they will find that there was only one beginning of life—possibly a molecule of A or ATP which formed by sheer chance and synthesized its mate, the nucleotide pair then building up into an RNA or DNA fragment large enough to manufacture a protein enzyme which would couple nucleotides together in DNA or RNA molecules of increasing complexity and utility.

The first nucleic acid molecule adjusted to its environment in which there was no free oxygen. It lived a plantlike life. Eventually, nucleic acids invented a system which broke down water so that free oxygen was produced. Then they produced a breed of nucleic acids which could use oxygen and required it—an animal form of life. Ultimately, cells formed, and the cells learned to specialize in highly socialized systems of higher life forms.

Miracle that its creation was, it is a greater miracle still that the first spark of life survived to grow, to reproduce, and to adapt itself to its changing environment over three billions years. It was tempered by the heat of molten fire and the bitter cold of a new planet, subjected to the powerful radiations of an aging sun, the tremendous quakes of a cooling and settling crust, the crash of comets, the crush of glaciers, recurrent droughts and deluges, the rise and eruption of mountains, the inundation of continents. It rode on winds of unbelievable velocity and violence.

It drew from its large and lonely environment other combinations of atoms, and, patiently, over a billion or so years, it achieved through trial and error the ingredients which made it grow and reproduce. It became two and found a measure of immortality—if one died, the other might survive. The two became four, the four became eight. Each division restored youth and made life more secure in a dead world. The spark became a flicker, the flicker a flame.

The first life has become the beauty and fragrance of plants, the speed and strength of animals, movement in thousands of forms under the sea, the plodding patience of animals that burrow under the earth, the grace of birds that fly, the mind of man.

Through the first life, a common ancestor, all living things are brothers. They are the products of a proud past, the progenitors of the future.

Dr. Harold Urey of the University of California has said that life, once eliminated from this planet, never would return again. The one important factor which made it possible three billion years ago—the scarcity of electrons around atomic nuclei—has been altered irreversibly with the gradual oxidation of substances, creating a preponderance of electrons.

Life, however, should continue to flourish for a long time, barring the actions of angry humans.

CHAPTER 17

CHROMOSOMES AND CANCER

Each person is tied to eternity by slender threads of DNA.

He starts life with one-ten-trillionth of an ounce of DNA as his inheritance; it represents the accumulated curses and blessings visited upon all his forebears since the first life; it is the legacy he will bequeath to future generations. DNA is the substance of his immortality. In it, he lived before he was conceived; his DNA survives in progeny, and in it he lives long after he has died. DNA is the stuff of which spectres are made; in it, the ghosts of bygone generations haunt a body of their own design.

The DNA in the fertilized egg is the loom on which will be woven the form and fabric of the body and the mettle of the mind. In large measure, it is a predestiny to health and to disease, to early death or a long life. It is the pattern of personality, and it sets the limits of one's potential.

The length, breadth and width of various DNA threads have been measured with more or less accuracy. A typical DNA molecule could be about 1/100,000 inch long and 1/10,000,000 inch in diameter. Its fourth dimension—time—is the greatest measurement of all. One's DNA extends from the mists of the immeasurable past to the farthest point in the unforeseeable future.

An individual's life begins when the male sperm penetrates the female egg, or ovum.

The sperm contains 23 sausage-shaped balls of DNA. The balls are called chromosomes. In these balls, or chromosomes, the long DNA threads are folded like a spring, with from 9.3 to 11 nucleotide pairs comprising each coil.

The ovum also contains 23 chromosomes.

The resulting cell—the fertilized egg—has 46 chromosomes.

Someone has estimated that the one-ten-trillionth of an ounce of DNA in 46 human chromosomes of the fertilized egg contains enough information to fill 50 sets of the 24-volume *Encyclopaedia Britannica*. The information is exclusively about the cell and the individual it produces—his race, color, number of fingers and toes, size and shape of his nose and ears, probable stature, and virtually all his physical characteristics and mental qualities.

The information is chemically controlled. The specific DNA produces specific RNA, which produces specific protein enzymes, which catalyze the many thousands of specific chemical reactions of the cell and of the individual.

The maternal DNA of the ovum and the paternal DNA of the sperm retain their identity; the chromosomes remain intact in the fertilized egg and in all the cells that arise from it. A-T and G-C nucleotide pairs or entire DNA molecules missing in the father's chromosomes may be supplied by the mother's chromosomes; and the offspring will have the mother's traits. If both lack a certain DNA molecule the particular trait it controls will not appear. If both have different DNA for a single trait— the mother for blue eyes and the father for brown, for instance—one or the other may dominate, or there may be a compromise color.

A trait is strong when both parents inherit it from both of their respective parents; it is weak if only one parent has it, and it is especially weak if the parent, in turn, inherited it from only one of his or her parents.

Chromosomes are of twenty-four different shapes and sizes. The largest is five times as big as the smallest. Twenty-two of the chromosomes in the egg are virtually identical with their paired 22 chromosomes in the sperm.

In the egg, the twenty-third chromosome is a relatively large one, and it is called the X chromosome.

In the sperm, the twenty-third chromosome may be a large X chromosome, like that of the egg. Or it may be a small one, called the Y chromosome. If the twenty-third sperm chromosome is an X, the fertilized egg then will have an XX chromosome pair, and the offspring will be a girl. If the sperm chromosome is Y, the fertilized egg will have an XY pair of chromosomes and the offspring will be a boy.

In the resting sperm, egg, fertilized egg, or body cell, the DNA threads are relaxed and loosely packed. During cell division, the threads condense in their chromosomes and become readily visible.

The fertilized egg divides into two cells, the two into four, the four into eight. At the end of nine months and after forty-five cell divisions, a baby composed of 26 trillion (26,000,000,000,000) cells is born.

The DNA fibers comprising the chromosomes of the fertilized egg might stretch about 6 inches if laid end to end; the DNA fibers in a newborn baby would stretch more than twenty times the distance from the earth to the sun. The DNA fibers in the 700-or-so trillion cells of an adult would cover a good distance across the Milky Way.

Some cells, like those in the bone marrow and those lining the digestive tract, are almost constantly dividing. Others, especially nerve cells, may never divide again after the system is fully developed. Perhaps most cells divide and die in specific daily, monthly, seasonal, and other rhythms which govern the function of various organs and systems. In the young, about 1.5 pounds of cells die and are replaced every day.

Nature's errors in producing new cells are numerous and often enormous.

The biggest blunders are reflected in the existence of an odd number of chromosomes possessed by some cells.

One group has reported finding odd chromosome numbers—most often 44, 45, or 47, but sometimes multiples of the normal complement—in as many as 10 per cent of the cell samples they removed from healthy people. Others challenge this finding; they contend the abnormalities probably developed after the cells were removed from the control of the body.

There no longer is any doubt, however, that a large number of diseases which have mystified medicine for ages are associated with chromosome abnormalities.

A few forms of cancer are among the conditions recognized as being marked by odd numbers of chromosomes.

The ability to count chromosomes accurately is a recent development in science. It was only as recently as 1956 that Drs. J. H. Tjio and Albert Levan in Sweden reported that human body cells contain 46 chromosomes —not 48 as all textbooks had asserted since the year 1926. They had devised a system of squashing cells so that chromosomes spread out and became countable. Dr. Theodore T. Puck of the University of Colorado found out how to make them grow on laboratory glassware as they do in the body, so that the chromosome number remained constant.

In the early 1950s, a happy laboratory accident also helped make chromosome-counting possible. Dr. T. C. Hsu, then a young scientist at the University of Texas Medical School, had a careless but lucky technician who misread instructions and washed cultures in a 0.08 per cent salt solution instead of the required 0.8 per cent. In this dilution, the cells ballooned out, bringing into clear perspective many of their internal structures, including the chromosomes. The surprised scientist spent four months trying to reconstruct the technician's historic error. The mistake became standard practice in preparing cells for chromosome counts.

In England, Scotland, Japan, France, Sweden, and the United States, groups of scientists began counting chromosomes. In a short time, the cause of several mysterious diseases which had defied scientific explanation came to light. They were traced to accidents to cell chromosomes during the early development of the individual.

Some of the accidents involved the X or Y sex chromosomes.

Klinefelter's syndrome was traced by scientists in Edinburgh and Harwell to male body cells containing an extra X chromosome; instead of the normal XY pair, the body cells of these unfortunate males contained an XXY combination. They were long-legged eunuchs with prominent breasts, wasted-away testicles and, often subnormal intelligence. This altogether-too-common condition was reported by Dr. Malcolm A. Ferguson-Smith to be at the root of 3 per cent of a series of Glasgow men under study for problems of infertility. Klinefelter's syndrome was found in one of every 400 male babies born and in a high percentage of institutionalized mentally defective boys in other studies.

A condition in females, called Turner's syndrome, is caused by what is known as an XO chromosome pattern, O meaning that one of the X chromosomes is missing. These girls, while of normal mentality as a rule, have infantile sex organs and any of a large assortment of physical anomalies—web neck, shieldlike chest, stubby fingers, distorted facial features, many pigmented moles, and eye, skeletal, and kidney malformations.

A vast array of sex chromosome curiosities have come to light in the last few years, including, besides XXY and XO, such combinations as XXXY, XXXXY, XXX (called superfemale), XYY (supermale), X½X, XXYY, 9XXY, and a number of mosaics such as XXXXY/XXY. The percentage of an individual's cells affected by odd chromosome numbers varies according to the stage of development attained when the chromosome accident occurred—the earlier in embryonic life, the higher the percentage of abnormal cells.

It is now known that accidents to several of the 44 nonsex chromosomes, called autosomes, also are associated with disease states.

Mongolism, long a mystery, has been traced by French scientists to the presence of an extra autosome Number 21, there being three instead of two of these chromosomes. One in every 600 or 700 babies is mongoloid, a child whose physical and mental development almost ceased at a point in embryonic existence. Most of these children die within a year. Perhaps it is more than coincidence that mongoloid children run twenty or more times the normal risk of acute lymphatic leukemia; and on a few of these pathetic youngsters is bestowed—and to a degree wasted—that rare blessing, a spontaneous and complete cure of this otherwise incurable blood cancer. While a variety of chromosomal abnormalities have been found in some patients with acute lymphatic leukemia—and none in others—autosome 21 does not appear to be affected often.

In chronic myeloid leukemia, white blood cells have a normal complement of 46 chromosomes, but in many cases a segment is missing from one of the Number 21 autosomes. This "Philadelphia chromosome" is the only specific abnormality so far associated more or less regularly with any kind of cancer; 40 per cent of its DNA is missing.

Chronic lymphatic leukemia involves no chromosome problems, so far as is known at this writing.

Dr. Theodore S. Hauschka of Roswell Park, long before chromosome counting became a popular scientific and clinical custom, noted that many kinds of cancer cells had odd numbers of chromosomes—often mutiples of the normal complement. With the introduction of precise methods of counting chromosomes, he and Dr. Avery Sandberg found that as many as one-third of the cells shed by a cultured human cancer had odd chromosome numbers. They reported that up to 10 per cent of the cells removed from healthy human marrow also had extra or missing chromosomes.

Several investigators have shown that some normal cells will become malignant spontaneously after they are removed from the body and grown in tissue culture. Dr. George O. Gey of Johns Hopkins University more than a quarter-century ago found that in tissue culture not only did normal cells sometimes become malignant, but malignant cells sometimes became normal—they no longer caused cancer when injected.

Dr. Hsu threw additional light on the mystery. He noted that when normal or cancer cells were removed from the host and grown in tissue culture, the number of chromosomes sometimes increased steadily for two or three months and then, after their number had doubled, gradually decreased. Cells with double the normal number of chromosomes proved to be extremely malignant when injected into animals. Cancer cells which had been cultured until their chromosome number had doubled and then receded to 150 per cent of normal no longer could cause cancer. Instead, Dr. Hsu found, they became a safe and reliable vaccine against transplanted cancer; when rats were vaccinated with them they became resistant to later transplants of that kind of cancer.

It now appears that a chromosomal error can occur as a result of several different situations—one of them being inheritance, that is, the defect is perpetuated in the seed itself. Studies of mongolism indicate that this disease sometimes is inherited and sometimes is due to a chromosome accident during development.

There have been instances in which mongoloids have lived to have children; one-half their offspring were mongoloid. In a few cases, the mothers of mongoloid children were found to have what appeared to be the normal 46, or even 45, chromosomes in their body cells; investigation showed, however, that the extra autosome 21 had attached to autosome 13, making the mother normal but a carrier of the chromosome for mongolism, which she passed along to her children. Male carriers for some reason seem to beget carriers, rather than mongoloids.

In many more instances, however, mongolism appears to be due to an accident which occurs to the ovum during its long period of development; this process begins before a girl's birth and lasts until she sheds the ovum in later life. The older the woman, the longer her ova have been developing and, consequently, the greater the chance of an accident occuring to a chromosome. For this reason, this kind of accidental (not inherited) mongolism is more common among offspring of older women than younger women.

In the normal developmental process, called meiosis, the 46-chromosome germ cell divides twice while the chromosomes themselves divide only once, leaving the mature sperm or ovum with only 23 chromosomes. Sometimes two chromosomes will stick together when they should pull apart, each going to a different daughter cell. When this occurs, one of the daughter cells winds up with only 22 chromosomes, while the other has 24. If the 22 chromosome ovum is fertilized by a normal 23-chromosome sperm, the body cells of the new individual will contain only 45 chromosomes. If the 24-chromosome ovum is fertilized, the resultant individual's body cells will have 47 chromosomes. If the missing or extra chromosome is an X or Y, sex mix-ups like Turner's or Klinefelter's syndromes may be the result. Many chromosomal accidents make it impossible for the embryo to develop for long, and there will be an abortion—often so early that the woman may not know she has been pregnant.

The vast majority of chromosome accidents found in children occur after conception—at some time during the development of the embryo or the fetus. In these cases, the body cells which are normal at the time of the accident stand a good chance of remaining normal and giving rise to normal daughter cells. By the same token, the chromosome-crippled body cell and all its cell progeny will be eccentric, and the organs and tissues they form from that time forward will be defective.

An accidental deletion or addition of even a very small chromosome can bring about darkened minds and malformed babies. Dr. Klaus Patau of the University of Wisconsin has found an extra small chromosome in two distinct congenital disasters—one characterized by deafness, convulsions, apathy, defective eye development, cleft palate, and anomalous thumbs, and the other by a small jaw, low-set ears, spasticity, heart defects, rocker-bottom feet, cataracts, hernias, and deformed kidneys.

Chromosome troubles appear during adulthood and even in old age. In these cases, the conditions are not as bizarre as those which occur in early life. Only the stricken body cells and their offspring are directly affected; and because growth slows down progressively with age, relatively few cells are involved. If the accident makes the cells cancerous, however, it can be a serious matter at any age.

Some of the agents which cause cancer now are known to cause chromosome anomalies. An Edinburgh group under one of the pioneers of human chromosome studies, Dr. W. M. Court Brown, have shown that therapeutic X rays can produce a veritable shower of cells with assorted chromosomal anomalies. There is increasing evidence that chemical carcinogens have similar effects.

If destiny is designed by the mathematics of probability—the chance of a stray ion or strange molecule colliding with a cell compound at a critical moment in time—the wonder is not at the number of diseases which befall us but that we live so long, so uneventfully and so well. One estimate, and probably a conservative one, is that during the average lifetime of a human, something like 2.4 quadrillion (2,400,000,000,000,000) cells are born and die.

It seems certain that nature has equipped its creatures with protective mechanisms—systems that do away with the damaged and defective cells. What the defenses are, how they function, and why, in so many cases, they fail remain unsolved problems.

The conflict between the normal and the abnormal cells perhaps is best illustrated by a grotesque kind of cancer called teratoma, an embryonic tumor usually of the ovary or testicle. This tumor type sometimes is called a "ghost twin" because it develops such tissues as hair, nails, eye elements, fat, lung, marrow, cartilage, bone, muscle, and brain—an eerie outline of an individual which never left preconception limbo. These strange structures so closely resemble the events in the development of a human that they have yielded valuable information on the normal processes of embryonic development.

A few scientists have studied teratomata with an eye to determining whether the deadly unspecialized cancer cells in these tissues can be made to differentiate—to reverse their malignant course and go toward normal. The evidence that this is possible is circumstantial.

Dr. Armin C. Braun of Rockefeller Institute has restored plant teratomata to almost normal. These are ugly tumors which retain the normal ability to form buds and leaves and which grow rapidly (but not as fast as the growing tips of buds, leaves and roots) because they retain an abnormal capacity to produce growth hormone. Dr. Braun snipped off the fastest growing tips of the autonomous tumors and grafted them serially to normal plants. With each successive transplant, the teratomata grew faster; eventually they attained the great growth rate of the normal tips of buds and roots —and at this point they became normal. The plan of this experiment was in contradistinction to the scheme of scientists seeking anticancer drugs;

whereas Dr. Braun sought to speed up growth and restore the tumor's dependence on hormones and nutrients supplied by the whole plant, others seek preparations which will slow it down—or kill the tumor cells. One wonders whether drugs which encourage growth might not be more successful against cancer than the present ones which inhibit growth.

Dr. M. C. Niu, variously at Stanford University, Rockefeller Institute and Temple University, also sought to "reform" teratomata—that is, to make them normal. In tissue culture he succeeded. He introduced RNA derived from normal cells into media containing teratoma cells. The tumor cells were transformed; when they were injected into animals, they no longer induced cancer.

Whether these and a few other observations offer hope that medicine someday may make genetic or congenital cripples whole again is for the future to determine.

CHAPTER 18

GENES
AND CANCER

About eighty million babies are born each year. Of these, about two million come into the world with obvious genetic defects and diseases.

In many others the inherited flaws are not apparent at birth, but they show up during childhood, adulthood, or old age. They may be hidden so long and so well that they are not recognized as inherited when they appear.

Some are convinced that among the defects is a predisposition to cancer. The susceptibility may be subtle; it may involve a slight malfunction of a gland, an inability to produce enough of a needed chemical, the over-production of another essential substance, or a metabolic mistake which displaces an atom in certain molecules. The cancer may not appear until environment provides the right set of circumstances to trigger it.

Genetic disease is caused by the presence of a bad gene, the absence of a necessary gene, or the displacement of a gene from its normal position inside the seed—sperm, ovum, or fertilized egg. Sometimes a whole chromosome or a considerable part of it is involved.

If a necessary gene is missing from, say, the father's seed, but is present in the mother's ovum, the offspring can be perfectly well. This is called a recessive trait; it may not show or it may be very weak.

If a bad gene is present in either sperm or ovum, it will show; if it is present in both sperm and ovum, the double dose of the dominant trait will show to an exaggerated degree.

For the above reasons, inbreeding is risky. Genetic faults which may not appear in hybrid humans may come out tragically in the products of consanguineous matches.

Special traits—good and bad—become watered down with each passing generation of outbreeding. In the process of meiosis, which produces mature sperm and ova, the host's genes are thoroughly shuffled and only one-half of each parent's genes (in 23 chromosomes) are passed along to the offspring. Unless there has been a double dose of a gene (from both the host's parents), the chances of any particular father's or mother's gene being transmitted to the new offspring are 50-50.

There is no general concurrence as to what a gene actually is. It is felt, however, that whatever genes are, they are strung on the spirally wound DNA threads of chromosomes as beads are strung in a coiled, two-stranded necklace.

DNA never has been found to exist in a free state within cells; so far as is known, it is always bound to protein. The role of the protein in chromosomes and genes is speculative.

Dr. Theodore T. Puck of the University of Colorado Medical School, who brought order out of worldwide chaos in genetics by organizing a group which devised a standard nomenclature for chromosomes, feels that a gene is one molecule of DNA. Composed of about 1,000 A-T and G-C pairs, the average gene, or DNA molecule, would be about a ten-millionth of an inch thick and 1/100,000 inch long. He feels that each chromosome, on an average, would contain about 10,000 genes. Under these calculations, the human sperm cell or ovum would contain about 230,000 genes, and the fertilized egg or ordinary body cell would have 460,000 genes.

Because an X chromosome is much larger than a Y chromosome, females (with an XX pair) would have 4 per cent more DNA than males (with an XY pair). "This greater gene complement of the human female would function as a greater factor of safety in helping to cope with life's stresses and may be the reason for the greater life span of women as compared to men," Dr. Puck has said.

Dr. Saul Kit of Baylor University estimates that the normal cell contains about 300,000 DNA molecules, all of them distinctly different, totaling about six billion A-T and G-C pairs. He believes that the cell may have as many as one million genes, a few of them about eighty nucleotide pairs long.

Dr. Kit feels that, in its natural state, a chromosome may be composed of only one long string of DNA—an enormous coiled thread interrupted by "nonsense triplets" of nucleotide pairs which serve as spaces or punctuation marks between gene molecules. This DNA, he speculates, might contain codes for the synthesis of very short transfer RNA molecules, long ribosomal RNA, and messenger RNA molecules.

For many years, scientists have set the number of genes per cell at 10,000. In the light of actual measurements of the DNA content of cells, this figure now is used only as a convenient round number and as a concession to convention.

The wide disparity in estimates as to the number of genes in a cell is narrowed considerably if one accepts the concept that the function of some genes may be as transient as baby teeth. These genes come into existence at a preappointed time in the development of the individual, do what must be done for the host to achieve that stage of development and then, no longer needed, rest or disappear; they make way for the genes governing the next stage of development. The human body, like other forms of life, is built from a genetic blueprint in which certain structures are produced in a highly specific sequence of events and on a rigid time schedule. It is conceivable that gene or DNA molecules may change progessively to govern the maturation of the cell.

Some feel that many genes may control a single trait. Some of them are involved in its inception, others in its periodic suppression, and still others in its ultimate denouement. These concepts envision a developmental gene which initiates a trait, modifies or suppresses it; a rate-setting gene which periodically inhibits the inhibitor; and finally a demolition gene which dismantles or permanently destroys the original gene. The activities of these gene sequences in governing growth and decline are as faithful as the seasons.

Other genes may be present but inactive during the lifetime of the individual. They are there to enable the individual to cope with unusual situations that might arise. They can produce adaptive enzymes which enable the bearer to detoxify certain poisons or live under unusual physical and chemical conditions which would kill organisms not equipped with these specific genes and enzymes.

These considerations help bridge the gap between the old concept of 10,000 genes controlling 10,000 enzymes which catalyze 10,000 different chemical reactions in each cell, and the new evidence of the existence of between 300,000 and 1,000,000 genes in a human body cell. The prodigious amounts of nucleic acid and protein in cells represent not only the essential machinery for life but thousands of "extras" for the protection, adaptability, smooth performance, and comfort of the cells.

Science one day will have more precise ideas of how many genes there are and just how they function. Meanwhile, a concept of some sort is not only a convenience but also is an absolute necessity in contemplating the past and present course of life.

Evolution, generally considered a ponderous process measured in millenia, may actually be a moment-to-moment matter. Its mileposts, which various authorities in the past have set as anywhere from one mutation in 100,000 individuals to one in 1,100,000, would seem to be far more frequent than has been supposed.

It may well be that everything which lives is a mutant—that its genes are unique in the history of life—that every blade of grass which has sprouted in all the springs of time and every leaf which has fallen during all the autumns has a distinct identity.

A mutation is a permanent alteration in genes or chromosomes. When the alteration occurs in the genes of the seed, it is inherited by offspring. When it happens to genes of a body cell it is called a somatic mutation, and is reproduced in daughter cells arising from the mutant cell. A major mutation may change radically the chemistry, form, and behavior of a cell or individual; a minor mutation may be imperceptible.

A lot of things can go wrong in the simple process of one cell dividing to become two cells.

And, under the laws of chance, a lot must go wrong.

Dr. Aaron Bendich of the Sloan-Kettering Institute has calculated that a single small DNA molecule composed of 1,000 A, T, G, and C nucleotides can exist in 10^{590} possible combinations. Ten to the 590th power represents one followed by 590 zeros. All possible combinations of the order of A, T, G, and C nucleotides in this tiny DNA molecule would weigh 10^{554} (one with 554 zeros after it) grams. The mass of the entire earth is estimated at only 10^{27} (one followed by 27 zeros) grams.

Accepting Dr. Puck's rough estimates, it would seem highly unlikely that any seed cell containing 230,000 DNA molecules would be alike in every respect to another seed cell. Each human female is born with from 200 to 400 eggs in her ovaries, and these are subject to radiation effects and chemical influences until they mature and are shed, month by month, during the reproductive years. The development of sperm also entails a series of enormous chemical changes, although over a short period—until they are discharged—as many as 400,000,000 sperm may be in a single ejaculate; only one fertilizes the egg, however.

The number of atoms involved in the blending of male and female DNA at fertilization and in the division of the fertilized egg or body cell can be calculated by multiplying 230,000 (DNA molecules in the ovum) $\times$ 2 (in the sperm) $\times$ 1,000 (nucleotide pairs in each DNA molecule) $\times$ 84 (atoms in each nucleotide pair) $\times$ an incalculable number of other molecules and atoms involved in the many chemical reactions of mitosis. A human cell contains about one billion molecules.

In the light of the .arithmetic involved, it is no wonder that brothers and sisters stemming from the same genetic lines are so different and that identical twins emerging from the same fertilized egg are actually far from identical.

It seems likely that every living creature is an experiment in Nature's ceaseless quest for new forms of life; each one is a "missing link" between the gradually disappearing life of the past and the emerging forms of the future.

Moreover, with increasing use of mutation-inducing agents in food, medicine, air, and water, evolution is accelerating. The changes once associated with the sweep of the centuries now are taking place with surprising speed.

The course of evolution is not a smooth one. For every radically mutant cell or organism which survives, many others die at once or before they reproduce. Only a few mutations are workable.

By the same token, a seemingly deleterious mutation may be a blessing in disguise. There are many examples of this. This is the case with sickle-cell anemia in which a gene defect results in one of the 560 amino acids comprising the hemoglobin molecule being altered. While about 8 per cent of American Negroes carry the sickling gene, only one in 600 develops the disease. All who have the sickling gene are immune to malaria—which throughout much of the world is still a great scourge. Another, inherited tendency, to retain salt in the system, enables the person to withstand difficult climatic conditions; Rh-negative women have been reported blessed with high fecundity. Some metabolic defects enable the carrier to survive on diets which would be inadequate for others. One can only speculate as to whether their inherited defect contributed to the talents of the many great artists and geniuses who suffered from genetic disease of one kind or another.

The rules and mathematics governing evolution of the species also apply to the prenatal and postnatal evolution of the individual.

Individual evolution is the process of growing up and growing old. A human being starts, like an early form of life, as a single cell; during his embryonic and fetal life, he traverses the selfsame course taken over three billion years by the life forms from which he sprang. During his postnatal existence, as he passes successively through infancy, youth, maturity, and old age, gene-controlled mechanisms (hormone-producing glands, for instance) turn on and then turn off.

In the fury of man's growth and during his gradual decay, accidents happen; the DNA molecules of new body cells constantly are being distorted by a ray or chemical. The distorted DNA may disappear with the death of the mutant cell, as presumably happens with the vast majority of mutant body cells. It may be perpetuated harmlessly in cells which form a benign lesion or tumor; these growths cannot invade other tissues or seed the body. Or it may live on in cancer—mutant cells which can reproduce and which move more or less freely through the body and prey upon the host.

The best evidence of the role of heredity—or DNA—in disease comes not from studies of body cells but rather from seed cells and the people who develop from them.

Studies of various inherited diseases in humans are of interest in cancer research for two reasons: (1) They offer clues to a supposed inherited proneness, or susceptibility, to cancer in some individuals; and (2) On a life-size scale, they suggest the general nature of chemical faults which result when a carcinogen makes a normal body cell malignant.

Scores of biochemists have discovered scores of chemical differences between normal cells and cancer cells. The differences, with few exceptions, have been quantitative rather than qualitative; that is, the cancer cell contains more or less of a certain chemical than a corresponding normal cell does. Only a few have reported finding that all cancer cells contain chemicals which do not exist in normal cells, or vice versa.

The chemical differences detected in cancer cells involve hormones, amino acids, sugars, fats, and proteins. The production and use of all these substances are under the control of cell genes, or DNA. For each of these cancer cell defects there is a counterpart in inherited human disease.

Many hormone problems are genetic. Some cases of cretinism, for example, are inherited. The victim lacks a gene which produces an enzyme which adds or deletes an iodine atom in the synthesis of thyroid hormone; if the condition is detected early in life and the victim given thyroid hormone, the condition is controlled. Similarly, an inherited virilizing condition—in which boys begin to attain a precocious manhood about the time they enter kindergarten and girls lose their femininity and become masculine in appearance—is due to the lack of a gene and its enzyme which remove an oxygen and a hydrogen atom in the synthesis of adrenal hormones.

There has been suggestive evidence that in some cancer cells one or another amino acid is not properly metabolized. As a counterpart in human heredity, one disease known as phenylketonuria is due to such a defect. In these cases, the victim lacks the gene and enzyme which convert phenylalanine into another amino acid, tyrosine, which ultimately becomes the body's pigment. The affected children are blond, fair-skinned, blue-eyed (because they form little pigment) and often clumsy, convulsive, and intemperate (because of a fault in nerve chemistry). If the condition, which affects one in 20,000 babies, is detected early and phenylalanine is taken out of the diet, a measure of control is possible; at two years of age, however, the brain damage is irreversible and death results. Along the same chemical assembly line, lack of the enzyme which converts tyrosine to pigment produces an albino. Another missing enzyme causes alkaptonuria—the patient in childhood excretes black or brown urine, in his teens and twenties has ochre-colored splotches around his joints, and in his forties suffers from arthritis.

Several genetic defects are reflected in the inability to metabolize sugar. In some cases the disease is marked by allergies to many drugs and some foods; even ordinary milk sugar can be poisonous. In gargoylism, the unearthly facial features result from the lack of an enzyme which normally breaks up those complex sugars known as polysaccharides. About one-half of the cases of sugar diabetes are due to the failure of a gene and its enzyme in the pancreas to synthesize enough insulin.

Some faults in fat metabolism also are inherited. In one of them, infantile amaurosis, a fatty substance piles up in nerves, and the child victims die after a year or two of blindness and paralysis.

Genetic defects in the manufacture of protein are numerous and varied. In hemophilia, blood fails to clot because a gene on an X chromosome is missing, and the coagulating protein it controls is not made. Because females have two X chromosomes, one from each parent, they do not show the bleeding disease unless both parents lacked the gene; but they can pass the defective X chromosome along to their daughters, who also will be carriers of the trait, and to their sons, who will suffer the pains and hemorrhages, the fear that any small cut or injury will kill them, and the anxiety incidental to their need for considerable amounts of blood and plasma to cope with a bleeding episode. Another protein defect is reflected in one form of agammaglobulinemia; in this, the victim fails to produce antibodies and consequently is severely affected by minor infections which normally would cause little trouble.

In many other genetic diseases the chemical defect is unknown, and it often is difficult to recognize the hereditary nature of the condition. Infantile autism is such a disease. In this, the youngster has an utter lack of interest in people, an obsessive preoccupation with things, a desperate need for sameness (his toys and other articles must be kept in the same place), often an inability to speak or understand the spoken word, and a future of schizophrenia but without hallucinations or delusions. The disease occurs in only one member of a family as a rule or, occasionally, in identical twins. The fact that in many cases both parents are emotionally rigid and compulsive (but regarded as clinically normal) suggests that the infantile autism patient has inherited a double dose of what otherwise would be a mild metabolic fault leading to a slight personality disorder.

Except for the familial occurrence of a few relatively rare cancers and precancerous conditions, there is no evidence that malignant disease is inherited. Beyond these few exceptions, the metabolic patterns or physical defects which would indicate a proneness to any specific kind of cancer or to cancer generally, at this time are not apparent. The biochemistry of many inherited noncancerous diseases, however, is still equally obscure.

Nevertheless, many feel that the predisposition exists in inherited genes of cancer victims and is expressed in the survival and growth of the damaged cells of cancer.

The problem of controlling cancer in a subject is akin to that of controlling bad seed within a species. Similar measures have been devised for both problems. Most of them are brutal. Only modest success has been achieved in either case; both problems continue to grow more severe with each passing year.

The most effective means—when it works—is nature's own remedy: let the unfit die of their own incapacity. It is probable that many potential cancer cells arise during the course of everyone's lifetime; they do not develop and multiply because the system, by means still unknown, lets them die.

Sterilization has been tried in both cases, and with fair results at best. In cancer, several agents—including X rays—permit the cell to live but prevent its reproducing. The agents themselves, however, can make normal cells malignant.

Extermination also has been tried in both cases. In cancer, good cells too often are poisoned along with the bad.

Eugenic quarantine has been tested. The Fore tribe in New Guinea has been quarantined in an effort to restrict to the tribe itself an inherited nerve disease called kuru. Superficial cancers have been tied off from the general circulation and allow to strangle for want of a blood supply.

A few scientists have tested gentler genetic measures against cancer. The clinical experiments are so new and so few that it is impossible at this time to predict whether they will prove useful. Test-tube results, however, indicate that they are worth pursuing.

One means calls for inserting good genes—or nucleic acid—into defective cells. The equivalent of this is done in a species by breeding the good with the bad in the hope that the sound partner will supply a good gene to offset the effects of his mate's missing or bad one. This reform measure is accomplished in the laboratory by placing a defective cell in an environment rich in the nucleic acid, or gene material, extracted from good cells.

Dr. Austin Weisberger of Western Reserve University bathed the diseased red cells from people with sickle-cell anemia in a culture to which normal red-cell DNA had been added. The evidence indicated that the sickle cells took up the normal DNA, incorporated it into their genes, produced healthy enzymes and hemoglobin, and became normal.

Dr. Salome Gluecksohn-Waelsch of the Albert Einstein College of Medicine in New York corrected in test tubes an inherited defect of mouse kidneys by other measures. When mutant kidneys, which develop slowly and inadequately both in embryonic mice and in tissue culture, were placed in a culture containing normal embryonic mouse ureters or spinal cord, the kidneys developed in a fairly normal manner. Something in the normal embryonic tissues apparently seeped into the mutant kidneys, supplied a factor they lacked, and enabled them to grow.

At the University of Miami, Dr. Wilhelmina Dunning found that if cancer-susceptible rats were put on a diet of nucleic-acid-rich yeast, their cancers developed slowly or not at all. The dietary nucleic acid apparently enabled the cancer-susceptible cells to repair their gene DNA defects.

Is it possible to influence the course of cancer in humans by comparable means?

Dr. Henry Koch, then in Tucson, Arizona, several years ago injected a dozen far-advanced cancer patients with placental extracts, which he reasoned would contain substances which made embryonic tissues mature. A few of the patients lived well beyond their prognosis, but the results were considered equivocal.

Dr. Sergio DeCarvalho of the Rand Development Corporation, Cleveland, Ohio, reported that in test tubes he had made cancer cells normal by bathing them in normal RNA and had made normal cells malignant by bathing them in cancer RNA. He then cautiously treated a series of advanced cancer patients with normal RNA. The clinical results were difficult to assess. They had the merit of low toxicity.

While there is considerable skepticism about the practicality of transforming cancer with normal DNA or RNA, few if any of the critics have actually attempted to duplicate the experiments.

Genetics has come a long way in the century since the Austrian monk, Gregor Mendel, offered to a heedless world his work on red and white flowers.

Under the biophysicist, radiation now is used routinely to mutate plants —to speed up the course of evolution. The results have served to satisfy man's great gustatory and esthetic tastes with a rich variety of nutritive and beautiful plants.

Under the scientific breeder, livestock have come to survive under adverse conditions, live longer, and produce more and better food for humans.

The greatest strides of all are being made at this writing in the laboratories of the biochemist, who in test-tube experiments is laying out the blueprint for the future of the human race. A beginning has been made in providing transplants for people with worn-out or diseased organs. It has been demonstrated that with specific DNA and RNA the day of tailor-made life is not far off; egg and sperm can be treated, genetic defects can be eliminated, and the offspring, a product of artificial insemination, can carry built-in traits of their parents' or foster-parents' own choosing. Some scientists even now are beginning to synthesize DNA according to their own specifications.

As the chemistry of inherited disease comes to light, it becomes possible to control it—as diabetes, cretinism, and other conditions now are controlled with drugs and diet.

It is only reasonable to assume that, when the genetics of cancer is understood, this disease, too, will yield to control by science and medicine. A step in this direction already has been made. Dr. Clement L. Markert of Johns Hopkins University has developed evidence which could be interpreted as a turning back of the genetic clock in cancer. He has found that two genes—which we will call A and B—control the cell's synthesis of an enzyme, LDH or lactic dehydrogenase, a protein comprised by an A chain and a B chain of amino acids. During embryonic life, the A gene makes virtually all the LDH protein—that is, A-chain protein which is particularly effective in an oxygenless environment. Following birth, the A gene slows down progressively and the B gene increases its activity, until, eventually, the LDH protein is composed almost exclusively of B-chain protein, which is most effective in an atmosphere of oxygen. In the mature person, the LDH and the genes which form it are almost purely of the B type. As normal cells become malignant, the genetic clock is turned back—A genes gradually increase the A-chain composition of LDH, while the B genes subside and B chains diminish. The more malignant the cancer, the more A genes and amino acids and the fewer B genes and amino acids in the tumor cells. Control of the activity of A and B genes might well mean control of cancer.

CHAPTER 19

VIRUSES AND CANCER

In the spring of 1961, a few widely scattered scientists put their findings together and came up with an alarming conclusion: millions of people in the United States and many millions in other countries inadvertently had been exposed to a cancer virus when they were given polio vaccines.

The cancer virus was a contaminant of the polio vaccine. It was called simian virus-40, or SV-40, because it was one of many unidentified particles which existed naturally in the kidney cells of rhesus and other Asiatic monkeys in which polio virus was grown. In these cells, the virus SV-40 appeared completely innocuous; the monkeys remained perfectly healthy and the cells undamaged.

When SV-40 was added to cultures of kidney cells removed from African monkeys, however, the cells blistered, bubbled, and died. When SV-40 was injected into newborn hamsters, it produced cancers.

Polio virus is grown in monkey kidney cells and is harvested from them in vaccines. The procedures which kill polio virus for injectible vaccines and which weaken polio virus in the live oral preparations do not affect SV-40. Because about 70 per cent of rhesus monkeys used to produce polio vaccines have been found to be carriers of SV-40, scientists estimate that a majority of people inoculated against polio up to the summer of 1961 had received SV-40 in both the killed and attenuated vaccines.

In the summer of 1961, procedures were found to inactivate SV-40, and American preparations used since then have been clean. The vaccines used in the Soviet Union and Cuba were decontaminated later.

There is not the slightest direct evidence at this time that SV-40 has induced cancer in any human. Adult volunteers have had their noses and throats sprayed with SV-40, and the only untoward reaction was a transient respiratory difficulty so mild as not to require medical attention.

Moreover, SV-40 has failed to induce cancer in mice and rats. It may be carcinogenic only to newborn hamsters and possibly one or two obscure experimental species, like an African rodent called mastomy.

It usually takes many years for cancer to appear in humans following contact with the cancer-causing agent, however, and it may be some time before the real consequences of SV-40 exposure are known. It is entirely possible that SV-40 may have immunized people against some forms of cancer. The impact of the virus on public health—good, bad, or indifferent—will be reflected in future vital statistics.

Meanwhile, the SV-40 incident serves to show that science's search for a cancer virus is of more than academic interest. More knowledge could prevent much unnecessary human exposure to cancer viruses, and it could bring about a means of controlling and possibly even of curing virus-caused cancer.

A chronology of events leading to the discovery of SV-40, the determination of its cancer-causing potential, and the speed with which it has been eliminated points up the practical side of cancer virus research. It indicates the ease with which catastrophic hazards to public health can arise in the swift sweep of modern scientific achievement, and the suddenness with which the dangers can be eliminated once they are recognized.

The fact that kidney cells of rhesus monkeys contain unidentified particles had long been known. Various scientists reported finding from 30 to 60 different simian bodies in them. The particles obviously were doing no harm in their natural environment.

In June, 1960, Drs. Maurice Hilleman and B. H. Sweet of the Merck Institute for Therapeutic Research reported that recruits given a Sabin vaccine produced antibodies against the SV-40 contaminants. They remarked on the durability of the particles which survived strong treatment with chemicals used to weaken or kill polio viruses. There was no evidence at that time that SV-40 damaged human cells growing in tissue culture. The scientists called the particles "just one more of the troublesome simian agents" to be eliminated from seed stocks and vaccines.

The Merck disclosures attracted the attention of other research groups, and within the next nine months a strong but strictly circumstantial case was built up against SV-40 as a potential human hazard.

In the virology laboratory of Dr. Francis L. Black at Yale University, Drs. G. D. Hsiung and W. H. Gaylord, Jr., isolated SV-40 from African patas monkeys housed in the same room with Asiatic rhesus monkeys. In their new host, the viruses damaged kidney cells. Dr. Hsiung showed the virus would survive for as long as fifty-eight days in cultures of human tissues, although it seemed not to multiply or damage the cells. One observation aroused the strong suspicions of the Yale group—SV-40, in the electron microscope, resembled polyoma, a rampaging virus which induces more than twenty kinds of cancer in mice, other cancers in rats, hamsters, guinea pigs, and rabbits and has infected humans—in the latter case apparently without causing cancer.

Several other researchers reported failure to infect cultured human kidney cells and other types of cells with SV-40. The cells were standard laboratory lines, and the infected cultures were watched for a couple of weeks.

Meanwhile, at Baylor University School of Medicine, a group working under Dr. Joseph L. Melnick made some disturbing discoveries. They recovered SV-40 from the throats and stools of children given oral polio vaccine. Some of the children had mild coldlike symptoms. The youngsters passed SV-40 in their stools for four weeks. The group set about finding a practical means of identifying SV-40 contaminants in polio vaccine and eliminating them.

The most provocative results of all were to be reported by a group headed by Dr. Bernice Eddy of the Division of Biologics Standards, National Institutes of Health. Ever since 1954, when she was testing polio vaccines for safety, Dr. Eddy had wondered at the fact that, if they were kept long enough, almost every cultured lot of rhesus kidney cells degenerated as though under vigorous attack by a virus. She remembered that two decades earlier a human had received a fatal infection from a monkey bite; virus-B was recovered from the victim.

In 1959, Dr. Eddy extracted cell-free filtrates from rhesus-monkey kidney and injected newborn hamsters with them. There were many native viruslike particles in the extracts; the question was: would any one or all of them collectively induce cancer? For 117 days the hamsters appeared perfectly normal. On the 118th day, however, one animal showed a small subcutaneous tumor. In short order, other injected hamsters developed tumors—some of them grew larger than the animals' bodies. Eventually about 90 per cent of all the hamsters had tumors. Transplanted to other hamsters, the cancers grew rapidly.

By this time, Drs. Sweet and Hilleman had isolated SV-40, and they gave samples of it to Dr. Eddy, who injected the virus into newborn hamsters and obtained results identical to those with monkey kidney extracts—tumors in five months.

In April, 1961, scientists at Yale called the circumstances to the attention of the American Cancer Society, which communicated them to the Surgeon General of the U.S. Public Health Service. Government scientists already were at work on the problem of eliminating SV-40 from polio vaccines, and in May, 1961, vaccines contaminated with SV-40 were banned.

In view of the accumulating evidence, two leading producers promptly stopped making polio vaccines. They were Merck, Sharp and Dohme and Parke, Davis and Company. For a few months, a curious dichotomy existed: the government, still seeking a means of purifying polio vaccines, nevertheless was conducting a vigorous campaign to have large populations inoculated; the polio season was approaching rapidly. At the same time, a regulation by the Division of Biologics Standards prohibited the marketing of vaccines containing a virus other than that specified (polio). Bureau of Census surveys showed that whereas from 1954 until the end of 1960, 93 million Americans under sixty years of age had had at least one shot of polio vaccine and just less than 40 million had had the full course, by the end of 1961 an estimated 98 million people under sixty had had at least one shot, and more than 50 million had had the full course. The annual polio immunization campaigns had been particularly effective with children; by the end of 1961, between 84 and 93 per cent of those fourteen years old and under had had one shot, and between 42 and 60 per cent had had four or more shots.

In September, 1961, Dr. C. W. Hiatt of the National Institutes of Health reported that during the summer he had succeeded in inactivating not only SV-40 but four other simian virus particles as well by a simple procedure. He added trace amounts of a dye, toluidine blue, to the vaccine and pumped it through a glass coil surrounding a brilliant incandescent bulb giving off ordinary white light. This destroyed SV particles numbered 1, 5, 12, 15, and 40. While other particles survived this treatment, there is no reason to believe that they are harmful.

Since the elimination of SV-40 virus from polio vaccines, nothing has come to light which suggests that humans actually have come down with cancer or been immunized against cancer as a result of their early inoculations.

Newly-developed facts about SV-40, however, have been found to place some of those inoculated against a respiratory disease in double jeopardy. Drs. John J. Trentin and Yoshiro Yabe of Baylor University College of Medicine and Frank Taylor of M. D. Anderson Hospital, Houston, reported in the spring of 1962 that one type of adenovirus itself causes cancer when instilled in the lungs of newborn hamsters. From five to fifteen weeks following treatment with adenovirus, between 80 and 90 per cent of the virus-treated animals died of tumors which filled their chests and, in some cases, spread to their livers. In these experiments, the Trentin group used adenovirus 12; others later induced experimental cancers with adenovirus 18 and adenovirus 7. Adenoviruses of types 3, 4, and 7 have been used in human vaccines. Two years after finding adenovirus 12 carcinogenic, the Trentin group produced a live vaccine against it; it was effective in hamsters and, to a degree, in mice, which were also found to be susceptible to the virus.

Adenoviruses, which were first isolated in 1953 in surgically-removed human adenoids, are a common cause of infection among children and, even more so, among recruits during their first year in military service. Adenovirus infection differs from the common cold in that its onset is more gradual and the symptoms are more severe and longer-lasting—fever, chills, running nose, watering eyes, sore throat, hoarseness, wheezing, cough, and general malaise. About one-fourth of a hospital population—sick with a variety of diseases—show antibodies against adenoviruses.

One cannot say with certainty whether a person receiving a vaccine containing two distinct viruses—like SV-40 and adenovirus—each of which causes cancer in newborn hamsters, would run a greater risk than is offered by a single virus. Virologists have found that the behavior of two different viruses toward one another and, jointly, toward the host is unpredictable. In some cases one virus will add to or multiply the virulence of the other; in other cases the result will be to suppress the effect of one or both. Scientists noted, for instance, that SV-40 weakened the immunizing effect of polio virus, its companion in the contaminated vaccines. They also found that SV-40 enhanced the growth of adenovirus 12 100-fold when both infected African green monkey cells.

Also highly unpredictable is the future behavior of a virus when it is removed from its natural host and introduced into a strange species. Most often the virus is completely destroyed in the new host. Occasionally, however, it assumes an unprecedented virulence; as one Irish scientist put it after recovering a polio virus from the feces of a child: "It went into the baby like a lamb and came out like a lion." After passage in the human, the virus caused polio in monkeys. In one set of experiments at the National Institutes of Health, a culture of SV-40 which originally grew poorly in hamsters became extremely virulent in these same animals after being grown in cultures of human thyroid or in the brains or under the skin of live African monkeys.

By now it is well established that SV-40 does infect human cells in culture and that it does great damage to them. Several groups found this out almost simultaneously.

One research team headed by Dr. Hilary Koprowski of the Wistar Institute, University of Pennsylvania, has reported that SV-40, besides inducing monstrous alterations in the size and shape of human cells, caused great changes in their chromosomes after eight to fourteen weeks in tissue culture. Similar chromosome changes now have been identified with a growing number of serious genetic, congenital, and other diseases (some caused by carcinogens), including a few forms of cancer. In some cases, chromosome number 21 or 22 was deleted; in certain kinds of human leukemia, these chromosomes are affected.

Dr. John F. Enders of Children's Hospital Medical Center at Harvard Medical School took a serious view of the situation when he and an associate, Dr. Harvey M. Shein, finally succeeded in growing SV-40 in cultured human tissues after many others had failed. Dr. Enders had won a Nobel prize for devising tissue cultures which had made possible the production of numerous vaccines. He and Dr. Shein first tested SV-40 against tissues freshly removed from aborted human embryos and babies born prematurely and dead. The virus grew in and damaged the young, fast-growing (fibroblast) cells of every fetal tissue tested—kidney, intestine, brain, skin, muscle, lung, liver, heart, adrenal gland, spleen, and testis. The Harvard scientists had kept their cultures going a month or more, whereas earlier unsuccessful experimenters gave up much earlier; and at about the end of this period the cell damage became glaringly obvious. The effect of SV-40 on cells was similar to that of polyoma virus.

Drs. Enders and Shein undertook a second series of experiments—this time to determine whether SV-40 damaged the tissues of young and newborn infants. Once again, the virus infected all the tissues tested. The purpose of these experiments the scientists explained in this way. "Since vaccines containing SV-40 have been administered routinely to three-month-old infants and, infrequently, to newborn children, it seemed of interest to determine whether cells from individuals of these ages are also susceptible to the agent."

SV-40, Drs. Enders and Shein showed, not only damaged and killed some cells but at the same time also stimulated the growth of other cells— a property possessed by many cancer viruses. They summarized their observations in an article appearing in the *Proceedings of the Society for Experimental Biology and Medicine* early in 1962:

> The demonstration of multiplication of SV-40 in human cells associated with cytopathic [cell disease] change is of significance from at least two points of view. First, it extends the serologic and clinical evidence suggesting that the agent is infectious for man. For ultimate failure to demonstrate multiplication in a human cell system would leave doubt regarding its infectivity for this host. Secondly, multiplication of the virus under these conditions may provide a useful means of studying its oncogenic [cancer-inducing] potentiality in populations of human cells.
>
> Although not conclusive, the observations indicate that SV-40 stimulates cell proliferation as well as inducing degenerative changes. It is common knowledge that initially a number of viruses stimulate cell division which is later followed by necrosis [decay]. Whether

in this respect SV-40 is similar or whether the cell proliferation observed may be a prelude to subsequent transformation, possibly
tending toward the malignant state, remains to be determined.

The impact of SV-40 on human health eventually will be known. When
the Yale scientists first communicated their concern to the American
Cancer Society, Dr. E. Cuyler Hammond, chief of the Society's statistical
studies, took immediate action. He incorporated into a massive, general,
and continuing survey of more than one million adult Americans questions about immune procedures used on them. Year by year, as more
and more of these million-plus volunteers die of various causes, computers
will determine whether there is any correlation between the cause of death
and their history of shots for polio, smallpox, and other diseases, as well
as a wide range of other factors.

The role of SV-40 might also be determined in a relatively short time
by checking the immunization histories of children who have died of
leukemia and other cancers. Ordinarily, carcinogenic agents are much
faster-acting in the young than in the old. It has been reported that all eight
youngsters who came down with or died of leukemia in Niles, Illinois,
over a short period had had their polio shots; while this is not statistically
very significant because a large majority of all children had been inoculated, it nevertheless suggests that further checks be made. Dr. Michael
Shimkin has reported that a five-year NCI follow-up has failed to show
childhood cancers which could be traced to SV-40.

Another possible indication of the effects of SV-40 might lie in a
study of mothers who bore congenitally defective children following polio
immunization during their pregnancies. Some authorities feel that childhood cancer often develops during the victim's nine months of residence
within the womb and may be due to congenital factors. Cancers sometimes coexist with congenital malformations, which can be caused by
viruses, radiation, pesticides, some drugs, nutritional deficiencies, and many
other means.

The SV-40 episode once again has raised to question the puzzling
practice of some physicians in immunizing newborn babies. Classical
animal experiments have shown that the newborn is extremely susceptible
to carcinogenic substances and that it can develop a tolerance to viruses
and other agents to which it is exposed during a few days after birth.
Unless the newborn infant temporarily has acquired enough of its mother's
specific antibodies to overcome the agent, it may develop no immunity of
its own. An unresolved question is whether neonatal immunization has
visited upon children a disastrous tolerance of both polio virus and
SV-40, which eventually—possibly many years hence—may lead to their
deaths from the overt or masked effects of infection or from cancer.

It may be important to learn early whether children who were immunized shortly after birth have been made tolerant to specific viruses. This can be determined by injecting the viruses and ascertaining whether antibodies are produced against them. There are several ways of ending the virus tolerance in animals and restoring an immune potential; perhaps the simplest method is to inject antibodies or antiserum specific for the agent. This procedure might be applicable to any infected and tolerant children.

While studies were made of a number of series of very young babies immunized against polio in such cities as Philadelphia, Cleveland, and New Orleans, the investigators were concerned not with the long-term observations but rather with the immediate effects. One group has reported that oral live attenuated polio vaccine has consistently excellent immunizing effects in infants more than ten weeks old and much less immunizing effect in those younger. The evidence indicated that the antibodies the baby acquires from the mother decay with a half-life of about three weeks after birth.

Whatever SV-40 may or may not have done to the public health picture, it has brought to light new and valuable information on viruses and their control. The Melnick group at Baylor discovered a way of doubling the durability and viability of SV-40. This is done merely by maintaining the virus in a hypertonic solution—adding common salts did the trick. The group found that they could stabilize polio virus and inactivate SV-40 by adding charged magnesium or calcium particles to the viral environment. The procedures also knocked out such viruses as vaccinia, cold sore, adenovirus, influenza, mumps, and parainfluenza. By manipulating temperature and acidity, viruses can be destroyed or preserved with great selectivity. Dr. Melnick and Dr. Sara Stinebaugh, his associate, also pointed up the well-established fact that some viruses take a long time to develop in tissue culture; some of their cultures of human cells were as long as thirty-five days in yielding SV-40. If the scientists had given up after two weeks, as many others did, they would have declared these experiments negative.

The SV-40 experience has indicated that it might be a good idea to examine the long-term effect of all vaccines. In the light of accumulating knowledge of virus behavior and the development of investigative techniques—and, indeed, in view of the rapid emergence of a large variety of new viruses—it seems prudent to reexamine the impact of common immunological practices on public health.

Vaccinia, like that received in smallpox shots, is commonly used in several laboratories to enhance the effect of carcinogenic chemicals in inducing cancer in experimental animals. The fact that the cancer mortality rate has risen over many decades in close correlation with the increase in smallpox vaccinations could be, and probably is, coincidence. Scattered reports of cancers appearing in smallpox vaccination scars also could be coincidence, although this seems unlikely.

At this writing, a lively controversy is being waged in British medical journals on the wisdom of mass smallpox vaccinations for very young babies. Dr. George Dick, head of the Microbiology Department of Queens University, Belfast, argues for abandonment of the practice and for a "sensible brake" on vaccination on the grounds that there were twenty-seven known deaths (and probably many more which were not reported) among the 2,600,000 infants under one year old vaccinated over a ten-year period. He contends that immunization resulted in thirty cases of smallpox and thirty cases of encephalitis during the decade and that a degree of control can be obtained by strict policing of ports of entry. Others have pointed out that vaccinia shots in themselves can be contagious and might induce congenital disease; in one case a pregnant woman infected by her vaccinated eleven-month-old son, gave birth to an infected, badly damaged and dying child. A German who has entered the debate contends that immunization is best done at four months of age, because the baby still has some protective antibodies from his mother and now is in a position to manufacture his own. After four months, he argues, there is increasing risk of nerve damage. No expert has defended the practice of immunizing newborn babies. University of Michigan studies of children inoculated during their first seven months of life have shown failures to immunize between 39 and 50 per cent against polio and 35 per cent against whooping cough.

There is no serious challenge to the general custom of immunizing against common and serious diseases when allowance is made for extreme youth and other factors. Infectious diseases still are dangerous. In the case of smallpox, recent Indian figures show 37.4 per cent of the unvaccinated and only 1.8 per cent of the vaccinated who contract smallpox die of the disease. In 1962, smallpox suddenly struck 67 people in Great Britain, killing 26 of them. Some do argue, however, that the risk of all immunization procedures must be weighed against the real risks of the disease; when the former prove greater than the latter, immunization should be abandoned. Whether cancer and possibly other long-latent sequelae are among these risks is yet to be determined.

A few philosophical scientists view with distaste the prospects of someday finding vaccines which will cure conditions as mild as the common cold. The cold, by and large, forces the fatigued to rest and stimulates the natural powers of resistance, which in clearing up the cold, probably rid the system of an accumulation of many sub-clinical infections by viruses and germs. Those who regard efforts to immunize against or cure the common cold as meddlesome medicine feel that success in this field may invite infections of greater magnitude and leave the patient with a resistance impaired by disuse. A few hold that the widespread and indiscriminate use of antibiotics already has atrophied the mechanisms of disease resistance in a considerable part of the population.

Against these arguments, however, are the irrefutable facts that immunization has virtually wiped out a plethora of plagues which once decimated large populations, and that modern drugs have greatly expanded the human life span.

Back in the early 1940s a soft-spoken, sensitive and fiery Spanish-born scientist proclaimed his belief that at least some human cancers were caused by viruses—not special cancer viruses, just ordinary viruses. The scientist, Dr. Francisco Duran-Reynals of Yale University, stood virtually alone in his contentions. The few accomplished virologists who might have agreed with him were silent; his utterances represented heresy to the solid body of conventional science, and cancer virologists found it expedient to pursue their studies quietly and apologetically; not only was their line of investigation at stake but so were their jobs. Medicine was even more hostile; to physicians who knew viruses only as a scapegoat diagnosis ("must be a virus—lot of sickness around town") the idea of linking common viruses and cancer meant that cancer was catching, and this, they reasoned, would make pariahs of cancer patients. It did not help matters that a few notorious quacks professed to be curing virus-caused human cancers.

Dr. Duran-Reynals patiently and eloquently spelled out the mounting clues to his scientific audiences, who could not but agree with his facts but found no difficulty in disregarding his conclusions. The chain of evidence was growing rapidly with each passing year. Dr. Duran-Reynals' own ingenious experiments were setting the pace for the growing ranks of microbiologists, microscopists, biochemists, biophysicists, and geneticists who were turning up remarkable new leads to virus behavior in bacteria and plant and animal cells.

Dr. Duran-Reynals confronted his silent, apathetic, or hostile peers with the meager history of cancer viruses in animals, his own elegant experiments, and a rapidly rising tide of findings by his younger contemporaries in his lonely campaign to countenance a virus cause of human cancer. In his own laboratory he had shown that vaccinia, the cell-growth-stimulating virus of cowpox, acted in concert with trace amounts of chemical carcinogens to induce and accelerate cancers in mice and chicks; that a cell-destroying chicken cancer virus, *Rous sarcoma,* could leap species barriers to infect ducks and turkeys, sometimes gaining great virulence in its passage; that a virus often was infective only in newborn and very young animals; that some hormones, like estrogen, restrain the virus by building up mesenchyme, the body's inner tissues, and others, like cortisone, help the virus by tearing the tissues down; that the selfsame chicken virus can cause acute and lethal hemorrhagic disease or, latently and chronically, cancer. He isolated a "spreading factor" hyaluronidase, which seems to suppress protective barriers of the body, and hypothesized that cancers produced something similar to enable them to grow without restraint and spread through tissues.

Two years before his death from cancer, an unusual malignancy which paralyzed him completely for many months and which some felt might have been caused by one of his laboratory viruses, Dr. Duran-Reynals had the satisfaction of hearing one of science's leading figures validate some of his sentiments. Dr. Wendell M. Stanley, who crystallized the first virus in 1935 and won a Nobel prize for it, in 1956 told the Third National Cancer Conference:

> Basic biologic phenomena generally do not differ strikingly as one goes from one species to another, and I regard the fact, now proved beyond contention, that viruses can cause cancer in animals to be directly pertinent to the human cancer problem. Acceptance of the viral etiology of human cancer as a working hypothesis will involve a marked change in attitude on the part of many investigators, but this is necessary if the right approach and the right design of experimentation are to result. What we do depends in large measure upon what we think.

Dr. Stanley's words were prophetic in part at least; many of the most vociferous critics of Duran-Reynals and his virology allies became silent; cancer virologists shed their timidity and cancer virology received an unprecedented stimulus. It now became quite respectable to talk about cancer viruses; and cancer virologists, released from the bondage of pathologists and other skeptics and cynics, now were free to attack one another—which they do with great vigor.

Time, his widow, his students, his associates, and other virologists also tended to vindicate Dr. Francisco Duran-Reynals. His widow, Maria-Luisa, now carrying on his work at Albert Einstein College of Medicine, Yeshiva University, continued many of her husband's experiments and expanded on them. She established the doses and schedules under which vaccinia and a carcinogen trace produced a great variety of cancer in mice. She has shown that in mice previously immunized against vaccinia, the virus loses its ability to promote cancer development.

Many of Dr. Duran-Reynals' findings still stand as basic principles in cancer virology. They apply to many tumors in many species.

The chain of evidence connecting viruses with cancer has been established link by link since the turn of the century. At first the field for only a few inquiring—and in most cases disbelieving—minds, virology has become at this writing the focus of cancer research.

The first virus of any kind actually identified was demonstrated in tobacco mosaic disease by the Russian, D. Iwanoski, in 1892, and in 1897 by the Dutchman, Martinus Beijerinck, who infected healthy plants with cell-free filtrates from disease plants. In 1903, Amédée Borrel of France pointed out that pox viruses made cells proliferate and advanced the opinion that cancer might be caused by such viruses; and in 1908 the Danes, Wilhelm Ellerman and Olaf Bang, gave substance to the speculation by transmitting a fowl leukosis with fluids from the diseased chickens. Dr. Peyton Rous of Rockefeller Institute transmitted chicken sarcoma in 1911. And in 1932, Dr. Richard E. Shope, also of Rockefeller Institute, scratched the skin of a healthy cottontail rabbit and applied fluids from rabbit warts, which sometimes turn into cancers, and produced warts. Taken out of the cottontail and applied to domestic rabbits, the virus' cancer-causing virulence increased threefold. Dr. Shope showed that the behavior of a virus depended in large part on the host and on environment.

Since his undergraduate days at Harvard, Dr. C. C. Little had been breeding cancerous male mice to cancerous females and watching the inherited incidence of the disease mount ever higher. As president of the University of Maine and the University of Michigan, he continued his experiments. Then he became director of the Jackson Memorial Laboratory in Bar Harbor, Maine, where he gathered about him a staff of scholars interested in the genetics of cancer and other diseases in an unprecedented variety of inbred animals. Genetic susceptibility to various viruses soon became established as a prerequisite for infection.

Dr. John J. Bittner was not convinced that genetics was the entire answer to mouse breast cancer studied at Bar Harbor. He removed newborn mice from their cancer-susceptible mothers and had them nursed by foster mothers; very few of these developed breast cancer. A single nursing, he showed, was enough to foreordain a destiny of breast cancer. This phenomenon indicates that the virus for breast cancer is transmitted in the infected mother's milk. Dr. Bittner called whatever caused the cancers an "agent," not a virus.

Before he died in 1961, Dr. Bittner, then at the University of Minnesota, showed that there was a good deal more to this mouse breast cancer than the virus, or "agent," alone. Genes were involved; the agent brought breast cancer only to specific inbred strains. *Hormones* were important; unless the animals were bred, given estrogen, or caused to have a false pregnancy (by tickling the vagina), there was no breast cancer. Other factors also had to be met: *age*—the agent had to be received very early in life; *tem-*

perature—the warmer the laboratory, the less the mice ate and the lower the cancer incidence; *diet*—skimpy wartime rations reduced the cancer incidence; *housing*—crowding reduced cancer, and isolation increased it; *carcinogens*—low doses of X rays and chemical carcinogens increased the incidence; *exercise* reduced the incidence. Dr. Howard Andervont of the National Cancer Institute, who paced Dr. Bittner in many of his findings, was first to show that, in a sense, the Bittner agent could be venereal; male mice with the agent, themselves not having cancer, transmitted it in seminal fluid to their agent-free mates, who in turn infected female offspring (which developed cancer) and male offspring (which didn't, but which perpetuated the agent).

Dr. Joseph V. Beard of Duke University worked with a chicken virus of amazing carcinogenic prowess and growth—about 15 trillion viruses existed in a teaspoonful of blood from an infected fowl. Candidly contagious, it caused cancer of the blood, bone, or flesh. It now is so common that it kills something like 50 million chicks each year in the United States; one cannot be certain that any flock is free of it. Dr. Beard and his group showed that this virus somehow formed an enzyme which broke down a principal source of cell energy, the compound called adenosine triphosphate.

In quick succession, a single virus during the 1950s took on dozens of roles in as many animal cancers. It began when Dr. Ludwik Gross at the Bronx Veterans Administration Hospital in New York made an extract of leukemic tissue of AK mice—a strain which inherited leukemia. He injected the cell-free fluid into newborn mice of a leukemia-resistant strain, called C3H; and in three or four months the C3H mice developed cancer. Mice infected within sixteen hours of birth came down with leukemia; others infected from the second to tenth day of life developed cancer of the salivary glands which, in humans, swell in mumps. The virus not only was contagious but it also could be transmitted congenitally to embryos. The reports, like all reports of unexpected developments, were received with a good deal of skepticism until they were amply confirmed. Dr. Gross had opened a new door on virus behavior.

Drs. Sarah Stewart and Bernice Eddy, at the National Institutes of Health, repeated Dr. Gross's experiments. The results checked out—Dr. Gross had reported accurately that the mouse leukemia had yielded a virus which in other mice induced not only leukemia but a solid cancer as well. Drs. Stewart and Eddy grew the virus—and, they discovered, a hidden companion virus—in monkey kidney tissue and then passed it back to mice; this time they reaped a cancer whirlwind. The mice now developed twenty-four distinct kinds of cancer. When the souped-up companion virus was transmitted to hamsters, it produced still more cancers. The same happened in rats, rabbits, and guinea pigs. Laboratory workers wondered whether this rampaging virus had infected them. It had; blood tests showed the human handlers had produced antibodies against it. Dr. Robert J. Huebner of NIH, a few years later, investigated wild mice on Maryland farms and in Harlem tenements and found that they had been infected with the virus. In early 1963, the virus was found in mice in Japan—an American export. The virus is called polyoma, a Greek derivative meaning many tumors.

The lengthening series of reports indicating the vulnerability of the young—and particularly the newborn—to cancer viruses stirred speculation; is youth an indispensable factor in virus-caused cancer? Dr. Charlotte Friend of Sloan-Kettering Institute found an answer: not necessarily. She discovered a highly virulent leukemia virus which infected mice of either sex and at any age. It gave leukemia to mice which normally resisted the disease. Killed, the virus was an effective vaccine against this form of leukemia.

The big question, which remains unanswered at this writing, is: Do viruses cause human cancers?

Dr. Duran-Reynals with vaccina and Dr. Trentin with adenovirus showed that human viruses cause cancer—but only in animals.

Scientific proof that viruses do cause human cancers would entail procedures which meet the rigid requirements of Koch's postulate. This means that the virus would have to be (1) shown to be present in every case of the disease, (2) cultivated in pure culture, (3) made to produce the disease when removed from culture and inoculated into humans, and (4) recovered from the deliberately-infected humans and grown again in culture. The law does not permit this in humans.

Dr. Leon Dmochowski of the University of Texas M.D. Anderson Hospital has produced excellent electron micrographs of viruslike particles in many kinds of cancer cells—animal and human. In some cases, they appear only in the cells of cancerous animals and humans and not in the healthy cells. In other cases, he finds them concentrated in the cells of cancerous animals and sparse in the cells of cancer-susceptible animals who have not developed cancer. He and Dr. Gross have found suspicious particles in the milk of women and mice with breast cancer. Dr. Dmochowski's enormous picture library indicates that leukemia viruses undergo a process of maturation as well as proliferation; long virus cylinders apparently break into short rods, and these, during the active infectious process, seem to become doughnut-shaped. Some of the suspected cancer viruses closely resemble myxoviruses which cause mumps, influenza, and other common human diseases. Others come in scores of shapes and sizes and they inhabit many cell sites—cytoplasm, nucleus, nucleolus, and membrane. Despite this persuasive pictorial evidence, however, Dr. Dmochowski concedes that the case for viruses as a cause of human cancer is strictly circumstantial. The viruses are at the scene of the crime, but, under the legal principle of reasonable doubt, they could be inveterate innocent bystanders.

A good working model for a cancer virus is one of the simplest viruses of them all—the bacteriophage. The principles which scientists fifteen or twenty years ago discovered in these tiny phage particles still serve as a hypothetical basis for the existence of human cancer viruses. Almost every highly acclaimed development in cancer virology during the last decade of dizzying progress has had its prototype in phage.

The virus, or phage, which infects bacteria inhabiting the intestine of humans and animals, is the best studied of all viruses. It is the best studied because it is simple in structure and behavior and can be obtained everywhere.

A common colon or sewage bacteriophage is sperm-shaped; it has only a big head and a tail. It is composed of a small bit of DNA as its core, and the DNA is covered by a protein overcoat. It infects a bacterium with a sort of copulatory gesture—it backs up to the cell, inserts its tail into an enzyme-produced pore, and convulsively ejaculates the DNA into the cell. The protein overcoat is left outside the cell as no longer useful.

Just as the sperm DNA joins with ovum DNA in fertilization, so does phage DNA impregnate the bacterium. In effect, the phage DNA becomes part of the bacterium's genes. Dr. Salvator E. Luria of MIT has called phage DNA "infectious heredity."

Once inside the bacterium, the virus DNA may behave in any of many manners. Scientists have words which describe the virus, according to its deportment:

Virulent. This phage commandeers the cell's entire synthetic machinery and chemical resources and forces the cell to manufacture a few hundred phage within the next twenty to sixty minutes (the warmer the environment the quicker phage is manufactured); the new phage then burst from the shell of the cell and each is ready to infect a new cell.

Temperate. These phage DNA particles become part of the cell genes and, as such, live in amiable coexistence with the cell.

Transforming. These are temperate phage which endow the cell with new inheritable chemical and physical traits; some of these traits enable the cell to resist invasion by virulent viruses, to grow and divide at an accelerated rate, to produce poisons against their natural enemies, to perform new chemical and physiological feats like synthesizing new foods such as vitamins or amino acids, and generally, to lead a richer more independent life. Temperate and transforming phage DNA reproduce and divide as genes when the cell divides, a daughter phage DNA going to each daughter cell.

Lysogenic. This is temperate phage DNA which retains its prerogative to resign as genes, to become virulent and destroy, or to lyse the cell when stimulated by light, heat, or certain chemicals in the environment or another phage.

When one temperate phage has taken occupancy in a cell a second, dissimilar, phage may also try to enter. If the second succeeds, any of several things may happen: (1) the two may live harmoniously with each other and with the cell, each enriching the cell with its genelike powers; (2) one may suppress the other; (3) one or both may be incited to virulence, reproduce rapidly, and destroy the cell; or (4) they may blend and produce offspring phage, called recombinants, in which the genetic or viral qualities of both are incorporated.

Phage DNA has one other quality of exceptional note. It is called *transduction*. This means that it can stick to and remove some of the gene DNA of the first cell it infects and implant it in the second cell it infects.

Scientists have been concerned with only one aspect of transduction—the virus transport and addition of foreign DNA to the genes of a cell. It could be that the first phase of transduction—the deletion of DNA from the cell originally looted by the virus—holds implications of major magnitude in the cancer problem. In keeping with other terminology, this virus activity would be known as *reduction*—the virus's original victim cell loses some DNA. If the reduced cell survives, some of its genes will be missing. So will the antigens controlled by the missing genes. If a cell becomes malignant by virtue of the loss of DNA, this could explain why the victim seldom produces antibodies against the cancer cell (there are no antigen markers present). It would indicate, on the contrary, that the cancer cell with impunity can produce antibodies against normal cell antigens of the host. And it suggests that one approach to the conversion of the DNA-deficient cancer cell would be through the *transforming* principle—expose the cell to the specific DNA that it lacks in hope that it will take it up, incorporate it in its genes, and become normal again.

That the process of *reduction* may be an actuality in cancer is indicated in the finding by Dr. Stephanie H. Barch at Michigan State University. She injected some rabbits with normal frog kidney and others with a frog kidney cancer long considered virus-caused. Antibody comparisons showed that, instead of having extra virus antigens, the cancer lacked antigens present in normal kidney tissue.

Viruses generally are of many sizes, shapes, and modes of behavior. Of the viruses definitely identified as causing cancer, there is no distinctive physical or chemical feature that would set them in a special class; cancer viruses seem to differ from one another a great deal. The one thing they have in common is that they cause cancer.

Most virologists concede that more than seventy viruses cause certain cancers in chickens, ducks, guinea fowls, frogs, guinea pigs, hamsters, mastomys, mice, pheasants, pigeons, quail, rabbits, rats, salamanders, squirrels, and turkeys. Some plant tumors, too, are virus-caused. A few of the cancer viruses are known to be among the 250 or so which cause assorted noncancerous human diseases.

Viruses are composed essentially of DNA or RNA wearing an expendable protein coat. Some contain a touch of fat or carbohydrate, which may or may not be essential to their operations.

Dr. Seymour Cohen of the University of Pennsylvania a few years ago stirred profound excitement among virologists when he showed that one bacteriophage had a distinctly offbeat DNA; instead of the ordinary A-T and G-C nucleotide pairs, these viruses contained DNA comprised by A-T and G-HMC pairs. Hydroxymethyl cytosine (HMC) is an ugly-duckling version of cytosine. Similarly, Dr. Robert L. Sinsheimer of the California Institute of Technology created a stir when he discovered another freak—a dwarf phage whose DNA was single-stranded rather than double-stranded.

Not only is the more recent knowledge of viruses being modified, corrected, amended, or discarded a year or two after it has become textbook truth, but some of the oldest principles seem to be tottering.

Viruses are said to be replicated inside cells. This means that cells somehow make replicas, or copies, of the original invading virus. Viruses, according to this fundamental principle, do not reproduce; reproduction is the province of cells and organisms. Actually, it now appears that the essential process of plant and animal reproduction is one of replication; the DNA in the fertilized egg is a copy of the composite DNA of both parents, and so is the DNA in every cell in the body a replica of it. It is simpler and perhaps more factual to say that both viruses and higher life forms reproduce—or replicate, if one prefers.

Even the virus' need for a cell in which to reproduce now can be questioned. Dr. Timothy Crocker and associates at the University of California Medical Center recently have made viruses multiply in tiny fragments of cytoplasm which completely lack cell nuclei and cell DNA. The virus in this case is the one which causes psittacosis in birds and appears to contain, of all things, both DNA and RNA.

An open mind and a decent degree of skepticism are important in following the fast-moving and fabulous events taking place in the field of virology.

Susceptibility is a word used to explain a host of major phenomena in biology and medicine. Basically, it means merely whether or not one gets sick. A few scientists now are trying to explain in precise terms the word "susceptibility." A great many questions will be answered if and when chemical equations ever replace this word.

Why does a single virus infect one, two or three species and not others? Why will a virus, infecting every member of the family, kill one, paralyze a second, leave a third with vague and transient joint aches, and permit the fourth to suffer no noticeable symptoms? Why does polio paralyze or kill one and leave 999 others who are infected with minor symptoms at most? Assuming that a common virus can cause human cancer, why would it give one man only a runny nose, another diarrhea, and a third a long, lingering and lethal sickness?

It is not enough to say that the more unfortunate were rundown—or particularly susceptible.

The late Dr. Jerome T. Syverton of the University of Minnesota once speculated that if you strip the protein coat off any virus, its nucleic acid might possibly infect the cells of just about any species. (Some carcinogens —phenols in particular—do destroy protein, incidentally.) He said that polio virus destroys human and monkey cells because the virus protein coat was so (genetically) designed that it could attach to the complementary gene-designed (lipoprotein) fat and protein structures which exist only on the surface of human and monkey cells. Species lacking these very special cell moorings for the virus protein are beyond attachment and attack. This could explain species and genetic susceptibility, at least to polio virus.

Dr. Theodore T. Puck of the University of Colorado Medical School showed that a sewage bacterium and the phage that normally infects it could exist indefinitely in distilled water without infection—or, indeed, without contact of any kind. They repel each other. The skin of the bacterium and the protein coat of the phage are predominantly charged with negative carboxyl groups (each surface also contains positively charged amino groups) and consequently thrust each other away. When calcium ions, with a double positive charge, were added to the water, the phage and cell came together with the speed of molecular collision and attached at their points of opposite electrostatic charge—negative to positive, and vice versa. In fifteen seconds the phage could still be washed off the cell surface, but the disinfected bacterium no longer was able to reproduce. When the phage entered the cell, it reproduced, and in twenty minutes several hundred new bacterial viruses emerged from the hollow cell corpse.

It is now apparent that virus infection is not a simple matter of a virus entering a cell and having its way with it. Many other factors determine the course of the infection, including prior infection by another virus, later infection by another virus, concurrent infection by a bacterium, the presence of certain toxic chemicals, the nutrition of the cell, and such physical factors as light and heat. Dr. Renato Dulbecco of the California Institute of Technology estimates that only one in every half-billion polyoma viruses injected actually infects a cell.

One of the strangest phenomena has been reported by Dr. Frank Fenner of Canberra—the resuscitation of a dead virus. In this case rabbits were injected with a heat-killed myxoma virus. If the rabbits were infected simultaneously with fibroma virus, which causes another type of tumor, the dead myxoma viruses repaired themselves, possibly by combining with parts of the fibroma viruses and they induced their typical myxoma tumors.

Dr. John E. Hotchin of the New York State Department of Health has found that the virus for lymphatic choriomeningitis usually will observe a good-neighbor policy while inside a brain cell on those rare occasions when the virus infects humans; the host usually is without disease symptoms. Injected into newborn mice, the virus multiplies but without apparent injury to the host, whose blood may be teeming with virus. However, if the virus is injected into a mouse already infected with the bacterium *Eperythrozoon coccoides,* the virus infection spreads like wild-fire and rapidly destroys the animal. If chronically virus-infected mice are later given an acute infection with the bacterium, both infections subside.

Dr. Neal B. Groman at the University of Washington in the early 1950s worked with Corynebacterium diphtheriae as a model of cell and virus interrelationships. As the name suggests, this bacterium causes diphtheria in humans. In its natural uninfected state, Dr. Groman demon-strated, the bacterium does no apparent harm to the host. When the bacterium is infected with a phage, however, it produces a toxin which brings on the symptoms of disease in humans. When the bacterium is infected with a second phage, the first infecting phage is suppressed, the toxin no longer is produced, and the host's disease symptoms subside. Dr. Groman showed that environmental temperature exerts a powerful influence in reproduction of both the bacterium and its poison-producing phage; at high fever temperatures, both were suppressed. The latter find-ing invites speculation on the advisability of the common medical practice of promptly reducing the patient's temperature—a symptom which may be more closely related to healing than infection. Dr. Groman found that the presence of ordinary unsaturated fatty acids prevented viruses from infecting cells.

A roughly similar pattern of virus teamwork exists in chicken cancers.

Dr. Harry Rubin of the University of California has reported two different and interesting reactions between a pair of closely related RNA chicken cancer viruses. One of the viruses is *Rous sarcoma,* or RSV, which causes either acute hermorrhagic disease in young chickens or, later in life, cancer of connective tissue. The other is the highly contagious leukosis virus, which, in various forms, causes cancer of the bone, blood, viscera, eye, and nerve tissue.

Leukosis virus can infect both ova and cells of the testes, although possibly not mature sperm. The maternal virus remains inside the egg and infects the young with leukoses congenitally.

Dr. Rubin first found that chick embryonic tissue already infected with leukosis virus was resistant to RS virus. He then discovered that when young RS virus infected an otherwise healthy cell, the virus transformed the cell into a cancer cell. Alone in the cell, however, RS virus could not reproduce. If at any time leukosis virus were added to the RS-infected cell, the RS virus began to reproduce. Evidently it took the help of leukosis virus for RS virus to reproduce.

Dr. Saul Kit of Baylor University showed how a minuscule amount of vaccinia virus DNA subverts the enormous supplies of cell DNA. The vaccinia virus, which is composed of only about 20 DNA molecules, enters a cell and unobtrusively takes residence in the cytoplasm—far distant from the 300,000 DNA molecules which comprise the cell's genes. For six or eight hours following infection, both the virus and the cell manufacture DNA; at this time the virus seems to have commandeered all available raw materials, and the cell RNA and DNA synthesizing machine shuts down. Between twelve and eighteen hours after infection, from 100 to 1,000 vaccinia viruses emerge from the pillaged cell.

A group working with Dr. Chester Southam at Sloan-Kettering Institute demonstrated that two viruses, themselves unable to cause cancer, doubled the potency of a chemical carcinogen. The viruses were herpes simplex, which causes cold sore, and nerve-attacking West Nile virus.

Somewhere in the welter of these seemingly unrelated, often contradictory, always confusing observations, there must be a thread of logic. Nature is much too orderly and the laws of cause and effect too rigid to permit willy-nilly virus behavior.

If the profound principles involved can be fathomed, man stands to gain a great deal. He can stop worrying about innocuous viruses and concentrate on what seems to be a mounting menace by harmful viruses. In 1950 only twenty-one human viral diseases were recognized; in a short dozen years the number has exceeded 200.

An urgent problem in virology is to determine whether man is susceptible to animal cancer viruses and, if so, how the virus is transmitted. With this knowledge, it might be possible to ward off some human cancers.

Those most exposed to animal viruses are the scientists who work with them. There is only the barest hint that it may be possible to trace a cancer in a scientist to one of his animal cancer viruses; Dr. Melnick has found that the antigen, or chemical marker, on the SV-40 virus is also carried by the cell it makes malignant; with fluorescent antibodies, the presence of an otherwise-undetectable virus can be discovered.

A few scientists have speculated that specific cases of human cancer might have developed because of infection with animal viruses. At this time, there is only the most tenuous evidence to support their sobering hypotheses.

Dr. Olive Stull Davis of Purdue University, after ten years of work with a virus which causes highly malignant lymphoid cancers in chickens, came down with lymphosarcoma in 1954. Under the microscope, her tumors closely resembled those of the chickens, which were virus-caused. She worked daily with the chicken cancers, handling them and the virus-loaded blood with hands that often carried scratches and open cuts. The effect, she feels, was tantamount to repeated inoculation with the virus. With her own cancer under reasonably good control with periodic treatment by supervoltage radiation, she has spent the past ten years trying to determine whether the chicken viruses can be transmitted to other animal species. The results so far are negative.

One group of scientists at the University of Minnesota noted that the children of four veterinarians in the Minneapolis area developed leukemia over a short time. Because the veterinarians handled both chickens and cows with leukemialike cancers, the Minnesota group have begun an investigation into the health of veterinarians' children. Another group at the University of Nebraska has reported finding an inordinate number of cases of human leukemia and lymphoma—about 200 among a population of 109,000 in five years—in a rural area of south-central Nebraska. The fact that there is a fowl and animal leukosis in the area has roused suspicions.

At this writing, the possibility of animal cancer viruses causing human cancer remains in the realm of pure speculation. It is known that about forty bacterial, viral, fungal, and protozoon diseases (zoonoses) are transmitted from animals to man: cancer is not among them. Dr. Neville Stanley of Australia has recently discovered a type of virus, reovirus, known to infect an enormous number of plant and animal species and man (the only animals so far found to be free of reovirus infection are whales). But, though reovirus resembles in some respects a plant tumor virus and can be transmitted from animals to man and probably vice versa, it has so far failed to produce tumors in any species.

Though there is now ample evidence that human viruses can play a decisive role in animal cancers, there still is no proof that human viruses cause human cancers. Dr. Robert G. Ravdin of the University of Pennsylvania showed that humans reject human cultured cells presumably made malignant with a human virus. He injected into healthy people and advanced cancer patients human normal cells which Dr. Koprowski had infected with adenovirus. The cells looked and behaved like cancer cells. But, after growing anywhere from seven to twelve days in the host, they died out completely. They were extinguished by natural resistance to disease.

Dr. Ludwik Gross of the Bronx VA Hospital has reported finding large particles in the milk of 80 or 90 per cent of young healthy nursing mothers with a family history of cancer. Similar particles were found in about 40 per cent of women without a family history of cancer. While the scientist feels that these particles might represent cancer viruses (as they seem to in inbred strains of mice highly susceptible to breast cancer and leukemia), the prevailing medical opinion is strongly in favor of these mothers nursing their children. Evidence of the benefits of breast feeding is strong. Evidence of a human cancer virus in milk remains highly speculative.

Particles, by themselves, do not necessarily indicate a cancer hazard. This is true even though the particles resemble a cancer virus. The common wart virus, which has infected most humans at one time or another, is almost identical in shape and size with the highly virulent polyoma virus, SV-40 and the Shope rabbit wart-and-cancer virus. Under several thousand magnifications of the electron microscope, the four viruses, which resemble a twenty-sided ball with forty-two spikes, look very much alike. They are also very similar in their chemical composition and behavior under various conditions. Human wart virus is not regarded as a cancer agent.

There is no evidence that cancer can be transmitted directly from one person to another. On the contrary, statistics indicate that cancers—and cancer viruses, if they exist in humans—select their victims by means other than contact. Healthy babies have been born to women with cancer. There is only one instance—and it is considered doubtful—in which a cancerous baby was reported born to a mother bearing a solid cancer. There is no known reason to avoid contact with cancer patients.

Animal studies show that cancer viruses are transmitted in many ways. The chicken leukosis virus, for instance, not only moves directly from the mother hen's blood and tissues into the egg and embryo, but it appears to be spread by direct contact between fowl, through the air, in water, in urine and droppings, and probably in many other ways, including seminal fluids. Some viruses are transported by a vector—often another species. One plant tumor virus is not infective unless it is first carried and treated by a leafhopper; another is delivered to the plant by bacteria. The vector—itself uninfected and unaffected—can add greatly to the virulence of a virus.

Viruses, like cells, mutate under the influence of chemicals, rays, and other physical agents. The mutation may prove lethal, or it may increase their virulence.

Among the happier phenomena of virus studies is the fact that viruses occasionally attack and destroy cancer cells. Some of them do this with great efficiency and selectivity.

Anticancer viruses have been reported since 1922, when a Rumanian bacteriologist named Constantin Levaditi disclosed that a neurovaccinia virus had multiplied well in skin cancers of both rats and mice. Since then, with increasing frequency, scientists in many laboratories have observed such incidents as these:

UNIVERSITY OF MINNESOTA—Nine of 11 viruses tested against a standard human cancer, HeLa, grown in culture destroyed the cancer cells. Among the tumor-destroying viruses were herpes simplex (cold sore), pseudorabies, vaccinia, polio, and five kinds of encephalitis. In this series only two viruses—Japanese B and St. Louis encephalitis—failed to attack the cancer.

HAHNEMANN MEDICAL COLLEGE—Influenza virus and vaccinia, with almost equal facility, destroyed ascites tumor cells in mice— within twenty-four hours virtually all cancer cells were dead. Within another twenty-four to seventy-two hours, however, the mice also were dead—of toxins unknown, probably in the decaying cancer cells.

UNIVERSITY OF MIAMI—An influenza-A-type virus injected into chick eggs or into the wings of young chicks blocked *Rous sarcoma* virus.

UNIVERSITY OF UTAH—A virus which makes flies susceptible to asphyxiation by carbon dioxide and which is passed from mother to offspring in the egg prevented fruit flies from developing tumors to which they were hereditarily susceptible.

JOHNS HOPKINS UNIVERSITY—Polio and several nerve-attacking viruses destroyed various cancer cultures selectively, without damage to normal adult cells. One of the viruses, however, attacked young normal cells (fibroblasts) as readily as it did cancer cells.

Drs. Chester M. Southam and Alice E. Moore at Sloan-Kettering Institute tested many viruses against mouse tumors including six which normally are transported by insects and spiders and which infect man and monkey. Three of the six destroyed mouse ascites tumor cells— which are suspended in body fluid—but had no effect on solid cancers. Following extensive animal testing, Dr. Southam treated fifty-seven patients who had hopelessly advanced cancer with a dozen different viruses, including many nerve destroying ones, mumps, and vaccinia. While in five cases the viruses appeared to destroy tumors, the patients were not helped to any degree. Two of the patients appeared to develop liver infections.

Viruses still are being used to treat experimental cancers in animals. At this time, however, there is little hope that they will prove useful against cancers in humans. Nevertheless, there is always the possibility that some small observation in some laboratory will suggest a new way to make viruses attack human cancer.

One of the fringe benefits of cancer research appears to be the development, at long last, of antiviral drugs. A few of the preparations cleverly concocted by biochemists to block nucleic-acid synthesis in cancer cells are showing promise of overcoming virus infections in animals and man. Some of them which, by virtue of their high toxicity or lack of anticancer effect, proved disappointing in cancer tests are selectively destroying viruses with pinpoint accuracy. The results have dispelled the belief that effective antivirus drugs never would be found.

The most promising antivirals so far discovered are analogues—counterfeit copies—of nucleic acid segments. The addition of a chlorine, bromine, iodine, or fluorine atom to A, T, G, C, or U molecules in many cases has proven much more lethal to viruses than to normal or cancer cells. The subtraction or transposition of other atoms within the natural molecules sometimes has similar effect. In a few cases even the administration of a natural nucleic acid segment seems to have had strong antiviral action; it may enable the cell to overcome the virus effect and fight back.

Dr. Herbert E. Kaufman at the University of Florida seems to be controlling, and possibly curing, a severe and blinding keratitis of the human eye caused by the cold-sore, or herpes simplex, virus. The drug used is IDU (5-iodo-2′-deoxyuridine), a counterfeit of a uracil derivative. No bad side effects accompany the treatment. Even advanced cases have cleared up under vigorous treatment with this drug. Designed originally by Dr. Arnold D. Welch and associates at Yale University, for leukemia, IDU proved of negligible value against any cancer, but did destroy smallpox viruses and chickenpox viruses in culture.

The most glittering prospects of antiviral drugs are now emerging from test-tube and animal experiments. Among the many leads now coming out of scores of laboratories are these samples:

Eight compounds (including mitomycin C, TEM, thioguanine and estradiol) show a completely inhibitory effect against the Friend mouse leukemia virus.

Thiosemicarbazones destroy several influenza strains and Newcastle virus by chelating, or clawing, metals (like copper, zinc, or cobalt) out of their nucleoprotein—some of them have shown strong anticancer activity.

Guanadine, used early or late, inhibits polio virus development in kidney cultures.

Benzimidazole preparations have suppressed such enteroviruses as polio and Coxsackie.

A Du Pont product, amantadine hydrochloride, has suppressed Asian flu virus and shows promise against other viruses;

The enzyme, trypsin, has destroyed the infectivity of mumps and rapidly wiped out three strains of herpes simplex; other enzymes—including papain, carboxypeptidase and RNase—have reduced the infectivity of Eastern equine encephalitis.

Other agents reported active against various viruses in tissue culture and animal tissues include 5-BDU, 5 FDU, 5-FU, B-phenylserine, aminopterin, heparin, sodium dextran sulfate, fungus-synthesized giberellic acid (which prevents plant stunting caused by viruses), acridine dyes (which can be labeled with tritium) and many others. Soviet scientists have stated that plain potassium permanganate acts against polio virus both in test tubes and in the digestive tract.

Physical factors, such as ultraviolet light, so far have proved unpredictable. While they seem to inactivate one virus, they may bring another— a dead one—back to life.

Beyond this, rapid strides are being made in understanding the vast field of immunity—natural resistance to disease. Some of the basic findings in this area already are being applied to the experimental treatment of many diseases, including cancer.

There is a dark side to the virus picture. With somewhere between 40 and 70 million Americans having been inoculated with SV-40, with almost everyone in the Soviet Union having received SV-40 in the live oral vaccine, and with many millions in other countries having been exposed, a sobering phase of science has come to light. The durability of the viruses in infected African monkeys (the virus has been recovered from monkey kidney more than one year after infection) is not a hopeful sign for humans. There has been a rise of other viruses—in some areas, for example, Coxsackie virus has begun to replace polio as a rising scourge among children and adults.

We live in an atmosphere loaded with viruses—bad, inconsequential, and good. Most of them we cannot always avoid. Our hope is to understand them and to learn to live with them and to use them intelligently.

Broad new vistas of preventing and treating virus disease are opening; if damage has been done in the recent rush of events and enthusiasm in public health, it may prove possible to undo at least some of it.

Some of the secrets of viruses are rapidly coming to light. The first cancer virus—and, indeed, the first DNA virus of any kind—has been crystallized. Dr. William T. Murakami of Brandeis has obtained polyoma in pure form. The virus—which is 90 per cent protein and 10 per cent DNA—yields two types of particles: a dense fraction containing almost all the highly infectious DNA and another particle containing little DNA. Both have the same antigens and attract the same antibodies.

A finding of great potential has been made by Dr. Maurice Green of St. Louis University. He obtained several of the twenty-eight known types of adenovirus and tried to determine whether there was any difference between those which cause cancers in hamsters and those which do not.

He found several important differences: the cancer-causing viruses contained 10 per cent less DNA than the others (11.6 per cent DNA and 88.4 per cent protein, as against 13 per cent DNA and 87 per cent protein); the cancer-causing viruses weighed 10 per cent less than the others. Whereas normal mammalian cell DNA contains 42–44 per cent G-C, and adenoviruses which do not cause cancer contain 56–57 per cent G-C, the cancer-causing adenovirus DNA contain 48–49 per cent G-C. Two other cancer-causing viruses—polyoma of mice and rabbit wart virus —had a G-C content resembling that of the cancer-inducing adenoviruses.

The tools that now have been developed promise to reveal many other virus secrets in the near future. They will disclose how a tiny bit of viral RNA can cause tumors and leukemia in chickens and rodents and polio in man and how viral DNA, the equivalent of a few genes or possible one-millionth of the cell's DNA, can bring solid cancers to animals and warts to man.

Research soon may show how viruses come into existence in the first place—whether there is such a thing as a *de novo* virus. Scientists at Oak Ridge have produced myeloid leukemia in mice with radiation, and with filtrates from the leukemia have induced the disease in a shorter time than radiation did. They feel that the radiation may have sensitized the original mouse to a virus in its environment, rather than rouse a latent virus. Meanwhile, other scientists at Stanford Research Institute have induced breast cancer in rats by feeding them the chemical DMBA. Filtrates from these tumors also induced breast cancer when injected into other rats. These results make one wonder whether the agents—radiation in one case, DMBA in the other—have not somehow brought about the formation in affected cells of a strange bit of RNA or DNA which, by itself or after synthesizing a protein coat for itself, became a virus—a *de novo* virus, a "make-your-own" virus, a "do-it-yourself" virus.

Some of the findings have implications for controlling cancer—possibly human cancer. Dr. Eddy has been able to prevent hamster cancers induced by either SV-40 or adenovirus 12. She discovered that if, during the latent period, she gave the animals whopping doses of the same virus (two and a half times the cancer-inducing dose twice a week for about twelve weeks), relatively few of the hamsters came down with cancer. The optimal time for the preventive doses was one-quarter through the (70–100-day) latent period.

If Dr. Eddy's treatment works in animals, it might conceivably work in humans shown to be infected by the same cancer-causing viruses, SV-40, and adenoviruses.

CHAPTER 20

IMMUNITY

Late in the thirteenth century a sick young Italian priest had a dream. He dreamed that his cancerous leg, which was to be amputated in the morning, had become well. When he awakened, the cancer had healed. He did not have the operation, and he lived in good health until 1345, when at the age of eighty he died of old age. He became St. Peregrine, the "Cancer Saint." More than three hundred cures of cancer and other serious diseases are attributed to prayers for his intercession.

In 1935, Sister Gertrude Kortzendorfer, an aging Sister of Charity who administered a New Orleans mental hospital, was surgically explored and diagnosed as having an inoperable cancer of the pancreas, which is 100 per cent fatal. Her sister nuns prayed to Mother Seaton, the now-beatified founder of the Sisters of Charity. Sister Gertrude became well suddenly. She died seven years later of a pulmonary embolism, and autopsy showed no trace of cancer.

The physicians and a pathologist who investigated the case were astounded. They had no explanation for it.

In 1952, four-year-old Ann O'Neill, the daughter of a Baltimore stone worker, was diagnosed as having acute lymphatic leukemia. She was given the standard treatments, had a mild and fleeting remission, and seemed to be on the verge of death when the nuns at Baltimore's St. Agnes Hospital prayed to Mother Seaton. There was a dramatic change for the better. The little girl became well and, at this writing in 1963, is without evidence of leukemia.

In the O'Neill case there is a reasonable explanation—chickenpox. Even as the nuns prayed for the tot, the massive, ugly sores of leukemia were joined by the tiny red pocks of the common childhood disease. Three days later Ann's condition improved remarkably: both the chicken pox and cancer cleared, and two weeks later she was in a state of complete remission which persisted through the years.

While some call these phenomena miracles, the medical profession knows them as spontaneous remissions, or spontaneous regressions. They are regarded as extremely rare; one rough estimate is that they occur once in every 80,000 cases of cancer. The estimate, however, may understate the frequency with which these blessed events occur; many physicians who have treated a good many cancer cases can recall witnessing at least one spontaneous remission, usually unreported in the medical literature.

Drs. Warren H. Cole and Tilden C. Everson of the University of Illinois a few years ago began collecting data on the spontaneous regression of cancer. Sundry medical journals had carried accounts of many hundreds of such cases since 1900. After weeding out those in which the diagnosis was not definitely confirmed microscopically, those lost to follow-up and the easily curable cancers, about 150 well-documented spontaneous regressions remained. Not all of them were permanent; in some cases the cancers returned after long remissions and killed the patients. Many of them, however, endured until death from other causes. The cases of spontaneous regression accepted by Drs. Cole and Everson include hypernephroma (30); neuroblastoma (29); choriocarcinoma (15); malignant melanoma (15); soft tissue sarcoma (10); and cancers of the bladder (10), bone (10), colon and rectum (6), breast (5), uterus (5), ovary (4), teratoma (3), stomach (3), oral cavity (2), unknown sites (2), and (1 each) lung, larynx, pancreas, and thyroid.

Scientists feel certain that there is an excellent biological reason for each spontaneous remission and that the answer lies in the field of immunity. Immunity is that majestic body chemical process by which each living thing defeats the diseases which would destroy it. There are many kinds, degrees, and phases of immunity, including some which themselves destroy the host; researchers only now are learning about them. Scholars in the field are convinced that when normal immune processes are understood, cancer will cease to be a major cause of death.

Evidence that immunity plays a role in cancer is abundant. These are examples:

Patient A has his original tumor removed, but his system is shot through with metastases and his blood contains millions of cancer cells. Following the surgery, he becomes well and remains well for years.

Patient B has a small, seemingly localized tumor and no detectable cancer cells in the bloodstream. Following surgical removal or radiation destruction of the original tumor, cancer colonies arise in various tissues

and kill him. The hidden metastases may flare up at once or remain quiescent for twenty years or longer.

Patient C has his original cancer removed, but metastases remain. His
cancer is ground up into a vaccine and injected under his skin. He responds
with the typical inflammatory reaction to the vaccine; the metastases
shrivel up and disappear for the time being.

Patient D has a condition identical with that of C. He has no good reaction to the vaccine. If the vaccine is composed of live cancer cells—
his own or another's—they may grow and, temporarily at least, form a new
tumor. He is not long for this world.

Countless factors influence immunity—or natural resistance—to cancer.
They are around us and inside us and include physical and emotional
stress, hormones, diet, exposure to viruses and microbes, toxins, fatigue,
allergies, genes, resistance to other diseases, the soundness of many
organs, and the ability of various cells to produce tens of thousands of
chemicals. Dr. Bernard Roizman of Johns Hopkins has noted that the
cold-sore virus, which is latent in most people, is triggered into action by
many means—heat, ultraviolet light, a run-down condition, or trauma. Its
eruptions have been both induced and suppressed by psychotherapy.

Proteins and many other molecules are produced under the direction
of genes. Individuals with similar genes produce similar proteins. Individuals belonging to different strains and species produce different proteins.

When strange proteins from another strain or species enter an individual,
the system produces other proteins, called antibodies, which neutralize
them.

When the strange protein molecules are on the surface of an infecting
virus or bacterium, the antibodies are attracted to the strange molecules
and destroy the virus or organism bearing them. The strange molecules
are called antigens.

The greatest conceivable achievement in cancer research might be to
find and synthesize an antigen—a strange molecule—which is common
to all cancers but not produced by normal humans. If a common antigen
were found, cancer's age-old threat to mankind would recede. The antigen
could be used as the basis for a vaccine to prevent and probably cure
cancer.

Polio epidemics have been reduced to the vanishing point because
polio viruses contain antigens, which have been used as a vaccine. The
antigens cause inoculated humans to produce preventive antibodies which
attack polios viruses the moment they enter the system. Other vaccines
have been made. They contain antigens from the viruses of smallpox,
rabies, and measles and the cellular organisms of anthrax, cholera,

typhoid, and paratyphoid, whooping cough, and many other sources of disease. Some vaccines are used to treat as well as prevent disease.

In some cases, vaccines can be injected into animals, like cows or horses, and the animals will produce antibodies against the antigens and the organisms carrying them. The antibody-loaded blood serum of these immunized animals can be injected, as antiserum, into sick humans, and the animal antibodies will then attack the disease-causing virus or organism in the humans. Antiserum, for instance, has saved the lives of people whose wounds became infected with the tetanus organism; the antibodies in the immunized horse serum attack the antigens on the tetanus organisms and destroy the organisms.

The big hope is that if a cancer antigen exists and can be isolated and produced in sufficient quantity, cancer can be controlled as infections are. Even now animals can be protected with vaccines against cancer viruses, and they can be vaccinated successfully with live, weakened or irradiated cancer cells. But these measures protect only against the specific cancer virus or transplant being tested.

Is there a common cancer antigen?

Five widely scattered scientists or groups—in Tokyo, Moscow, Houston, New York and Stockholm—have reported finding antigens which appear to be common, not only to all human cancers they have examined, but to animal cancers as well. Many others have reported finding antigens which are tumor-specific; that is, they exist in a certain kind or class of cancer and not others. A few scientists have reported finding antigens in every animal and human cancer examined; but, they said, each antigen was specific for the tumor that yielded it. No two tumors had the same cancer antigen.

The discouraging thing about the reported common cancer antigens is that each investigator has described a different kind of antigenic molecule. If all the reports turn out to be correct, it would mean that cancers contain not one but several common antigens, a happy circumstance. Most investigators in the field, including those who have faith in the existence of specific antigens in specific cancers, are extremely skeptical of reports of any antigen common to all cancers.

An antigen, the molecule which marks its virus or bacterial carrier as foreign, can be flamboyant or subtle. Its strangeness can be reflected by a completely eccentric molecule, a displaced atom, or a combination of atomic groupings. In the molecular world, an antigen stands out as an ethnic stranger, its foreignness as marked as skin color, hair texture, nose shape, eye slant, language, accent, and any one or combination of ethnic characteristics which distinguish humans.

To be subject to attack by antibodies produced by native systems, the antigen must be a large molecule. The enormous protein molecules are antigenic to a foreign system. So are naked nucleic acids, the large sugar clumps called polysaccharides and fat (lipid) molecules.

Small molecules, when naked and alone, escape antibody attention. However, they become antigenic and subject to antibody attack when they attach to the surface of a large molecule, such as a protein. One can induce an antibody reaction against small molecules by combining them with native proteins and using the combination as a vaccine. In an antigenic combination, the small molecule, which has become an atomic grouping on a large molecule, is called a hapten; it has become as conspicuous as a bump on a log.

Antigens are made under the direction of nucleic acids—the DNA and RNA in cells and the DNA or RNA of viruses. The number of various combinations of antigens in life is astronomical. Dr. Lawrence Levine of Brandeis University has estimated that 10^{200} (1 followed by 200 zeros) combinations of DNA exist in 10^7 (10,000,000) species. Antibody reactions are so specific that in the laboratory they will show the presence of one antigenic, or foreign, molecule among 10^{12} (1,000,000,000,000, or one trillion) native molecules. Dr. Nathan Kaplan of Brandeis has found antibody detection of antigens so sensitive that he has been able to trace the subtle changes wrought in enzymes over a billion years of evolution.

Antigenic differences exist between humans. Usually they are subtle. Some of them are pronounced. In many cases, the slighter the chemical difference from native compounds, the more troublesome the antigen can be. Some people have genes which result in the production of an Rh protein antigen on red blood cells; if the offspring of an Rh-positive father and Rh-negative mother is Rh-positive, there is a risk of maternal antibodies attacking the embryo's red cells and killing the unborn baby. Two other common blood protein antigens are called A and B, and certain chemical incompatibilities exist between A and B people and also between them and O people, who have neither the A nor the B antigen. The injection of an antigen sensitizes the person lacking it to that antigen, and on the second exposure the antigen-antibody reaction may be violent; an A or O person receiving a second transfusion of B blood, for instance, may go into shock. A few cases of infertility between A and B, A and O, and B and O couples have been traced to antigenic differences; evidently the female produces antibodies which destroy the incompatible sperm before fertilization can take place. Humans have many other antigens—studies at Roswell Park have shown that white blood cells contain unsuspected antigens. This discovery suggests that an epidemiological survey of prior transfusions given patients with various diseases might prove fruitful. (Could cancer and various other cell-"tolerance" conditions have been caused by the transfusions?)

Different disease causers can carry common antigens. The virus of smallpox and the virus of cowpox, for instance, each have an identical protein which is foreign to the human system. For this reason it is possible to vaccinate humans with the mild cowpox virus and have it protect against the virulent smallpox virus.

It is generally supposed that in order to incite antibody attack, the antigen must be exposed. A virus floating free in the sensitized blood would be attacked by antibodies, but a virus nucleic acid hiding inside a cell, with its DNA blended with gene DNA or its RNA blended with the cell's protein-manufacturing RNA, would be safe. Antibodies, it is believed, do not violate the sanctity of the cell any more than police enter a home without a writ permitting search and seizure. A hapten also is safe from antibody attack if it is inside a rolled-up protein molecule ball, rather than on the surface. This is, and for a long time has been, the generally accepted concept of antigenicity and antibody attack; it may or may not be correct.

Dr. Levine and a Rutgers group headed by Drs. Werner Braun and Otto Plescia have shown that foreign or chemically disturbed DNA is antigenic when it is naked outside the cell. Dr. Helene W. Toolan of SKI found microsomes the most antigenic structure of the cancer cell. Their evidence gives no hint, however, that antibodies will enter the cell to attack a foreign DNA or microsome.

These lines of research are intimately connected with the cancer problem. If antibodies could be induced to enter cells and attack strange DNA, they could destroy DNA-different cancer cells with great selectivity.

If antibodies cannot enter a cell, what hope is there for the immunological approach to cancer—even though it should turn out that cancer is virus-caused?

Research on viruses which infect bacteria has lit a very lively hope that virus-caused diseases, including virus-caused cancers, may be subjected to vigorous antibody assault. Dr. Seymour S. Cohen of the University of Pennsylvania has made two critical discoveries in this regard: (1) at least some viral DNA contains a bizarre DNA segment (hydroxymethyl cytosine instead of the normal cytosine) which sets it apart from all normal cell DNA, and (2) while the strange viral DNA inside the cell may be sheltered from antibody attack, it produces at least 30 different antigenic proteins, any one of which on reaching the cell surface would mark the cell as diseased and subject it to antibody destruction.

Dr. Cohen's research on bacterial cells may apply quite directly to cancer research. One of the bacterial virus-produced proteins, for instance, is an enzyme which exists in great abundance in the animal and human leukemic cell and which protects the leukemic cell from destruction by antivitamin drugs. The enzyme is dihydrofolate reductase. It is conceivable that vaccines or antisera might be pitted against a leukemia-specific version of this enzyme.

Dr. Lev A. Zilber of the Gamaleya Institute of Epidemiology and Microbiology, Moscow, has devised a brilliant technique for the detection of cancer antigens. It has had great impact on worldwide cancer immunology. In technical terms, he sensitizes guinea pigs with an acid protein fraction of tumor tissue at pH 4.5, desensitizes the animals three or four weeks later with similar fractions from normal tissue, and then injects the tumor fraction into the animals. If the injection sends the (cancer-sensitized) animals into shock, it is regarded as containing a tumor-specific antigen. Under this test, many tumors of various animal species and of humans have shown they contain one or more antigens not present in normal tissues.

"Much is still obscure," Dr. Zilber has written. "And yet there is hardly any doubt that there exists tumor immunity. Our main task is to isolate and concentrate these antigens. As soon as this problem is solved, the clinicians will receive preparations which might possibly be used for diagnosis and prophylaxis of tumors and for their treatment."

Dr. Zilber's method is a modification of a little used and highly sensitive "Schultz-Dale technique" for the detection of antigens. In this, a known antigen (let us call it A) is injected into a female guinea pig; this sensitizes the animal. The guinea pig is killed, and its sensitized uterus is exposed to test substances in which normal antigens have been neutralized and which may or may not contain antigen A. If antigen A is present in the test substance, the uterine horns register shock—they go into a violent spasm.

With these and other antigen-detecting techniques, scientists have reported identifying cancer-specific molecules in many tumors. Dr. Maurice M. Rapport of Sloan-Kettering Institute and Yeshiva University has found a fat-containing hapten—cytolipin H—in all the animal and human tumors he has tested; he feels that each organ (as well as all cancers) may have an organ-specific hapten. Japanese have said that all the cancers they have examined produced a "toxohormone" (possibly a small protein) which permits tumor growth. A Stockholm scientist, Dr. Bertil Bjorklund, has reported finding a lipoprotein antigen in human cancers. And Dr. Harris Busch of Baylor has said he has discovered a unique protein (histone) closely associated with DNA in the nuclei of cancer cells in rat, mouse, and human.

All of these reports will become significant or fade into oblivion as time passes. If any of the reported antigens really represents a cancer-specific molecule, a giant step may have been made toward the control of cancer.

Many other reports of a less general nature also hold forth hope that there may be an antigen in at least some cancers. Drs. L. E. Hughes and B. Lytton of Kings College, London, have produced delayed allergic skin reactions in one-quarter of their patients by injecting them with extracts of their own tumors.

Dr. Arthur E. Bogden of the Biochemical Research Foundation, Newark, Delaware, has made the rather surprising discovery of a substance in rat cancers which is immunologically identical with the human blood group A antigen. It can be separated into two antigenic molecules: (1) an alpha-3 globulin which makes normal and malignant tissues grow, and (2) an alpha-2 globulin which gives each individual tumor a distinctive character. These antigens are glycoproteins—that is, a protein (globulin) with a carbohydrate attached.

Dr. Bogden's extensive studies have turned up other leads which well might have clinical significance. In rats, he can tell with certainty whether or not the animals will die of transplanted cancers; if their blood contains a specific beta-globulin the animals will survive; if it does not, they die. He has concluded that if the tumor and normal cells of the host contain the same antigens, the host surely will die; if the genes (and, necessarily, antigens) of the tumor and the host are different, the host's antibodies well may destroy the tumor. In his experiments, healthy rat blood killed human red cells, whereas the blood from cancerous rats did not; it may be that the cancers produced something which either suppressed rat antibody production or robbed the antibodies of their destructive potency. In cancer, Dr. Bogden has reported, normal red cells acquire antigens and they are clumped by antibodies; this causes anemia.

Dr. Felix Haurowitz of Indiana University, an authority on antibody production and behavior, believes that these all-important proteins are manufactured by many cells, but particularly by highly-specialized cells in the marrow and the lymphatic system of liver, spleen, and tissues which lie just under the skin. The antibody-manufacturing system is called the RES, or reticuloendothelial system.

Antibodies are tailor-made to attack specific viruses, bacteria, and all manner of foreign invaders. Antibodies can stick virus particles together or clump cells in an inert mass, precipitate molecules out of solution, and disintegrate cells and particles. They are generally considered gamma globulins, but some evidence suggests they may be other globulins as well.

Dr. J. R. Marrack of Cambridge, an eminent immunologist and pathologist, has said that the normal gamma globulin (antibody) molecule has at least six sites which can combine with as many mirror image sites on an antigen molecule. A single infectious virus or organism, he adds, may have one or many antigens and may attract a number of different antibodies. During a lifetime, one produces a "whole museum of antibodies," he has said.

Dr. Marrack is skeptical of all reports of antigens specific for cancer. He feels that specific antigens may be present, but he doubts that they have been detected by present methods. If cancer antigens do exist, he believes, antibodies may fail to destroy them for any of several reasons: the antibody-producing system or the antibodies themselves may be defective; the chemicals which bind antigen to antibody may be weak or unstable; there may be an incompatibility in the kind and number of binding sites on the antigen and the antibody; there may be an excess of antigen for the available antibodies; or a state of tumor tolerance may have been induced in the host.

Many factors can contribute to antibody defects and deficiencies. Age is one; the newborn baby doesn't begin to make antibodies until his second month and he reaches full production only in his third year of life, and old age decreases antibody production. Diet is another; general malnutrition or a dietary deficiency of ascorbic acid, thiamine, or other vitamins depresses antibody formation. Many of the chemicals which cause cancer in experimental animals and many of the drugs—and the radiation —used to treat human cancers lower blood antibody levels. Dyes and several other chemicals lodge in the RES and block it, and an injection of polyamino acids inhibits the scavenging capacity of RES cells. Low antibody (or gamma globulin) levels are associated with several diseases, including cancer, sarcoidosis, septicemia, meningitis, pyoderma, purulent conjunctivitis, otitis media, and purulent sinusitis.

Not only cancer, but, in experimental animals, even cancer susceptibility sometimes is reflected in antibody production defects. Drs. Samuel Albert and Ralph M. Johnson at the Detroit Institute of Cancer Research measured the metabolic function of antibody-producing lymph nodes and found it definitely sluggish in animals with a genetic proneness to cancer, and weaker still in susceptible mice infected with a breast-cancer virus, and in those in whom cancer transplants later took and grew. One investigator, Dr. W. C. MacCarty, has reported that he could tell pretty well by the lymphocyte reaction around a tumor how the patient would fare. A strong reaction he regarded as a good sign.

In medicine, two kinds of allergies are recognized: (1) those producing an immediate reaction—within seconds or minutes of exposure to the allergen (or antigen), the antigen-antibody union in a sensitized person evokes any of a host of symptoms, slight or serious; or (2) those producing a delayed reaction—the response appears usually a day or two after contact, or, occasionally, weeks or even months later. In some cases both immediate and delayed reactions take place.

The reaction occurs in the skin (endothelium) lining the lymphatic and blood vessels and body cavities. Taking part in the reaction are the white cells called lymphocytes and also mast cells; the latter are ubiquitous storehouses of potent compounds, including histamine, serotonin, epinephrine, heparin, and possibly other closely related amines. In an emergency, these chemicals increase blood flow to the area and facilitate the transmission of stimuli along nerves. If the allergic reaction affects vessels lying just beneath the skin, it takes the form of a wheal, itch, eruption, rash, or dermatitis; if it attacks mucous membranes, the effect can be runny nose, coughs, sneezes, blocked breathing tubes, or inflamed sinuses; if it touches joints, the soreness can be of long or short duration, and in the large, deep vessels anaphylactic shock, circulatory collapse, and sudden death may result.

The most commonly recognized allergens are large protein, carbohydrate, and fat molecules and an enormous number of small molecules which, as haptens, attach to the large molecules. They are in pollens, animal and human hair, foods, dusts, drugs, smokes, and many other substances. Viruses, bacteria and fungi are allergens, and so are some of their products. Heat, cold, light, emotional upset, infection and injury are considered by some to be allergens, although it is possible that they merely serve as coallergens—that is, they prepare the thin skin or other tissues so that ever-present but undetected allergens can reach the target.

Sometimes the allergic reaction results from the combining of an allergen with a single molecule—a common protein antibody circulating in the blood; and in other cases it seems to be induced by the union of the allergen with an entire antibody-producing factory—a whole lymph cell. One can induce an allergy in an otherwise allergy-resistant person by injecting a lymph cell to which the allergen has been attached or by injecting a normal lymph cell from an allergic person and then injecting the allergen.

It is important to science and medicine to determine the immune situations in which only a molecule of antibody or a whole lymph cell is needed. On such knowledge may hang the success of future attempts to graft organs from one person to another, or to cure cancer. If only lymph cells are involved in allergic reactions, the rejection of transplants or the destruction of cancer cells, experiments with antibody molecules alone might well prove futile.

Is cancer related to allergy? A case—perhaps a tenuous case—could be made for the argument that it is.

At the McArdle Memorial Laboratory for Cancer Research, University of Wisconsin, Drs. James and Elizabeth Miller and Charles Heidelberger have shown that carcinogens which cause liver cancer bind with a protein in the target cell, and the protein with the bound carcinogen disappears from the cell. The fact that this binding occurs only in normal cells, and not cancer cells, has given rise to what Dr. Harold P. Rusch, director of the laboratory, calls the "protein deletion" hypothesis of cancer; that is, the normal cell becomes cancerous as a result of the loss of this protein. Whether the lost protein serves as a sort of antibody or whether the carcinogen acts as a hapten which transforms the protein into an antigen or allergen is not known. Nor, indeed, do the scientists know how general the protein deletion process is in cancer; it could be restricted to a few cancers or apply to many or all of them.

In sacrificing a specific protein to bind a carcinogen, the cell apparently loses one of its normal antigens. In this case, unless the protein is restored, protein-deleted cancer cells might regard normal protein-rich cells as antigenic and produce antibodies against the normal cells.

Thus, protein deletion poses two distinct immunity problems: (1) the need to remove the protein–carcinogen antigenic combination from the body, and (2) the destructive activity of the protein-depleted cancer cell against its normal protein-containing neighbor cells.

Allergies are believed induced by many kinds of stresses—physical, chemical, and emotional. Once started, the allergies continue in the absence of the stress; the mere suggestion of the stress is enough to evoke the reaction. Some allergies, like asthma, are relieved by stresses, including antigens, infection (nonrespiratory), major surgery, traumatic shock, and widespread cancer. In experiments at Seton Hall College of Medicine, the paralysis of allergic encephalomyelitis in rats was suppressed by such stresses as restraint (taping the feet to a board) and cold baths. One wonders whether the current fad of stress-avoidance is medically sound in all cases.

Some authorities feel that some carcinogens act by breaking protein molecules at sulfur-to-sulfur or hydrogen-sulfur (sulfhydryl) bonds. At Walter Reed Hospital, Washington, D.C., scientists put human allergic blood serum in test tubes and added to it several sulfhydryl compounds. Under this treatment, the serum antibodies lost their ability to cause an allergic reaction. Would sulfhydryl-rich drugs help allergic patients? Would they help cancer patients?

As noted earlier, mast cells and their contents promote allergic reactions. Histamine is regarded as the key chemical in this; but Dr. Mary Alexander Fink, then at the University of Colorado, showed that serotonin is 1,000 times as potent as histamine in promoting an allergic (Schultz-Dale) response. Mast cells also promote the "take" and growth of transplanted cancers. Dr. Kenneth Scott of the University of California discovered that if he ruptured mast cells before transplanting a cancer, the tumor would not take. When he ruptured the mast cells after transplanting the tumor, cancer grew rapidly. He found that the cancer cells themselves produce an iodine-containing compound which shatters the mast cells, spilling their circulation-increasing and nerve-exciting chemicals into the area and stimulating tumor growth.

The eventful twentieth century began with a nightmarish question by Dr. Paul Ehrlich. In discussing his discovery in 1900 that one human produced antibodies against cells from another human, he raised the question: could a person produce antibodies against himself? He dismissed the possibility as being contrary to the law, *horror autotoxicus,* self-poison horror, an unthinkable situation in nature. He was convinced that even though he had demonstrated that antibodies could be produced against tissues of another individual within the same species, it would be impossible for one's antibodies to eat away his own brain, heart, and other organs.

A generation later, a young Heidelberg immunologist, Dr. Ernest Witebsky, expressed skepticism of the soundness of *horror autotoxicus.* He felt that, under some circumstances, the system might produce antibodies against itself. He was impressed by a finding by others in 1904 that red blood cells in syphilitic patients often disintegrated after the patient was exposed to cold and then returned to room temperaure. If one's own antibodies destroyed red cells under these conditions, they might destroy other cells. In fact, Dr. Witebsky thought, they might even destroy one's own cancer.

Dr. Witebsky in work done later at the University of Buffalo repealed the law of *horror autotoxicus.* During the early 1950s he and Drs. Noel R. Rose and Sidney Shulman demonstrated thyroid-destroying antibodies. The Buffalo scientists reproduced in rabbits a disease like the human condition called Hashimoto's thyroiditis by injecting them with a thyroid protein called thyroglobulin.

The evidence showed that when a globulin leaked (or was deliberately released) from the capsule containing the thyroid gland, antibodies formed against the errant protein, migrated back to the thyroid, and eventually ate away part of the gland.

Other autoimmune conditions were produced in experimental animals —male sterility with injections of seminal fluid or testis extracts, and encephalomyelitis with brain extracts.

Dr. Witebsky's success opened the floodgates of investigation into autoimmune disease. In the relatively short time since his classical work on thyroiditis, a score or more of common and serious conditions have been reported as autoimmune in nature. How many of these conditions actually are autoimmune time alone will determine; it is prudent to allow a substantial margin for overenthusiasm in any fast-flowering fashion in science and medicine.

Autoimmunity has been claimed as the cause of diseases affecting germ cells, hormones, joints, muscles, skin, blood cells and particles, glands, digestive organs, lungs, liver, kidneys, heart, brain and nerve, eyes, breast, and other structures.

In some cases, autoantibodies attack the tissues; in others, fixed and circulating autoimmune lymph cells, including the scavenger cells called phagocytes and histiocytes, may do the damage. In only a few diseases, however, is there clear-cut evidence of culpability. Although quite definitely of autoimmune origin, the conditions often leave no trace of antibodies or cells which might damage the affected tissues.

In all cases, the big question is, where does the antigen come from? The process by which normal cells and structures become antigenic is the essence of autoimmunity and the key to the possible prevention and control of these diseases.

The antigen may be—as in the case of Dr. Witebsky's peripatetic thyroid globulin—a protein which escapes from the precincts to which it has been assigned. (Dr. Abraham G. Osler of Johns Hopkins has discovered that many, and perhaps all, organs produce organ-specific proteins which seem to be at home in many species providing they are in the accustomed organ.) Infections and injuries also have altered tissues, cells, and particles so that they gave rise to antigens. Drugs and other chemicals also can change a cell to make it antigenic. Dr. Nathan Kaliss in Bar Harbor, Maine, reported a decade ago that antibodies may form against antibodies.

Dr. Frank J. Dixon of the Scripps Clinic and Research Foundation has listed in *World Wide Abstracts* these diseases as reported associated with autoimmune responses: disseminated lupus erythematosus, rheumatoid arthritis, scleroderma, polyarteritis nodosa, rheumatic fever, glomerulonephritis, Hashimoto's thyroiditis, thyrotoxicosis, lupoid hepatitis, primary biliary cirrhosis, macroglobulinemia, ulcerative colitis, and Addison's disease. He named as diseases resembling human conditions induced in laboratory animals by autoimmune measures: acute demyelinating postinfectious encephalitis, multiple sclerosis, Landry's paralysis, peripheral neuritis, chronic thyroiditis, sympathetic ophthalmia (of the uvea), phacoanaphylactic endophthalmitis (of the lens) and aspermatogenesis (depleted sperm). Several investigators have reported that some insulin-resistant diabetes cases have been traced to the binding of insulin in an antibody. Others have named as autoimmune diseases some kinds of cirrhosis, arrested breast development, lung destruction, and heart damage.

Some strange interrelationships between autoantibodies have come to light. Various investigators have reported, for instance, that Addison's disease of the adrenals is characterized not only by antiadrenal antibodies but by antithyroid antibodies as well. Hypoparathyroidism seems to be caused by the same combination of autoantibodies. Antibodies against syphilis organisms have been found to react also with beef heart, those of infectious mononucleosis react with sheep red blood cells—relationships which seemingly have nothing whatsoever to do with human disease.

If autoimmunity is at the root of 10 per cent of the diseases for which it is blamed, it would be reasonable to suspect it of a role in cancer. More than any other diseased body cell, the cancer cell seems to merit attack and destruction by autoantibodies.

A number of recent discoveries inspire the suspicion that autoimmunity in cancer may be more frequent than generally is supposed.

At the University of Pittsburgh, for instance, a group was surprised to find that a patient with disseminated lupus erythematosus, presumably autoimmune, also had Hodgkin's disease. That was in 1959. They searched their records to learn whether the two diseases had been reported as concurrent in any of their earlier patients. The reports showed no earlier patient who had the two diseases. During the next two years, however, the alerted group found that three more of their lymphoma patients also had lupus or rheumatoid arthritis. A check of the literature turned up a substantial number of isolated cases, casually mentioned, of lymphoma complicated by such probable autoimmune diseases as lupus, rheumatoid arthritis, scleroderma, and polyarteritis nodosa. Inasmuch as lymphoid swellings and lymphoid disease occur in 50–75 per cent of rheumatoid arthritis patients and large percentages of patients with other autoimmune diseases, the scientists wondered whether there wasn't a connection between lymphomas and autoimmune conditions.

It may be significant that bacterial polysaccharides, injections of which cure some experimental cancers in animals, prevent rat arthritis. Drs. Fae D. Wood and Carl M. Pearson of U.C.L.A. have induced arthritis in rats with injections of a Freund-type wax adjuvant (tuberculosis germ fractions and a water-in-oil emulsion) and prevented the disease with lipopolysaccharides from several bacterial strains.

Dr. Louis Pelner of the Swedish Hospital, Brooklyn, a leading chronicler of cancer's idiosyncracies, has summarized in the *Journal of the American Geriatrics Society* the reported association of various kinds of cancer with a number of other diseases. Frequency of the associations ranged from rare to occasional, and only in some instances were the collateral conditions recognized as of allergic or an autoimmune nature. They included:

Acanthosis nigricans, a discoloration often around the beltline or in armpits—stomach cancer.

Thrombophlebitis—cancer of the pancreas or bronchi.

Hypertrophic pulmonary osteoarthropathy—bronchogenic cancer.

Dermatomyositis—several forms of cancer.

Arthralgia or rheumatoidlike arthritis—lung, breast, and prostatic cancer.

Scleroderma and lupus erythematosus—visceral cancer.

Nerve and muscle disease—lung and other cancers.

Mental symptoms, including anxiety and depression—cancer of the pancreas.

Peripheral neuritis—multiple myeloma.

Cushing's syndrome (overactive adrenals)—cancers of the lung, ovary, thymus, pancreas, and prostate.

In some cases, surgical removal of the cancer cleared up all symptoms of the associated disease.

It is noteworthy that, according to tests at the University of Southern California, patients with lung cancer, emphysema, and pulmonary tuberculosis have high concentrations of antilung antibodies, as compared with normals and people with other lung diseases.

Dr. Jack G. Makari of Muhlenberg Hospital, Plainfield, New Jersey, has reported the simultaneous presence of both cell-bound autoantigens and autoantibodies in minces of a great many cancers.

Occasionally, during the nineteenth century, one physician or another commented on the complete and apparently permanent disappearance of cancer following a severe, fever-inducing infection. The infection most often mentioned was erysipelas, caused by streptococci which enter the system through the nose, mouth, or a wound or scratch. Erysipelas usually starts with a chill, induces a temperature which remains high for several days, makes the inflamed face look neon-lighted, often spreads to other tissues, is painful and prostrating, and commonly kills untreated victims. Modern sanitation, hygiene, and medicine have pretty well eliminated this ancient scourge from the Western world.

Some nineteenth-century physicians, impressed with the reports of remarkable cancer remissions, had their patients sleep in "erysipelas beds" —beds recently vacated by erysipelas victims—and wrapped them in bandages cast off by erysipelas patients. Some of these cancer patients developed erysipelas and died of it; others survived erysipelas and were cured of their cancers.

Dr. William B. Coley of New York, after finding deliberate infection dangerous and unsatisfactory, injected cancer patients with toxins of dead erysipelas (beta-hemolytic) streptococci and another bacterium, prodigiosus, which enhanced the reaction. In 1893 he announced that several of his patients has shown a complete remission. A few other physicians also used "Coley's mixed toxins," and they too reported varying percentages of success. Sarcoma, which is a difficult-to-cure cancer of connective tissue, seemed most amenable to this treatment, although many other types of cancer also were reported as yielding to it.

Dr. Coley treated many hundreds of cancer patients with his toxins, both alone and in combination with surgery and radiation; up to the time of his death in 1936, he seemed to have achieved a good measure of success, considering the fact that a large majority of his patients were beyond hope of cure by any other means.

"Coley's mixed toxins" never did catch on with the medical profession; some of the cures are described as "spontaneous regressions." For one thing, it usually was a rough treatment.

Variations of Coley's mixed toxins still are being used experimentally by the New York Cancer Research Institute and a score or so of affiliated physicians in the United States. Dr. Coley's daughter, Mrs. Helen Coley Nauts, executive secretary of the group, has compiled an analysis of more than 1,200 cancer cases treated with Coley's toxins and 300 additional cases in which various intercurrent infections also occurred. Almost 300 of the toxin-treated cases, according to the report, showed complete regression. One series of thirty specially-studied inoperable cases were said to have survived from one to forty-seven years following toxin therapy, twenty of them for more than twenty years. A total of 460 of the treated and infected—some of them also given surgery or radiation—were followed from six to fifty-nine years; and in some of these the disease eventually recurred. The record compares most favorably with that of modern treatment for cancers beyond surgical and radiation cure.

Dr. Murray Shear at the National Cancer Institute and Dr. Hugh Creech at the Institute for Cancer Research in Philadelphia have modified the toxins, which are polysaccharides, from *prodigiosus* (now called *Serratia marcescens*) in efforts to weaken the poisonous effects and strengthen the antitumor activity. Their efforts have not met with spectacular clinical success, although many remissions were reported. Doses which cure one-third of cancerous mice kill another third, a forbidding ratio in treatment of humans. More than 200 patients have been treated with Dr. Creech's preparations; while a few have shown very good remissions, the doses used were too light and safe to cure. Two-thirds of the lymphoma patients showed regressions—often lengthy ones; one-third of sarcomas regressed somewhat; carcinoma and melanoma were resistant. Radiation often increased the antitumor effect of the polysaccharides. One of Dr. Creech's polysaccharides proved to be 1,300 times as cancer-destructive in mice as the original erysipelas toxin. Within a half-hour of administration of a potent polysaccharide, patients undergo a severe chill; in short order other violent events take place—nausea, vomiting, high temperature and, sometimes, shock. The extreme discomfort lasts five or six hours (in erysipelas severe symptoms may go on for a week or more). The system and the tumor quickly become resistant to the polysaccharide; if the first dose doesn't cure, it is unlikely that succeeding doses will. A fifth dose fifteen times the strength of the first is almost without effect.

Some physicians are acutely aware of the fact that millions of people have died of infections and other diseases when the cure was just around the corner; in some cases it reposed in folk medicine and current clinical impressions but awaited medical confirmation by some reputable and bold scientist.

This conceivably could be the case in present-day immunological treatment of cancer. A few physicians in experimental medicine have preferred to give their hopeless patients the benefit of a gamble rather than sacrifice them pending clinical proof of a theoretical cure. Their efforts, by and large, have encountered much the same skepticism and criticism accorded the sound scientists who first validated the viral theory of cancer.

Drs. John and Ruth Graham of Roswell Park were convinced by their own studies that many human cancers were antigenic. They noted that patients with a strong immune response to their own tumors did very well, as a rule, whereas those who showed little resistance soon died of their disease. For those who could not be helped by other means, they devised a vaccine composed of cancer cells freshly removed from the patient's own tumors and Freund's adjuvant (a mixture of killed tubercule bacilli, mineral oil, and an emulsifying agent which stimulates an immune reaction). Some of the patients were also given a small dose of X rays to enhance the effect of the vaccine. In an effort to measure the worth, if any, of the vaccine, they gave one of three treatments at random to each of a series of their patients: (1) conventional X ray, (2) conventional drug, and (3) vaccine with or without X rays.

Seventeen months and ninety-two patients after the start of their experiment (virtually moribund patients who lived less than one month were excluded), the Grahams totted up the score. The survivors were 40 per cent of those given the vaccine, 24 per cent of those given X rays, and 17 per cent of the drug-treated patients. The vaccine had produced no major complications; ulceration at the site of vaccination was regarded as a good sign; those who showed none soon died of their cancers. A few of the vaccinated patients showed a remarkable recovery from their cancers—in one or two the disease had cleared up completely.

Six years and 232 patients after they began their experiments, the

Grahams' account was more detailed. Of their vaccinated patients, 31 per cent were alive more than one year (as compared with 22 per cent of those given conventional treatment). Ulcers at the site of vaccination remained a good sign—all those who did not ulcerate were dead within six months, and one-third of those who did react were alive at the end of a year. One of the earliest-treated patients no longer seemed to have cancer, and a few more recent patients appeared to have been cured (the Grahams, however, carefully avoid the word "cure").

The Graham vaccination technique was applied to about fifty far-gone patients over six years by Dr. Russell H. Wilson and James Finney at the VA Hospital in Dallas. The clinical results of treatment were not particularly impressive; in two-thirds of the cases the vaccine did not seem to delay the inevitable death of these terminal patients. Large rises in antibody titers to some of their cancers were recorded, however. Some of the tumors shrank.

In a series of twenty-five patients treated by Drs. Charles A. Ross and George E. Moore at Roswell Park with human cancer cells grown in tissue culture, three results were particularly noteworthy: (1) an eighteen-year-old girl with a malignant granular myoblastoma of the mouth showed regression of a metastatic mass in the chest and general improvement; (2) a fifty-year-old man with bone cancer which had spread to his lungs had complete disappearance of all but one spot on a lung, which when removed turned out to be a healed cancer; and (3) another man, twenty-three years old, temporarily lost all symptoms of a bone cancer which also had spread to the lungs. The latter two cases also had been given a drug, AB-132, which occasionally has good but brief beneficial effects and has serious toxicity.

Several physicians have used antisera against human cancer. In these cases, they usually inoculated human cancer or cancer extracts into horses or other animals, withdrew the animal serum and injected the antibody-containing part of it into patients. Several procedures were used to eliminate from the serum all antibodies against normal human tissues.

Dr. Sergio DeCarvalho of the Rand Development Corporation, Cleveland, has extracted protein antigens from human normal and cancer tissues and injected them into horses. He removed from the horse antiserum what he calls purified gamma globulin—presumably antibodies against the human normal and cancer antigens. The antibodies against normal tissues were eliminated from preparations by using human normal antigens as blotters, leaving only the anticancer antibodies for use in patients. In a report detailing the results of treatment in thirty-one patients, Dr. DeCarvalho stated that of fifteen leukemic patients, thirteen had remissions lasting from four weeks to more than twenty-nine months; in fifteen of sixteen patients with other cancers, "a nearly constant feature was the alleviation of pain, partial or complete recovery of functions impaired by cancer growth, and partial or complete clearance of objective tumor lesions for from two weeks to eleven months." The side effects, he reported, included mild inflammatory reactions at the site of injection and a slight elevation of temperature. At this writing, he is using purified antibodies as a vehicle to transport anticancer drugs and radioactive isotopes to tumors.

Dr. DeCarvalho has used other immune measures in test tubes, animal, and human experiments, including direct vaccination with laboratory-produced antigens. He has reported transforming normal cells in culture into malignant cells by adding RNA from cancer cells to the medium, and the reverse by adding normal RNA to cultures of cancer cells. He devised what, theoretically at least, is an ingenious system for the production of tailor-made (autologous) vaccine materials: it calls for transforming human amnion cells by treating them with RNA from the patient's cancer cells and then extracting antigens from the transformed cells. The transformed cells thus become a factory for the production of custom-built antigens. If these achievements can be duplicated, they would suggest new methods of treating cancer.

Dr. William Harrington of the University of Miami, after extensive animal experiments and a few human trials, concluded that lymph cells, rather than antibodies, were the body's main defense against cancer. He also felt that leukemic cells would mutate and become antigenic under exposure to several anticancer drugs, and that normal lymph cells then might destroy the mutated leukemic cells. He gave four leukemic patients nitrogen mustard for ten days—to mutate the leukemic cells and increase their antigenicity; he withdrew the leukemic cells from the patients and mixed them with Freund's adjuvant to further enhance their antigenicity; he then injected the highly antigenic mixture of cells and adjuvant back into the donor-patients. Three of the four patients enjoyed excellent remissions; in the fourth, the treatment almost wiped out the normal blood-forming cells of the bone marrow.

Animal experiments have indicated that it might be a good idea to inject sensitized lymph cells, which are antibody-producing factories, rather than antibodies alone into cancerous animals. Drs. Russell S. Weiser and Charles A. Evans of the University of Washington found that sensitized lymph cells selectively killed mouse-cancer cells both in test tubes and in animals. They stimulated production of the anticancer lymph cells by first injecting cancer into mice which were resistant to that particular kind of cancer. When the cancer had been destroyed, the scientists took the lymph cells from the cancer-cured mice and used them in two experiments: (1) When the sensitized lymph cells were added to cultures of cancer cells, they swarmed over the cancer cells; the cancer cells stopped dividing under this attack, their protoplasm filled with bubbles, and between six and forty-eight hours later all of the cancer cells were dead. (2) When cancer-susceptible mice were injected with sensitized lymph cells and then with cancer, the lymph cells destroyed the cancers and the animals did not become ill.

Similar protection was effected in rats in experiments by Drs. Robert W. Preston, Robert Shrek, and others at Northwestern University. In this case, the scientists made a paste of various organs of rats which had been injected with and recovered from a (Bagg) lymphosarcoma. Pastes of cells from the cured animals' lymphatic organs (spleen, thymus, nodes, or blood lymphocytes) injected from three to six days after inoculation with the lymphosarcoma cured 83 per cent of the animals. Sensitized lymph cells which had been stored in the refrigerator for as long as four weeks cured 77 per cent.

The technique of inoculating cancerous hosts with sensitized lymph cells is called adoptive immunity. An appreciable proportion of transplanted cancers in animals have been cured by injecting them with sensitized spleen or lymph node cells from resistant strains previously injected with the cancer.

How about human patients?

Drs. M. F. A. Woodruff and B. Noland of the University of Edinburgh have transplanted human spleen cells to eight human cancer patients. They obtained the cells from patients whose spleens were removed because of hemolytic anemia or thrombocytopenic purpura or during operations for hypertension or gastric cancer. The procedure relieved some of the symptoms in every patient, and five seemed to improve; but it is difficult to say whether any survived longer than they otherwise would.

The transplant of lymphocytes or whole lymphatic organs from one person to another is risky. It is possible that the transplanted cells will produce antibodies against the new host and destroy him. Dr. Carlos Martinez of the University of Minnesota recognized this danger in animal transplant studies. He found that he was able to transplant organs successfully between unrelated adult animals if he first injected donor spleen cells into the recipient—either a single massive intravenous injection or repeated small injections. The injected cells and the transplants, however, often produced fatal runt disease in the new host. Dr. Martinez found that, if he ruptured the cells before injecting them, they made the new host tolerant to a later transplant without inducing runt disease. This latter technique is now being tried on a few human kidney transplants.

Among the many factors which make comparison of laboratory results and clinical results illogical, one in particular stands out: in the laboratory, the scientist knows that he is treating a mouse which has cancer only, whereas in the clinic, the experimental physician usually treats patients who have been altered not only by their cancers but by several earlier drastic anticancer treatments as well and who often are more dead than alive. Some physicians feel they might have better luck with immune therapy if their patients had not been given prior treatment and stood at least an outside chance of cure.

While most cancer immunologists are preoccupied with the role of antibodies and lymph cells, the evidence indicates that many other immune substances, known and unknown, may be more important to the control of cancer than are antibodies and lymph cells as such.

Dr. David Pressman of Roswell Park, a pioneer in efforts to produce cancer-specific antibodies, has found these proteins highly unpredictable. He has tagged cancer antibodies with radioactivity in the hope that the antibodies, acting as a "guided missile," would destroy tumors with their combined biochemical activity and radiation. He has found that antibodies produced against specific animal tumors—transplanted or induced —are capricious; they often concentrate in normal tissues as well as cancers. They also localize in fibrin, a tough anticlotting protein which forms in the vicinity of tumors.

Dr. Pressman's group and another headed by Dr. William F. Bale of the University of Rochester have shown that antibodies prepared against fibrin concentrate to varying degrees in some transplanted, induced, and spontaneous tumors. The Rochester scientists suggested that it might prove practical to treat widely metastatic human cancer with antifibrin antibodies.

Several groups, including one at the National Institute of Allergy and Infectious Diseases, have produced experimental evidence which indicates that antibodies may not be necessary for recovery from virus infections. This finding raises the question as to whether or not antibodies would be involved in a defense against virus-caused cancers.

Dr. Manfred M. Mayer of Johns Hopkins, who has isolated and purified several of the blood proteins involved in immunity, believes that while antibodies may destroy viruses and toxins, they are powerless by themselves to do away with cells—bacteria and cancer cells specifically. He has shown that cellular destruction entails a synchronized attack by a sequence of at least six proteins which comprise complement, ions (charged particles of calcium, magnesium, manganese, nickel, and cobalt) and antibodies. In his laboratory, Dr. Mayer has established the precise sequence with which each of these forces act in an assault upon a cell. He feels that antibodies initiate the series of reactions which enables the complement fractions, with a high degree of tactical strategy, to injure cells, neutralize viruses, stimulate activity of scavenger cells (phagocytes), and institute allergic reactions in tissues.

Dr. Mayer believes that another blood anticancer protein, properdin, actually is a combination of several complement fractions. Other investigators feel properdin may be a distinct entity.

A Sloan-Kettering team led by Dr. Chester M. Southam, in a series of experiments a few years ago, showed that the blood of far-advanced cancer patients was deficient in properdin and that this presumably accounted for their immunological impotence. The scientists first transplanted cancer cells under the skin of hopelessly ill cancer patients and found that in their new environment the cells grew very well. Similar transplants to a large number of healthy volunteer prisoners at Ohio State Penitentiary resulted in the rapid destruction of the cells. The principal difference in the two human guinea-pig groups was that the cancer patients lacked properdin while the healthy prisoners, on the other hand, showed high properdin levels. Dr. Antonio Rottino of St. Vincent's Hospital, New York, discovered that about one-half of his cancer patients had low properdin levels; apparently the properdin decreased as the patients went downhill. Other investigators found that animals also became properdin-deficient as their tumors grew.

One observation indicates that complement and properdin may belong to the same system: polysaccharides appear to attach to the target tumor or bacterial cells and sensitize them to antibody-complement-properdin attack. Sensitization is accomplished as well by zymosan, a polysaccharide extracted from the walls of yeast cells, as by bacterial polysaccharides. A group working with Dr. Shear at NCI has used zymosan effectively against experimental animal cancers.

It may turn out that one of the more important medical discoveries of the twentieth century is a small natural protein known as interferon. It was called interferon by Drs. Alick Isaacs and Jean Lindemann of the National Institute for Medical Research in England, when they discovered in 1957 that it interfered with the propagation of viruses in chicken eggs. On a weight basis—gamma for gamma—interferon is ten or more times as potent against viruses as antibiotics are against bacteria. Drs. Enders and Monto Ho at Harvard (Dr. Ho is now at the University of Pittsburgh) showed that interferon suppresses mammalian virus growth; it makes cells resistant to viruses. It does not seem to kill the viruses, however.

Interferon still is so new (it has not yet been obtained in completely purified form) that there is a good deal of speculation as to what it does and how. Most who have studied interferon believe it is produced by virus-infected cells; it also is possible that it might be produced by islands of normal cells in an infected cell colony. Some believe that, when an acute infection occurs, interferon is produced and suppresses, not only the new virus of acute infection, but also old viruses of a chronic infection;

this would account for an acute secondary infection clearing up an old chronic infection. Others feel that interferon is a whole family of specific proteins, rather than a single general protein which suppresses all viruses, and that a distinctive kind of interferon is produced against each infecting virus. Dr. Ho believes that while interferon does not prevent a virus from entering a cell, it does block the virus from using cell chemicals and from developing. In this way, he has said, interferon could account for the masking of cancer viruses—for the fact that they become lost after entering a cell.

In the present state of ignorance, interferon or interferonlike chemicals could explain a long list of phenomena encountered in biological research. So far as anyone knows, it could play a role in the suppression of cancer growing in laboratory dishes and, the most remarkable event of all, spontaneous regression in humans. A Belgian scientist, Dr. Edward E. de Maeyer, has reported that carcinogenic hydrocarbons—and possibly cortisone—block the production of interferon and permit a cancer virus, polyoma, to proliferate.

Some years ago Dr. Vincent Groupe of Rutgers University discovered that the chicken cancer agent, *Rous sarcoma* virus, often was neutralized when released from cancer cells. Something in the cell environment destroyed the viruses' infectivity. When the cells were cleansed of the fluid which had surrounded them, the virus again became infective. Small doses of virus injected into chickens seemed to disappear, even though they induced cancer. Large doses, on the other hand, produced a prolific harvest of viruses; they seemed to overwhelm whatever (interferon?) held the small doses in check.

Dr. Jorgen Fogh of SKI also found something which inhibited the growth of tumor cells. First he discovered that when human amnion cells were grown in laboratory dishes, about one in 10,000 cells spontaneously became malignant—they produced tumors when injected into tolerant rats or humans. Filtrates (presumably containing nucleic acid from the malignant cells) also transformed normal amnion cells into cancer cells. Something in normal cells, however, halted the growth of the malignant cells; the more normal cells present, the slower the growth and fewer the malignant cells in any culture.

Various scientists have reported these fractions in human blood: (1) a glycoprotein or lipoprotein, called MFlo, which inhibits cell division and is deficient in the serum of patients with untreated, recurrent or metastatic cancer; (2) a heat stable factor, resembling the complement fraction, C′4, which with human or rabbit (but not guinea pig) complement destroys mouse ascites tumor cells; (3) lysozyme, a small protein which is leaked by white cells in the presence of certain bacteria—it kills the bacteria; (4) phagocytin, a white-cell substance which destroys bacteria resistant to lysozyme; (5) haptoglobin, which appears in the blood as immunity develops; (6) a factor in normal serum, coupled to an inhibitor, which rapidly destroys human tumors in tissue culture; (7) C-reactive protein, which appears in blood during periods of stress; (8) something in cancer patients' serum which destroys their own tumor cells (indicating an 82 per cent assurance of cure), and (9) something else in cancer patients' serum which permits growth of their own tumor cells (the chances of death by cancer in this case are 87 out of 100).

Many other natural anticancer substances have been reported. Outside stimuli must be applied for some of them to reach effective levels.

Dr. George W. Woolley and others at SKI destroyed several human cancers growing in test tubes merely by raising the temperature to 103 degrees. More than ten hormone products have been found to induce fever temperatures. The hormones were steroids formed in the gonads and adrenal cortex. Substances which stimulate the reticuloendothelial system (RES)—polysaccharides and lipoid material from several bacterial species among them—have similar temperature-raising and anticancer (particularly antisarcoma) activity. Lipids have been found to enhance the polysaccharide reaction to protein antigens; and the lipid and polysaccharide activity, in turn, has been increased with the addition of injected potassium. Workers in the Soviet Union have introduced such temperature-raising and shock-inducing preparations as KR, or cruzin, an endotoxin from the organism which causes Chagas disease; the preparation was abandoned and its discoverers banished under the Stalin regime, but under Khrushchev cruzin was retested and reported to have limited merit. Mouse tests of cruzin in the United States proved negative for cancer.

Cancer patients are said to be tolerant of their tumors. Otherwise, the patients would resist these ugly cells and, immunologically, destroy them. Cancers seems to be intolerant of the patients—they consume their victims.

What induces tolerance? What ends it?

The answers to these questions could solve much of the cancer problem. They also could make it possible to transplant organs from one person to another.

Research into the tolerant state has moved rapidly in recent years. Many reasons for tolerance have been established; the reasons already have been translated into a few death-delaying clinical experiments, which appear to be heralding the day when one may trade in his tired glands, worn-out organs and injured tissues for a functional set from a freshly dead, dying, or generous living donor. In a few centers, blood and tissues from the dead are being refrigerated and stored as spare parts for the living.

Generally, science is concerned with four kinds of grafts: autologous —the removal and replacement of one's own tissues; isologous—grafts between identical twins; homologous—grafts between two people or animals of the same species; and heterologous—grafts between individuals of different species.

In humans, three kinds of grafts—autologous, isologous, and homologous—have been successful so far, but for the most part in only a few cases. The autografting of a severed arm or leg back to the owner has been accomplished in several instances. A kidney has been isotransplanted from one identical twin to another and, in a number of cases, homotransplanted. Lungs and liver have been grafted—with a degree of success. Blood transfusion between unrelated people, a homologous transplant, for many years has been a routine medical procedure. Thyroid and parathyroid glands have been reported homografted successfully.

In animal experiments—which many regard as a prelude to clinical events in the almost immediate future—there have been transplants of a spectacular nature. Livers, lungs, kidneys, stomach, the entire upper intestine and lower bowel, the spleen, marrow, and numerous glands have been removed, stored, sometimes refrigerated or kept functioning in perfusion chambers, and then restored to their original owner. Many of those who have performed these operations in mice, rats, dogs, baboons, and other animals feel that they can be done in humans with equal or greater facility. In cancer treatment, these procedures would enable the surgeon to remove the cancerous organs, treat them vigorously with surgery, drugs, radiation or other means outside the body, and autoimplant them in their original owner—hopefully, minus the cancer.

Homologous transplants have been made from one to another individual of the same species, and the transplants have remained functional for hours days, weeks or more than a year. Heterologous transplants—as from mouse to rat or human to hamster—occasionally have been made to work for varying periods.

The key to the success of most transplants has been youth. The younger the donor and the younger the recipient, the more successful the transplant. In some cases, embryonic tissues have been grafted to adults of the same species, including humans. And adult tissues—even from other species, including humans—have been transplanted to newborn animals, like hamsters, or animals suddenly aged with heavy doses of X rays or cortisone.

Cancer, chemically and biologically, can be considered eternal youth. It may be the most transplantable of tissues; and—perhaps because cancer's youth is transmissible—the far-advanced cancerous human and animal are, with the exception of embryos and the newborn, the most tolerant hosts for foreign cells and tissues.

In the first few days or weeks of life (according to observations in animals), baby tissue learns what is itself—or native to the genes—and what is foreign. Based on these early experiences, the individual's defenses develop a self-or-stranger-type memory; during the rest of its life, the host will accept what is itself and reject or destroy what is unfamiliar. Bacteria, viruses, and chemicals introduced into the baby's system before its immunological memory is developed will be recognized henceforth as itself, and the system will not produce antibodies against them or otherwise destroy them. If spleen or other lymph cells from a child or adult are injected into the newborn baby, the baby throughout all its years will accept transplants from the donor.

Animal studies indicate that the memory in which self-or-stranger data are stored is the reticuloendothelial system (RES), composed of lymph cells throughout the body and in the marrow. In the newborn, the primitive memory center seems to be situated in the thymus gland. During the early weeks of life, some scientists feel, memory-imbued lymph cells migrate from the thymus to the spleen, liver, kidneys, appendix, and other areas and establish outposts of the memory and early-warning self-or-stranger system. If the thymus is removed at birth—at least in animal experiments —the self-or-stranger system never is established and as the infant develops through its childhood and adult years (if it lives that long) it will fail to produce antibodies against invading viruses, bacteria, and other antigenic substances. In this tolerant individual, cancer cells will grow profusely. So will transplants of other tissues. Removal of the thymus in effect stops a biological clock; the animal or human does not develop an immunological memory. At least, this is the situation in animals.

Radiation impairment of the thymus—the immunity memory—in the newborn may explain some kinds of cancer, especially leukemia and other lymphomas, in the young. Other events, particularly aging, may account for immunological amnesia and cancer in the adult. In these cases, the memory clock is not only run down, it is turned all the way back to infancy and stopped.

Scientists have found that the immunological clock can be turned back or stopped in adult animals in many ways. It can be done with fluids from embryonic cell cultures. It can be done by injecting substances, such as dyes or thorotrast, which lodge in and block the lymphatic and marrow elements of the RES. It can be done with many carcinogens, including radiation. It can be done with anticancer drugs. It can be done by inserting a new memory—that is, by injecting massive amounts of mature lymph cells (from the thymus, spleen, appendix, or other lymphoid organ) of another animal; the recipient of the lymph cells then will accept, as familiar, grafts of other tissues from the donor. It can be done with cortisone-type lymphocyte-destroying hormones. It can be done in a female by mating her frequently and for a long time with a compatible male; something in the sperm or seminal fluid eventually makes her tolerant of transplants from the male.

A stopped immunological clock can be restarted. This has been done by injecting antisera against the agents which stopped it, with massive doses of the agent and sometimes with radiation. And immunity can be stimulated in many ways. The Dameshek group in Boston injected antigens directly into the thymus of hamsters and thereby greatly increased the size of spleens and lymph nodes and the output of antibodies and antibody-producing lymphocytes.

A decade or so ago a group headed by Dr. George D. Snell at Jackson Memorial Laboratory in Bar Harbor, Maine, reported, on the basis of their genetic observations, that grafts and transplants between unrelated individuals are possible. The only thing the donor and recipient needed in common would be certain tissue-compatibility, or histocompatibility, genes. One of the critical genes, called H-2, they located at a specific spot on the ninth chromosome of the mouse; mice bearing identical H-2 genes could exchange organs and tissues.

Drs. Snell and Nathan Kaliss showed that under the influence of H-genes, cells produced an enhancing substance (ES) which blocked lymph-cell growth and function and, consequently, immunity to cancer and other strange cells. They injected ES from the blood and tissues of can-cerous mice into cancer-resistant mice, and the latter then tolerated the cancer graft and died of it. Each mouse produced its own ES as directed by its H-2 locus. The ES was infectious and, in recipients, made tissue trans-plants infectious.

It now appears that tolerance can be conferred on animals by injecting the prospective recipient with certain proteins (presumably produced under the direction of H-genes) of the prospective donor.

Dr. Benjamin B. Kamrin of Seton Hall a few years ago made nonlitter-mate rats tolerant of skin grafts with prior injections of blood fractions con-taining what he identified as a mixture of alpha and beta globulins.

Dr. J. F. Mowbray of London, during his research at Harvard in 1963, reported isolating an amazing nontoxic glycoprotein, comprising 0.2 per cent of all plasma proteins, which permits the transplant of tissues between different species. In physical properties (electrophoretic), the protein resembles RNase and phosphatase. Primed with this protein (which he identified in the blood of rats, rabbits, cows, dogs, and humans, and which seems to be produced by the thymus), rabbits became tolerant of foreign rabbit skin, human albumin, cow gamma globulin, and tetanus toxoid.

A single dose blocked antibody production; five doses over twelve days produced tolerance toward homologous skin for more than six months.

In the light of recent findings in basic research, clinical experiments in the immunotherapy of cancer so far undertaken seem unsophisticated. Nevertheless, the results have vindicated the experimental physicians' abiding concern for their patients and their determination to use the knowledge available to challenge death to the (usually bitter) end. Critics contend that there is a risk in immunological treatment of cancer—a risk of accelerating the disease, of adding distress to the great burden of pain suffered by some advanced patients, of inducing sudden and fatal anaphylactic shock. What some critics fail to consider is that few things in life are as risky as terminal cancer. Experimental treatment, of course, should be done only by experts.

Dr. Michael B. Shimkin, as head of research at the NCI's Laboratory for Experimental Oncology in San Francisco, more than a decade ago undertook many heroic measures on behalf of his hopeless patients. He reproduced some of the suspected causes of spontaneous regression in childhood leukemia by infecting dying children with diseases which could be controlled—hemolytic staphylococcus, chicken pox and a cat (pancytopenia) virus. Some of the patients recovered from cancer to return to school and to play for a few weeks or months. He cross-transfused young leukemics with their parents or with adult patients who had other kinds of cancer, in the hope that the nonleukemic body and blood would destroy the leukemic cells. There were temporary remissions. Several other experiments were undertaken, none of them disastrous, some of them dramatically but briefly beneficial, some of them completely ineffective. The experiments ended when Dr. Shimkin was promoted to an administrative post at the seat of the NCI in Bethesda, Maryland.

Dr. William H. Beierwaltes of the University of Michigan some years ago removed a melanoma from a patient, injected the tumor into a horse, and treated the patient with antiserum from the horse. The patient went into shock and almost died. But during the next few weeks scores of the ugly black cancers on his skin and in his lungs and stomach withered away and disappeared. The patient lived for several years with no signs of melanoma. Similar treatment—but cautious enough to avoid shock—was ineffective in a dozen other melanoma patients.

A spontaneously-cured melanoma patient in Jacksonville, Florida, gave 250 cubic centimeters of his blood to a young man whose melanoma had produced large lumps on the head, armpit, and right buttock; six weeks after the injection all the lumps began to shrink, and in six months they had disappeared. The sera of both melanoma-cured patients were tested against mouse melanomas grown in tissue culture; neither had the slightest effect.

The dramatic possible cure of a patient riddled with melanoma was reported in the June, 1964, issue of *Cancer* by Drs. Kenneth H. Burdick and William A. Hawk of the Cleveland Clinic. These physicians injected ordinary cowpox vaccine into the ugly black nodules on the skin of a sixty-nine-year-old woman at various intervals over eleven months. The shots were followed by a vigorous reaction and the disappearance of all cancers, not only on the skin, but also in the groin, liver, and viscera. Completely depigmented patches marked the location of the eradicated skin cancers. When the investigators reported, the patient had been free of cancer for two years. Two other patients responded well to vaccinia treatment of melanoma, and five showed no benefit at all.

A few physicians have called for extensive and intensive studies of spontaneous regression for clues to nature's own way of curing cancer. As things now stand, very few of the clues can be exploited clinically. Moreover, it is difficult to prove cause and effect in regression—either spontaneous or, indeed, quite often in treatment-induced regression. There have been instances in which advanced cancer regressed completely when a patient was given antirabies serum for dogbite or antitetanus serum for a contaminated wound. The treated patients went into shock. The implications may seem strong that the antisera and ensuing shock induced the regressions; but the procedures were repeated in other cancer patients without benefit. By the same token, almost all anticancer drugs which seem of value are without good effect in a majority of patients.

Drs. Cole and Everson cite as factors of possible significance in their extensive investigation of spontaneous regression:

NERVE CANCER (neuroblastoma) in very young children: age and time play important roles; children under one year of age stand better than a one-in-five chance of spontaneous regression; another authority has estimated that any child who can live with neuroblastoma for fourteen months stands a one-in-three chance of cure.

MELANOMA in women: grows worse during pregnancy but may relent dramatically following delivery.

BLADDER CANCER: frequently regresses when, in the first phase of a two-stage surgical operation, the urine is diverted from the bladder to the bowel; presumably something in the urine is needed to maintain the vitality of this cancer.

CANCER OF THE KIDNEY (nephroma), CHORION (uterus) and BONE: metastases in the lung and elsewhere sometimes disappear following removal of the original cancer.

CANCER OF THE BREAST: radiation treatment of a recurrence in one breast has made cancer in the other breast disappear.

CANCER OF THE COLON AND RECTUM: an abscess nearby has caused the cancer to regress.

Dr. J. Englebert Dunphy, first at Harvard and later at the University of Oregon, in his practice has seen three dramatic spontaneous regressions. He feels that the tissue changes in early cancer closely resemble those of early and incomplete wound healing; in spontaneous regression, the softened connective tissue firms up and completes the healing.

While a few regressions have been obtained by deliberate infections, the injection of toxins, the reproduction of fevers, the inducement of shock and a few other violent stresses, spontaneous regression remains nature's secret. The immunologic treatment of cancer offers neither a completely safe procedure nor in any degree a sure cure. Neither does any other treatment.

Immunology, still undergoing acute growing pains, has opened enormous vistas of potential cures for cancer. It is reasonable to assume that, as new techniques are developed, some of the substances in blood, fluids, and tissues which have been found to destroy cancer will be isolated, purified, identified, and possibly synthesized. Some of them, singly or in various combinations, may be indicated for treatment of sick humans.

Numerous other natural substances not mentioned in this account have shown decided cancer-killing activity in test tubes or in animals or both, and these may prove of value in the treatment of human cancer. They include specific and nonspecific RNA, DNA, RNase, DNase, a number of enzymes, amino acids, and several dozen natural compounds and complexes which at this stage are still called "X," the algebraic equivalent of the legal John Doe—identity unknown.

Something, an X, inhibits viruses in the female genital tract, including *Rous sarcoma* virus. Cervicovaginal secretions have destroyed the infectivity of cancer and non-cancer viruses.

There is an X in DNA digests which stimulates the production of DNA, the multiplication of cells (including antibody-producing lymph cells), and the cell secretion of antibodies. Dr. Werner Braun of Rutgers believes some versions of X might be of clinical value in cancer.

Some hold that cows may be made to produce an anticancer "colostrum." In this sense, colostrum means milk containing an X—possibly antibodies—against a cancer antigen. (Some investigators have professed to have made cows produce colostrums against infectious agents by injecting the agents into their udders and thereby immunizing, or sensitizing, the animals.) Scientists at Johns Hopkins and the U.S. Department of Agriculture injected cows' udders with a mince of human breast cancer and then treated seventeen breast-cancerous women with the colostrum. The milk seemed to contain anticancer antibody, but none of the patients showed objective benefit from the treatment.

Another X—this one called fetuin—has been isolated (still in impure form) from embryonic and calves' blood by a group headed by Dr. Theodore T. Puck of the University of Colorado. It seems to play a critical role in the development of the fetus. Whether fetuin will affect the embryonoid cancer cell remains to be seen.

Fever-inducing substances have been isolated from the blood, and they are still another X. One is an enzyme called lysozyme, a product of white blood cells known as granulocytes. Lysozyme has been found deficient in the sera of patients with chronic lymphatic leukemia, and high levels of it have been reported in acute monocytic and granuloeytic leukemia. The enzyme, used in treatment of many virus infections and various kinds of cancer, has reduced inflammation and relieved pain, often permitting withdrawal of narcotics; some of its effects are those of radiation. Various patients respond to lysozyme in different degrees. Lysozyme was discovered in 1922 by Sir Alexander Fleming; he noticed that it wiped out bacteria in a nasal mucus culture. The enzyme, readily recovered from many tissues and abounding in the whites of eggs, was rediscovered in the 1960s by scientists in Italian, French, English, Brazilian, and American universities as a highly exciting substance.

Dr. Robert W. Wissler is seeking an X which makes capillary walls permeable to anticancer antibodies and complement. Some anticancer viruses seem to contain this X.

Another X is exuded by lymph cells sensitized against cancer. Sensitized lymph cells from cancer-resistant rats injected with mouse cancer have been put in tiny boxes (millipore chambers) with pores large enough to permit particles but not cells to pass through; the boxes were buried under the skin of mice, and the imprisoned sensitized rat lymph cells oozed something (X) which destroyed cancer cells in the mice. Because the rat cells were protected by the box from contact with mouse cells, they did not produce antimouse antibodies and runt disease, and were not destroyed by mouse immune substances. With so many valuable immune substances in lymphocytes, one wonders whether the widespread custom of snipping out the appendix, adenoids, and tonsils has influenced cancer rates. A few have questioned the practice of removing apparently healthy lymph nodes during some types of cancer surgery.

And then there are the magical X's, known as the transforming principle. Some believe it is RNA. Some say it is DNA. Experiments indicate it probably is both. Dr. M. C. Niu of Temple University has used the RNA of cancer cells to transform cultured normal cells into cancer, and vice versa. He also has used RNA from various organs to make embryonic cells mature into donor-type cells. University of Michigan studies showed that DNA or RNA injected into their bellies stimulated mice's production of antibodies.

Dr. Antonio Rottino of St. Vincent's Hospital has reported isolating an

X from tumor-bearing humans, mice, fruitflies, chickens, and bacterial cultures which induces cancers in several species. He has extracted from the same sources another substance which suppresses X.

In the glittering magic, miracles, and mirages of science, quiet but powerful lines of investigation sometimes are lost sight of. Important biological phenomena are ignored until someone glamorizes a small part of one as the cause of one ailment or the cure for another.

One of the basic mysteries of life which deserves a good deal more attention than it has received—and particularly in cancer research—is the process by which microscopic organisms may assume many different forms. A virus which attacks bacteria-causing soft rot in onions, for instance, assumes many shapes. It can be with or without head or tail, with two tails, rod-shaped, or resembling a dumbbell. Some forms, like common molds, live one phase of their lives as individual blobs of protoplasm; under the stimulus of a natural chemical called acrasin the blobs stream together to live a multicellular sort of existence. The deadly anthrax bacterium changes shape radically as it transforms from a killer to an innocent organism. Strains of jellyfish live alternately as colonies or as individuals, depending on available food and other economic conditions. All humans at one time in their lives existed as a single cell.

Some organisms exist at various times as a particle and as a cell. The bacterium which causes whooping cough is an example of this. When threatened with attack, chilled, aged, or treated with certain chemicals, the bacterium turns into a particle; it reverts to normal when the threat of destruction is removed. These particles are called L-forms, or Listerforms. They probably are numerous, particularly among fungi and gramnegative bacteria. Not much is known about them, because few modern scientists have evinced much interest in them or their remarkable changes of form. Many still dispute contentions that a particle can become a cell; they say this idea went out when spontaneous generation was discredited.

A decade ago it was regarded as heresy to attribute cancers to viruses. Today, with cancer research very virus-minded, it may be heresy to suggest that some of the "viruslike particles" discovered in cancers may not be viruses at all but rather something like L-form organisms.

A few scientists for many years have been reporting pleomorphic (manyform) organisms in all kinds of cancers. On some occasions the researchers were abused, but usually they were ignored—which in science is worse than being abused. Their work had little impact on research and none on medicine.

By now several bits of isolated circumstantial evidence support suspicions that pleomorphic, or L-form, organisms have a role in cancer. No one has undertaken the herculean task of adding it up, however. It is conceivable that they and their products could incite the allergic, immune, and autoimmune manifestations in the disease.

Dr. Irene Corey Diller of the Institute for Cancer Research in Philadelphia for almost two decades has reported finding one kind or another of L-form organisms in a great many animal cancers and some human tumors. Most of those who commented advised her to pay no attention to them—they were laboratory contaminants, and they could be found in the air everywhere. Under stringent sterile precautions, however, the organisms still appeared in her cancer cultures and not in normal cell cultures.

Dr. Diller succeeded in isolating some of the organisms. They usually were an odd breed of changing shapes and sizes, sometimes bacteroid, sometimes fungoid, as are the acid-fast mycobacteria of tuberculosis and leprosy. They infected human leukemic and scavenger cells—the histiocytes in connective tissue and phagocytes in circulating blood. She found them in many other animal cancer cells and in the pre-cancerous cells of the mouse breast. When she injected large doses of the motile rod forms (from very early isolates) into mice, the animals died quickly and violently; small doses of weakened organisms induced inflammatory changes, abscesses and tumors in various organs and degenerative changes in many tissues, and they increased the cancer incidence. Small doses of cortisone enhanced the infection. The liver was a frequent target. A vaccine of killed organisms was injected into mice with transplanted tumors; it gave strong protection against some cancers, none against others. The vaccine given to day-old mice caused overgrowth of lymphatic tissues and inflammation of the liver, kidneys and spleen.

When Dr. Diller placed well-known fungi—baker's and brewer's yeast—into cancer cultures, the yeasts killed the cancer cells and encircled the nuclei. And sometimes the yeast cells killed the cancer cells without even making contact with them; apparently they secreted some kind of poison. Injected into mice with transplanted tumors, the yeasts destroyed the cancers completely in up to 95 per cent of the animals; in mice with ascites cancers, however, the organisms were destroyed by defense cells.

Two polysaccharides—zymosan and hydroglucan—were isolated from the yeast cells; they stimulated the RES and cured some mouse cancers but had no effect on others. At this point, scientists interested in polysaccharides looked into this phase of Dr. Diller's work.

Other groups have supported Dr. Diller's evidence of a relationship between microorganisms and cancer, and they have added to suspicions that fungi may be a more common public health problem than is supposed.

Concurrently with Dr. Diller, a group at the Presbyterian Hospital, Newark, New Jersey, reported that they had grown in embryonated eggs a number of pleomorphic organisms isolated from the blood and blood-forming tissues of cancerous humans and animals. Drs. Eleanor Alexander-

Jackson and Virginia Wuerthele-Caspe declared that the organisms, which sometimes assumed the size and shape of some viruses, existed not only in several hundred cancer patients they had tested but also in patients with scleroderma and a few other slow-acting proliferative diseases. Some apparently healthy humans also harbored the organisms; these investigators wondered whether this indicated a prelude to cancer. Injection of the organisms into animals induced tumors, they reported.

Clostridium is a spore-producing bacterium; various strains cause botulism, gas gangrene, and tetanus in man. Drs. J. R. and G. Moese of the University of Graz reported in 1963 that, by injecting spores from a nonpathogenic strain, Cl. butyricum, they had melted away mouse tumors. Scientists elsewhere soon found these spores would destroy cancers in hamsters and rats, as well as mice. Tested in thirty-six humans, they destroyed the tumors in twelve and damaged them in three more. But sometimes they accelerated cancers in animals. They are not yet considered fit for clinical use.

Investigations at the University of Pennsylvania have brought to light the presence of pleuropneumonialike organisms (PPLO) and sixteen other kinds of organisms, including L-forms, in cultured benign and malignant tumors and normal cell lines; but the investigators said these might be chance contaminants.

Dr. Daniel R. Boggs of Kearns, Utah, has reported that thrush—a disease caused by yeastlike *Candida albicans*—often is found in patients debilitated by cancer and other serious diseases. He reported that his studies showed the patients as a rule had received antibiotics and cortisone as treatment, and he voiced his own and others' suspicions that the hormones and other anticancer drugs may depress the patients' resistance, permitting the organisms to grow. Thrush usually begins with ulcers on the tongue, which spread to involve the mouth, larynx, pharynx, digestive tract, lungs, and skin. Thrush usually does not kill the patient; cancer fells him first.

Dr. Eliane LeBreton of Villejuif, near Paris, injected a common peanut mold, *Aspergillus flavus,* into rats and produced liver cancer. Influenced by this observation and recent reports that moldy peanuts as turkey feed had decimated British flocks with acute liver disease, Dr. Shimkin in 1963 asserted that mold and mold products—including some antibiotics—now must be viewed with suspicion as possible carcinogenic agents. He raised the question as to whether the peanut mold, which flourishes in certain Asian and African areas where liver cancer among children and adults is almost epidemic, might not be responsible for some human liver tumors.

One scientist in a large cancer hospital recently reported that "there is no doubt that the incidence of mycotic [fungal] infection has increased at this hospital." The increase, he said, had been progressive since 1950. One

of the fungal agents, *Aspergillus,* had infected thirty patients and contributed to the deaths of at least eleven. The infections were considered a
consequence of the patients' lowered resistance, due in part to the anticancer drugs they had taken. It was not suggested that the organisms caused
or contributed to the cancers.

It may turn out that viruses, fungi, bacteria, and the whole field of immunity have nothing to do with human cancer. To further ignore the able
and reputable investigators who entertain the suspicions that they do and
to completely discount evidence of their involvement, however, could well
delay an understanding of cancer and control of the disease.

CHAPTER 21

LEUKEMIA

Of all the diagnoses, the most fateful is leukemia. It is destiny, signed and sealed, the setting for an early Christmas, the essence of the six-months-to-live story situation.

Leukemia, meaning "white blood," is cancer of the tissues which manufacture blood cells. The tissues are the bone marrow and lymphatic tissues spread throughout the body. Leukemic cells—young, useless, predatory and constantly proliferating—invade the marrow, swell the spleen, liver, and lymph nodes and often infiltrate the lung, stomach, esophagus, tonsils, bladder, and urethra. A number of malignant diseases involving lymphatic and marrow tissues are closely related to leukemia; they include lymphosarcoma and Hodgkin's disease and, perhaps more distantly, mycosis fungoides, multiple myeloma, chloroma, and myeloid metaplasia. One source lists more than seventy kinds of leukemia and allied diseases lumped into a category called malignant lymphoma.

Leukemia is called incurable. Still, there are several well-documented cases in which youngsters dying of the disease became beneficiaries of that rare miracle, "spontaneous regression," and were completely cured.

Leukemia is considered a disease of children. It now is five times as common in older people, and in adults the incidence is increasing at an astounding rate.

It is considered a rare disease. Yet it is much too common. Of all diseases, leukemia is the leading killer of children; in 1963, an estimated 11,500 adults and 2,300 children died of it. Leukemia claimed almost one-half of all youngsters lost to cancer. An additional 700 or so children and 14,000 adults fell victim to lymphomas.

One gets the impression that leukemia always is rapidly fatal. Yet some patients live ten or twenty or more years with chronic leukemia under reasonable control, and die of diseases of old age.

Some say the cause of leukemia is not known. X rays and benzol compounds, and possibly arsenic as well, cause leukemia in humans; and many other causes have been traced in animals.

In leukemia, the bloodstream is said to be glutted with white cells. In aleukemic leukemia (meaning no-leukemia leukemia) the white-cell count can be perilously low. In any case, the patients are susceptible to infection and hemorrhage, because the cells are defective.

Almost all scientists consider leukemia a cancer, and for more than fifteen years it has been classified as such in the official international catalogue of diseases. In laboratory animals, however, it can be caused with any of several viruses, thus making it an infectious disease.

Perhaps more than any other kind of cancer, leukemia's identity is lost in an enormous snarl of clues—age factors, hormones, infections, occupational exposures, genetic vagaries, congenital accidents, stresses, racial influences, geography, and all the rest.

Somewhere in this maze is a component or a combination which is the answer to leukemia and the key to other cancers. The job of combining out of this tangled mess the significant factors is a difficult—but not insuperable—one. Some feel that this now hopeless disease will be the first major cancer to be cured by means other than surgery or radiation.

Every now and then a dramatic situation yields a promise of penetrating the inscrutable exterior of leukemia. In most instances the evidence hints at a virus or other infection as the cause.

Scientists at the University of Minnesota discovered that within a short period children of four veterinarians developed acute lymphatic leukemia. The veterinarians had treated cows which had lymphosarcoma of unknown genesis and chickens with contagious virus-caused leukemoid diseases. Were the veterinarians the unwitting carriers of the disease to babies who had not yet become "immunologically competent"—that is, who were too young to produce sufficient antibodies against infectious agents?

In Niles, Illinois, a Chicago suburb of 18,863 people, eight children came down with leukemia—three during an eight-month period in 1957–58 and five during ten months in 1959–60. Seven either attended or had older brothers or sisters attending a parochial school with 1,416 students. All lived within a two-mile square area. Dr. Clark Heath, then of the Communicable Disease Center and now of Harvard University, investigated. He found no history of unusual exposure to radiation or toxic materials; no contact between the victims or their families; all eight families were of different national origins, had different physicians, went to different hospitals, moved to Niles from Chicago at different times; they came mostly from middle-class homes, and their diets, habits, sports, and other characteristics were those of the average suburban American family; radiation from the soil and buildings was moderate; the leukemics had had the usual history of mumps, measles, and other childhood diseases, and, like other children, they had taken their shots for smallpox, polio, and other infections.

Dr. Heath discovered that during the period of the leukemia outbreak, two other children had come down with nonleukemic cancers and two adults developed leukemia—all of them living in a single block within the parish. Five other children in the same area had been diagnosed as having leukemia, but the diagnoses later were reversed: they had or had died of other diseases. Dr. Heath found that during these critical months eight cases of rheumaticlike illness had occurred among parish school children, and another unusual number of youngsters had died of congenital heart disease.

Dr. Heath concluded that the leukemia outbreak was due to an unidentified infectious agent.

Meanwhile, a dozen other clusters of childhood leukemia were reported from widely separated communities, including Chicago, New York, Philadelphia, Cheyenne, Bergen County, New Jersey, Orange, Texas, and Seattle's suburban Mercer and Whidbey Islands; some, or perhaps all, of them may be a statistical mirage. One other report, under investigation at this writing, cites twenty-four cases of leukemia centering around Lewiston, Idaho.

Despite the outbreaks, epidemiologic data—with a substantial margin for error—indicates that while adult leukemia is increasing rapidly, the rate of childhood leukemia has remained steady. A personal inquiry of the local public health authorities has shown that the incidence of childhood leukemia and lymphoma in Chicago and the State of Washington lurched upward in the mid-1950s and has continued to rise. During the last decade or so, congenital malformations and deaths from them have begun to soar. Some consider childhood leukemia often congenital in origin.

In leukemia, perhaps more than in other forms of cancer, statistics serve as only a rough measurement of the size of the threat and the speed of its advance. The undiagnosed and misdiagnosed cases, of course, are not included. Dr. Mila I. Pierce, a University of Chicago pediatrician of considerable experience, has reported 10 per cent of her cases of childhood leukemia as of congenital origin—a much higher percentage than is generally recorded. She added: "The association of other congenital defects— mongolism, cardiac defects, abnormalities of the bones and so on—with congenital leukemia suggests that an intrauterine disturbance occurs between the sixth and ninth weeks of gestation and initiates the leukemic process in the fetus." She points out that the initial signs and symptoms of childhood leukemia are those of many common minor infectious illnesses; and, as a matter of fact, leukemia very often follows a cold or other contagious disease which just does not seem to go away. Sometimes leukemia may be confounded with its complications which become the immediate cause of death—brain hemorrhage, bleeding into the mouth, throat and digestive tract, bowel ulceration and hemorrhage, secondary infections and septicemia, kidney infiltration, central nervous system involvement and, in the very young, separation of cranial sutures, following headache, vomiting, or swelling of the nerves. Dr. Pierce mentions as conditions with which leukemia should not be mistaken in diagnosis, acute lymphocytosis, infectious mononucleosis, rheumatic fever, disseminated lupus erythematosus, aplastic anemia, septicemia, Hodgkin's disease, reticulocytosis, and histoplasmosis. By misdiagnosing leukemia and treating the wrong patient for leukemia, one can induce leukemia or another grave or fatal disease.

Dr. Lauren Ackerman, the distinguished pathologist of Washington University, has pointed out that some anticonvulsant drugs cause swellings of lymph glands which can be confounded with leukemia. Others have said that antibiotics and other drugs often are used against viral infections in children and seldom reported, and a few have wondered whether these have played any part in transforming a stubborn infection into leukemia. Dr. Alice Stewart of Oxford University has expressed the view that some early childhood leukemias follow changes induced by radiation and chemicals in immature ova from which future patients spring. The change, she believes, may alter cells which form the infection-combating RES (reticuloendothelial system), the lymphatic organs and marrow which give rise to defensive lymph cells. "Before the discovery of sulfonamides and antibiotics," she has written, "the usual cause of death among children with congenitally defective RES was pneumonia. Now such children survive the infections only to die later of leukemia. The drugs probably have increased the early peak of leukemia mortality, the risk of death among mongols and the number of sibships with more than one instance of leukemia or lymphosarcoma."

The idea of leukemia being transmitted from animal to man has not had wide acceptance, but a growing number of investigators seem to be tolerant of it. Dr. Johannes Clemmeson of Copenhagen has argued that in view of the present lack of knowledge about the genesis of the disease, physicians must consider any and all clues, including animal vectors. Lymphosarcoma among cows, for instance, has spread steadily across Western Europe since its discovery in Germany in 1871, and in the last thirty or more years it has infiltrated many herds in the United States. Drs. Robert R. Marshak of the University of Pennsylvania and Lewis L. Coriell of the South Jersey Medical Research Foundation have investigated the disease intensively;

they have given the sick animals many tests—complete physicals, electrocardiograms, frequent blood counts, marrow biopsies, platelet counts, sedimentation rates, urine and feces analysis, blood nitrogen, thyroid tests, chromosome counts, exhaustive autopsies and efforts to make whatever causes the disease, like viruses, grow in chicken eggs, tissue cultures, and laboratory animals. While the cause of the disease so far has not been discovered, the scientists have found that in cattle it follows the selfsame unswerving course as in humans, showing the same initial symptoms, attacking the same organs, killing in the same way and perhaps with a bit more speed. Suggestions of genetic influence seem to be only about as strong as they are in humans. One inspection of cattle brought to slaughter showed a lymphosarcoma rate of 17.6 per 100,000; the disease was highest in Holsteins but also was found in Guernseys, Ayrshires, Jerseys, and Angus.

Several bits of evidence indicate that there is at least a one-way transmission of leukemia—from man to animals. Dr. Ludwik Gross, in his book called *Oncogenic Viruses,* cites experiments over the past sixty or seventy years in which a succession of scientists induced cancers, including leukemia, in rabbits, rats, chicks, and mice with human tumors and extracts of them.

That viruses do cause animal leukemias there can be little doubt. Dr. Joseph G. Sinkovics of M. D. Anderson Hospital, reviewing the literature, has enumerated eighteen viruses and virus variants recognized as causing leukemia and leukemia-related disease in mice and rats. Various viruses exist naturally in certain animal strains, grow strong or weak when injected into foreign strains, infect only newborn or very young mice or infect young and old alike, induce lymphatic leukemia in one strain and a different leukemia in another, cause leukemia in some foreign species and solid cancers in others, are brought to life in irradiated animals or are extracted from solid and sometimes regressing cancers, and sometimes, weak or killed, the viruses serve as antileukemia vaccines.

So far as anyone knows, leukemia may never start as leukemia. It seems to start as something else—either a seemingly well-defined infection or a vague illness. By the time the diagnosis of leukemia is made, the case is hopeless.

One psychiatric group studied the pre-disease histories of thirty-two women who came down with leukemias and lymphomas. They reported that within four years prior to their diagnosis, thirty of them had suffered a shattering loss of a son, daughter, father, mother, or husband, or had been separated or threatened with separation. The other two had also undergone severe emotional trauma. The group concluded that great emotional disturbances could trigger the onset of leukemia or lymphoma and exacerbations of the disease during its long or short course.

The acute disease in humans and animals observes a seasonal variation; like infections, its peak is during the winter and early spring. In chickens, spontaneous leukemia is twice as severe in the early spring as in early fall; even leukemia transplants to laboratory animals are twice as successful in the spring as in the fall. It is largely a disease of cold and temperate climates; there is little leukemia in the tropics.

The onset of leukemia usually is insidious in both children and adults. Early leukemia is remarkably free of pain; the swollen tissues seldom are tender. In children, it often follows a slow recovery from a cold or a contagious disease. The child is pale, apathetic, somewhat feverish, bearing bruises of unknown origin, and without appetite. Eventually bleeding tendencies—from the gums and under the skin most often—are found. Backaches and bone pains add to the discomforts of sore mouth and sore throat. Chronic leukemia, most often reserved for adults, may be preceded by a year or two of unexplainable great fatigue, easy bruising, bleeding, itching, flatulence, dyspepsia and perhaps an enlarged spleen and lymph nodes. Patients may have any or all of these symptoms—or still other signs of the oncoming disease.

Leukemia's advance may be extremely fast, moderate, or very slow. Acute leukemia usually pursues a rapid downhill course; but even here, fleeting remissions occur in 5 per cent of the untreated patients. The subacute and chronic leukemias may become acute without warning. One experiment—by Dr. Robert Shrek of the VA Hospital, Hines, Illinois—has shown some prognostic value. He removed lymphocytes from eighty patients with chronic lymphocytic leukemia or lymphosarcoma, put the cells in glass dishes, and irradiated them; in sixty-one cases the diseased lymph cells survived X rays no better than lymphocytes from normal people, and these patients lived an average of twenty-two months; in the other nineteen cases, the lymphocytes resisted radiation, and these patients survived an average of only four months.

Dr. James F. Holland of Roswell Park has said that the acute leukemias usually end in any of three "complicating catastrophes": infection, bleeding, or destruction of a vital organ. Fatal infection, he said, is a consequence of the patient's shortage of normal disease-fighting white-blood cells against a death-dealing agent which is bacterial more often than viral. Bleeding occurs because of a lack of thrombocytes, or platelets, the sticky disks which patch up leaky or ruptured vessels, an excess of enzymes which dissolve fibers, and deficiencies in clotting proteins. Instead of manufacturing normal white cells, lymphatic tissues and marrow produce leukemic cells which, with ameboid motility, infiltrate and destroy the protective covering of nerves, brain, mucous membranes, skin, marrow, the sacs enclosing the heart and lungs, and the kidneys. Anemia occurs in almost all acute leukemics. Singly and in combination, these conditions often become painful. When the end finally comes, many patients and their tired and tortured families and physicians have a sense of sad relief.

A good deal of study and speculation has gone into the question as to when the destiny of leukemic doom is sealed. There is a wide range of conclusions—anywhere from several generations before the victim's birth to a short time before the disease is diagnosed.

Despite striking instances of leukemia "running in families," including fraternal and identical twins, the consensus is that the disease is not inherited. Reports by sixty-four hematologists on 2,448 cases of acute leukemia (four-fifths of them in children) disclosed ten instances in which at least two siblings (including one set of fraternal twins) in a single family had leukemia. Records compiled at the Children's Research Foundation in Boston show one family in which three of seven children died of acute leukemia and a fourth of lymphosarcoma, another in which four of twelve children had acute leukemia when they became young adults, and still another in which five of eight children had acute leukemia, and all five died before their eighth birthday. A Bucharest investigator has listed eighteen sets of identical twins who developed leukemia, usually either simultaneously or a short time apart—most of them as infants, but a few in old age.

That at least some of these dramatic situations are not sheer coincidence is almost certain. Factors other than hereditary easily could account for them, however. Among the possibilities are: (1) irradiating the young girl's or woman's pelvis, or strong leukemogens (leukemia-inducers) in drugs, food, or some other environmental source might have wrought the leukemic transformation in many or all of a future mother's immature ova; (2) a chronic or recurrent viral or other infection during successive pregnancies or a cyclic stress at a critical period in gestation might be responsible, and (3) because family members share the same childhood environment, the cause might be related to familial encounters with a leukemogen.

One study of 285 leukemic children by Dr. Daniel Stowens of the University of Southern California showed that in one-quarter of the cases, at least one member of the family, usually a grandparent, had diabetes. Among nonleukemic controls, only 4 per cent showed a similar family history of diabetes. Dr. Stowens reported that 10 per cent of the children with acute leukemia had high urine sugar levels and that all of those examined at autopsy had significant alterations of the insulin-producing cells of the pancreas. If these findings are borne out by other studies, they may indicate that diabetes, often inherited, in some cases could constitute a genetic hormonal predisposition to leukemia.

The existence of congenital factors in leukemia is confirmed by several situations. In twenty-one recorded instances a child has been born leukemic—never, however, of a leukemic mother. More often leukemia and another congenital condition, notably mongolism, coexist in the same victim. Brothers and sisters of leukemic children have a remarkably high incidence of mongolism. In both leukemia and mongolism, cells often have an odd number of chromosomes. In these cases, the culpable agent may pass from the mother through the placenta, or it may arise in the placenta itself.

The placenta, which shelters the embryo from many prenatal diseases and disasters, is covered by microvilli—30 miles of slender, streaming fingers of protoplasm, exposing 160 square feet of surface to maternal blood which flows through them at the rate of 500 cubic centimeters a minute. The maternal blood nourishes the fetus with hormones, thousands of enzymes, water, oxygen, electrolytes, glucose, amino acids, vitamins and other nutrients, and it removes fetal wastes. Metabolic accidents of many kinds could lead to fetal death, malformation, or leukemia—excess hormone production by the mother or by the placenta, failure of the system to bind the enormous output of hormones with protein and thereby neutralize them, blockage or rupture of the placenta, destructive antibodies seeping into the fetus through the amniotic fluid, or an unfavorable shift in the fluid flow between mother and fetus. There is a question as to whether placental cells—trophoblasts—may not themselves form the seeds of future cancers in the offspring, as they do occasionally in the mother when they fail to undergo sudden senility, die and be discharged on delivery of the child. In some enzymatic respects these embryonic cells resemble cancer cells.

There is one report of a leukemic mother dying one week after giving birth to a child who developed leukemia nine months later. Leukemic women usually bear perfectly healthy babies, however, providing they live through their pregnancy in good shape and do not take radiation or drug treatment which would abort or mutilate the fetus. About 40 per cent of leukemic pregnant women have a normal baby. In Hodgkin's disease, it is different—about one-tenth of the successfully-delivered babies are born with their mothers' disease.

Some years ago at the University of Chicago, Drs. Leon Jacobson and Matthew Block had the rare opportunity of studying eighteen adults, mostly women, for from three to thirty months, during which they progressed from a mélange of puzzling pathologic states into acute leukemia. Prominent among their sizable catalogue of preleukemic symptoms were multiple allergies. The records do not indicate what happened to the al-

lergies as these patients became leukemic, but it would be interesting to know whether they persisted during the leukemic state. Later studies by groups at the University of Minnesota, Roswell Park, and other institutions have shown that a high percentage of patients with cancer—and particularly with leukemia and lymphomas—are anergic; that is, they lack the ability to give a normal response in a situation calling for allergic reaction. The anergic patients, after being sensitized with an allergen (allergy-inducing substance) like a tuberculin, viral or fungal antigen, do not respond with the typical skin rash or other delayed reaction when exposed a second time to the same antigen. Anergy seems to progress as the cancers advance into late stages.

One other observation may fit into the possible relationship of allergy and anergy to leukemia. A group working with Dr. Sidney Farber at the Children's Cancer Research Foundation, Boston, discovered that 32.4 per cent of the mothers of leukemic children suffered from such allergies as hives and hay fever; this contrasts with the finding that 11.8 per cent of mothers of children with other, nonleukemic, cancers and 20 per cent of mothers of children with no serious disease were similarly allergic.

Questions naturally arise: Could leukemia (or lymphomas) and the resultant anergy represent the body's too-successful effort to overcome allergy? Could anergy be the consequence of an overworked and exhausted allergic response?

Epidemiological studies of leukemia have been of limited help. The disease has a way of shifting its unwelcome presence so consistently that last year's statistics are out of date this year.

Geography is important, but throws little light on the cause of the disease. Childhood leukemia in the United States is reported highest in New Jersey (4.8 per 100,000 population), Montana and Oregon (4.7). It is reported lowest in Nevada (0.7), South Carolina (2.2), Georgia, Florida (both 2.6), West Virginia, and Mississippi (2.8). All leukemias, childhood and adult, in modern countries are highest in Denmark (about 7.5), United States (about 6.2) and Sweden (6.0). They are lowest in Japan (2.8), Portugal (3.3), and Ireland (4.7).

Sex is a significant factor, but a confusing one. Males are much more susceptible than females. In the United States the leukemia ratio is about three males to two females and in all other countries this proportion exists to a greater or less degree. In experimental animals, by contrast, the female is the more susceptible, and injections of female hormones, estrogens, cause leukemia in some strains and in castrated males.

Dr. Brian MacMahon of Harvard University has cited these grim selections: While leukemia is low in Israel, it is twice as high among Brooklyn Jews as among their Catholic and Protestant neighbors; it is much commoner in areas of high background radiation than low. In France, there is six times as much adult leukemia in granite regions as in neighboring areas. It is 50 per cent higher in United States urban areas than rural districts. The older the mother when the first child is born, the higher the child's chances of developing both leukemia and mongolism; leukemia is twice as common among the first born of old mothers as in the later born of young mothers. In Brooklyn, Negroes proved little more than one-half as susceptible as Whites. When one identical twin develops leukemia, the second has a 25 per cent chance of dying of the disease.

Leukemia is highest among urban populations, the better educated people, and those enjoying a high standard of living. With the exception of breast cancer and leukemia, malignant disease is most frequent among the less well-to-do.

Radiation causes leukemia both in animals and humans. It does so in one large dose or multiple small ones. On this there is virtually no dispute. There is, however, considerable difference of opinion as to the size of the radiation dose which is dangerous for humans, and this is a sensitive subjects for physicians who feel that fear will restrain their patients from having necessary X-ray examinations and treatments. The lot of physicians themselves hardly instills confidence; as a class, radiologists, dentists, dermatologists, and general doctors have high leukemia rates, although they have become more respectful of radiation. A study, reported in December, 1963, by a Cal Tech scientist, indicated that even the experts, board-certified radiologists, have from three to twenty times the leukemia and related diseases of the general population. They were especially subject to multiple myeloma and aplastic anemia. In the light of the doctor's own unfortunate exposure, the patient may be justifiably squeamish about X rays. The answer is to go to physicians who know radiation technology, have good equipment, and make it a point to determine the patient's prior radiation exposure and don't irradiate except for good cause.

Reports too numerous to list here have indicted radiation as a major culprit in human leukemia. The disease has been found in elevated rates among patients irradiated in childhood or as adults for a variety of conditions, including enlarged thymus, goiters, ankylosing spondlylitis, acne, and numerous other conditions. And, of course, pelvic irradiation of the pregnant woman presents a risk for the offspring.

Several authorities have said that benzol and benzene compounds are highly suspect as leukemogens. These are coal-tar products widely used as solvents and in the manufacture of many products. Dr. William Dameshek of the New England Medical Center has suggested that physicians periodically examine the blood of patients taking a variety of drugs—

certain antiepileptics, antihistamines, dexedrine, chloramphenicol, tars, phenols, and chyrsarobin; while the preparations have not been proved to cause leukemia, they do induce blood changes which conceivably might lead to leukemia. He also has voiced suspicions of certain cleaning-up solvents, gasoline, oils, and greases, including some handled by garage mechanics and oil-industry workers. Insecticides, arsenicals, floor waxes and solvents, including paint removers, have been mentioned by others.

Dr. R. Wayne Rundles of Duke University names as "possible and conjectural" causes certain antibiotics, insecticides, sedatives, pep pills, tranquilizers and analgesics.

Animal experiments have yielded valuable information on leukemia, although in many respects mice seem to react differently than humans, and even between strains and within inbred strains of mice there is wide variance of the response to leukemogens and the course of the disease.

Heredity is important in animals. More than 90 per cent of one mouse strain develops spontaneous leukemia; in some others, the disease is extremely rare and difficult to induce.

Leukemia often can be induced readily in young animals but not in older ones. In at least one strain of mouse, the offspring of young mothers are more susceptible to leukemia than those of older mothers and those in late litters; this is the reverse of the reported situations in humans in which the risk of leukemic offspring rises with maternal age.

In some experimental mice, estrogen induces leukemia; male hormone suppresses it dramatically and progesterone slightly; removal of the ovaries sometimes has a moderate inhibiting effect; removal of the testes shortens the latent period and increases the incidence; cortisol slows the development of leukemia, and adrenal removal enhances the effect of X rays and leukemogens. There is a strain difference—and a difference of opinion among scientists—as to whether thyroid hormone has an inhibitory effect.

Severe restriction of caloric intake slows the development of leukemia.

The late Dr. Arthur W. Kirschbaum showed that in his mice the various factors—hormones, age, genes, and leukemogens—were additive and possibly worked through a common pathway. He also showed that something in the milk of leukemia-resistant mice tended to suppress the disease; susceptible new-born mice nursed by resistant foster mothers were slow in developing leukemia, and some seemed to escape it altogether. He made the observation, which at this writing seems to be gaining in significance, that a carcinogen, methylcholanthrene, induces leukemia in a mouse strain resistant to lung cancer, and it induces lung cancer in another strain resistant to leukemia. This and similar findings by others now are stimulating speculation as to the relationship of leukemia and solid tumors.

One of the most intriguing chains of evidence as to the nature of leukemia extends over two decades. It centers around the thymus, a gland of —until recently—obscure function which is located between the neck and the chest, behind the breastbone. It is composed largely of lymph cells, or lymphocytes, and it reaches its growth peak during infancy, after which it gradually slows down until, at puberty, it atrophies. Until recently, this was almost all that was known about the thymus.

It now appears that at least in some mice, the thymus plays a key role in the cause of leukemia. Indirect damage to the gland induces the disease. In some mice, radiation and viruses cannot induce leukemia in the absence of the gland.

Back in 1944, Dr. Jacob Furth and his associates, during the methodical testing of gland influence on the incidence of mouse leukemia, removed the thymus gland of mice which almost invariably develop leukemia. The thymectomized mice never did become leukemic.

Six years later, Dr. Henry S. Kaplan at Stanford University reported a series of experiments on mice which normally became leukemic after being irradiated. He removed their thymus glands before irradiating them, and these animals failed to develop leukemia. He then removed the thymus, irradiated the mice and several days later transplanted either their own or another mouse thymus to them. These thymectomized animals with the grafted thymus readily developed leukemia if they received the new thymus within eight days following irradiation. Obviously, something in the blood of the irradiated animals damaged the thymus and brought on leukemia.

In 1959, Dr. Ludwik Gross of the Bronx VA Hospital found that a leukemic virus also acted on the thymus. When he removed the gland and injected the virus, the mice did not develop leukemia. If he waited until one month after virus infection to remove the gland, about one-half the mice developed leukemia. If he thymectomized, infected, and then grafted a new thymus under the skin, 90 per cent became leukemic.

Perhaps the most significant thymus observation was made in 1960, when Dr. Robert Good and Dr. Carlos Martinez of the University of Minnesota teamed up to study the organ. Dr. Good had found that a substantial number of cancer patients, and particularly leukemics, lacked gamma globulin, the stuff that antibodies are made of, and consequently were defenseless under infections. Lymphoid cells, like those in the thymus, manufacture gamma globulin. Dr. Martinez had developed ingenious techniques for the transplant of glands between different strains of mice. They wanted to know what function the thymus performed in the normal animal. They removed the thymus from mice at birth and waited to see what the effects would be. They found that the thymectomized mice lost a great deal of their ability to populate the spleen, liver, and other organs with lymph cells and to produce antibodies; in the absence of the thymus, the mice would even accept tissue grafts from unrelated strains of animals. Predatory bacteria grew with impunity in thymus-less animals and destroyed them.

The experiments convinced most scientists that in prenatal and young animals (and perhaps humans as well) the thymus seeds the system with lymphoid cells which become lifetime lymphocyte and antibody factories. The findings had bearing not only on the antibody lack in cancer patients but also in people in need of transplants or ill with rheumatoid arthritis and many other diseases due to errors in natural immunity.

Dr. Kaplan has sought to offset radiation effects by manipulating the thymus. He X-rayed a strain of mice which, in response, developed lympho-sarcoma. Between 50 and 100 days after irradiation, he gave the animals either (1) a single massive dose of X rays to the thymus, or (2) an adrenal stress hormone. Either treatment destroyed the damaged and regenerating thymus. One-half the mice were cured of their early leukemia, and the rest survived with their disease for a long time.

Research into the function of the long-ignored gland, the thymus, is proceeding at a rapid pace at this writing. Several scientists have reported isolating hormones and other substances from it.

Early in 1964, Harvard scientists produced evidence that the thymus, instead of disseminating migrant cells which seed the body, actually pro-duced a hormone which stimulated lymphoid cells throughout the body to become bastions of natural resistance to disease. Drs. Margaret MacGilli-vray, Valerie Jones, and Sidney Leskowitz at Massachusetts General Hos-pital thymectomized newborn rats and later implanted into their belly cavities micropore filters containing newborn thymus tissue. The pores in the filters were too small to permit passage of cells. Something, however, seeped from the tissues through the pores into the animal systems which stimulated the development of depleted spleen lymphocytes, restored a lost capacity to produce an allergic response, and, to a degree, reinstated the animals' immunity. Circulating lymphocytes remained depleted.

Dr. Albert Szent-Gyorgyi, who obtained his Nobel prize for isolating ascorbic acid and later achieved the remarkable feat of making dead muscle move by applying adenosine triphosphate (ATP) to it, had long been fascinated by the mystery gland, the thymus. In his laboratory at Woods Hole, Massachusetts, he has found that irregularities in the thymus were somehow related to certain muscle diseases. Gifted with great curiosity and a remarkable capacity for recall, he remembered the work of a German scientist who in 1915 had fed thymus extracts to tadpoles; instead of maturing into frogs, the tadpoles became giants—nonmaturing giant tadpoles. In his search for the elusive chemicals which had accom-plished this arrested development, Dr. Szent-Gyorgi isolated two substances—promine, which made tissues (including cancer) grow, and retine, which arrested growth (including growth of animal cancers). Later, he found promine and retine in many tissues; human urine was rich in it. He has been purifying promine and retine—which may be almost identical substances but poles apart in their response to enzymes—in the hope that retine may be of use in cancer treatment.

Other scientists have found that the thymus somehow influences other hormone-producing glands, particularly the adrenals and thyroid. Drs. C. P. Li and others at the NIH have found that a water extract from calf thymus inhibited Coxsackie virus in tissue culture, and a dilute acetic acid extract showed impressive antibacterial activity against pseudomonas organisms.

The wonders and the mysteries of life, the tangled systems which govern it, and the chemical catacombs which undermine it are reflected realistically in the significance of this single, seemingly insignificant gland, the thymus. It stimulates the appendix, along with other lymphoid organs, and one cannot help but wonder what effect simple appendectomy might have on leukemia and immune diseases. Dr. Bernard Grad of McGill University has reported that a large dose of thyroid hormone, which reduces body weight and may keep the thymus healthy, decreases spontaneous leukemia in mice; antithyroid drugs or a little thyroid hormone plus a fattening diet increase the leukemia incidence. Dr. Patricia P. Weymouth of Clarkson College has noted that a large dose of X rays or of cortisol increases the enzymes which break down nucleic acids in the thymus, and this may be the mechanism by which radiation depopulates the gland of its cells.

The key to the multiple functions of thymus may lie in the nature of the lymph cells which comprise it, and much too little is known about them.

One attractive theory is that the lymph organs constitute the principal, or sole, blood-manufacturing system in the embryo, and that many lymph-cell functions gradually are taken over by bone marrow at birth. According to this idea, when the marrow is impaired at any stage of life, the lymphatic tissues revert to their prenatal function of making blood. Lymph cells, or lymphocytes, comprise 1 per cent of the body's weight; they are ubiquitous, forming solid concentrations in the thymus, spleen, liver, and many other organs; they drain from all the body's tissues in lymph, and they are transported everywhere in the blood. They age by dividing into increasingly smaller lymph cells, and at the end of two or three divisions they disintegrate. Lymph cells are remarkably versatile; as the situation demands, they can transform into blood-manufacturing cells, virus and bacteria destroyers, antibody producers, fiber-spinning cells, scavenger cells which sweep germs and debris out of the system and, time may show, perhaps many other kinds of cells.

Lymph cells—free floating in blood and fluids or fixed in organs—are caused to age rapidly and die when exposed to adrenal stress hormones. They also may exert a reciprocal effect in maintaining adrenal hormone production. Dr. J. Comsa of the University of the Saar found that removal of the thymus depleted the guinea-pig adrenals of cholesterol, from which the adrenals make hormones, and of ascorbic acid which regulates adrenal hormone release. It takes forty days for other lymph tissues to take over the thymus' function and restore adrenal hormone production in thymusless guinea pigs.

The spleen, like the thymus, also contains a great many lymphocytes, or lymph cells. Back in 1950, while Dr. Kaplan was working with the thymus and radiation, Dr. Leon Jacobson at the University of Chicago was undertaking similar experiments with the spleen. Dr. Jacobson found that if he removed the spleen or shielded it in a lead container while a mouse was being irradiated, the animal did not die under enormous X ray doses. The protected spleen was able to sustain and eventually restore the blood-forming system. He prevented or cured lethal radiation sickness by injecting animals with minced spleen or spleen extracts shortly after their exposure to the rays.

Dr. Jacobson also showed that radiation would not kill an animal if a marrow-rich bony part—like a leg—were shielded during irradiation. Marrow cells, like lymph cells, also protected against radiation effects if they escaped the rays.

It became clear that both types of blood-manufacturing cells—lymphocytes and their counterparts in the marrow, myelocytes—undid the damage done by radiation.

The door had been opened to a theoretical cure for leukemia.

A group headed by Dr. John J. Trentin at Baylor University and, almost simultaneously, an English team of scientists cured leukemia in mice with large and lethal doses of X rays. The radiation dose, in curing leukemia, so completely erased the mice's lymphatic and marrow immune mechanisms that rat tissues transplanted to them grew and thrived. To rescue the animals from radiation death, the scientists then injected the irradiated animals with bone marrow. The rescue was highly successful, regardless of whether the marrow came from related or unrelated mice or even from rats.

The mice, delivered from leukemia by radiation, and then from radiation death by marrow injections, now faced another fatal condition, runt disease. In runt disease, the foreign (rat or mouse marrow) cells grow and produce antibodies against their host, block its growth, destroy its organs, and kill it.

Scientists in several centers began a great and gallant series of clinical experiments in efforts to cure leukemic children with massive radiation doses and then overcome the radiation effects with injections of human marrow. In some cases the marrow had been withdrawn from the patient's own bones, stored during irradiation and then restored to the patient. In others the injected marrow was from generous donors, or from stores of fresh or frozen marrow. Spleen cells and fetal liver cells also have been used.

No child has been cured of leukemia by radiation followed by injections of marrow, spleen, or liver. A few seem to have been helped, but this is hard to say for sure. Doctors, however, have kept the radiation dose well below the lethal level; they refused to gamble all of the patient's short survival on a cure-or-kill wager.

Acute leukemia refers to cases in which death may be expected within three months; in subacute leukemia, the victim is expected to die somewhere between three and twelve months hence; in chronic leukemia, the predicted survival is at least one year. Chronic lymphatic leukemia strikes principally among old people; its course usually is so slow that most of these patients die of other diseases, including other cancers, before their leukemia can do them in.

Until 1948, when radiation, benzene products, transfusions, and arsenic were the standard treatments, these rough classifications served a fairly good prognostic purpose. Fully 50 per cent of children with leukemia were dead within four months of diagnosis, and 90 per cent were gone by the end of the year. In 1948, a series of new drugs began entering the picture and, for children, the classifications suddenly became anachronistic. With the advent of counterfeit molecules of the vitamin, folic acid, and the war gas, nitrogen mustard, the first dent was made in leukemia's armor. In the best hospitals, child survival almost doubled under the drugs. Five years later the hormone cortisone became available and in short succession thereafter, a great many antileukemic drugs, including DON, 6-MP, azauracil, TEM, thio-TEPA, Myleran, and chlorambucil.

In 1963, about 50 per cent of leukemic children given the best treatment were surviving fourteen months and 10 per cent thirty months. One girl at Children's Hospital, Boston, lived eight years and two months, being helped by first one drug and then, as she became resistant, another preparation.

Two of every three leukemics can be given some help by one or more measures. The longer lease on life signifies a great deal to scientists; some now feel a cure is possible.

Memorial Cancer Center in New York has listed these drugs as being in common usage against various types of childhood leukemia: (1) the antifolic, Methotrexate, for patients in fairly good condition and (by injection into the spine) for patients with central nervous system involvement; (2) purinethol for those resistant to Methotrexate; (3) cortisone-type drugs—prednisone in severe illness, prednisolone during active bleeding, and the adrenal stimulant, ACTH, and (4) Cytoxan, a nitrogen-mustardlike preparation.

Memorial recommended the following for chronic granulocytic leukemia: in the early state, nitrogen-mustard-type compounds, Purinethol, Fowler's solution, and urethane; in intermediate stages, high doses of X rays to spleen, Myleran, nitrogen mustard, and Purinethol; and in the late stages, Purinethol, Methotrexate, and adrenal cortical hormones.

In Hodgkin's disease, high doses (2,000–3,000 r) of X rays were recommended for early and intermediate stages and lower (600–2,000 r) palliative doses when the blood picture is relatively normal. Nitrogen mustard was suggested as an adjuvant to radiation or to surgery, and chlorambucil, nitrogen mustard, and prednisone were used in various stages as indicated.

The plant extracts leurocristine and vincristine also have yielded brief but striking remissions to leukemic children who had exhausted other means of help and to some Hodgkin's patients.

Evidence of the possible curability of Hodgkin's disease is given by Dr. Henry Kaplan of Stanford. With the exception of four failures while he was establishing the dosage, every single patient has had lasting help from a single series of treatments. Eleven are now without disease from three to more than ten years after treatment with extremely high doses of radiation delivered by a six-million-volt linear accelerator.

A few other scientists are not convinced that lymphomas are incurable. Dr. Harold W. Dargeon at New York's Memorial Cancer Center reported in 1960 that of seventy-five patients his group had treated for lymphosarcoma between 1926 and 1959, a total of fifteen were alive and without recurrence more than five years, two more than fifteen and one more than twenty years. In addition to surgery and/or X rays, the patients were treated with drugs like nitrogen mustard and Coley's toxins (fever-inducing poisons produced by bacteria).

Despite the drugs which reduced the number of leukemic cells in their bloodstream, children still faced that unavoidable moment with destiny when their vessels broke and released the final flow of blood into their tissues. They died of hemorrhages which nothing could stem. Dr. Gustav Freeman, then at Children's Hospital, Boston, and now at Stanford Research Institute, went to work on the problem of patching up these fragile vessels. He devised a technique for extracting platelets, or thrombocytes, from donated blood and storing them. Platelets are the sticky particles which automatically vulcanize a blowout in a vein, artery, or capillary; they are almost always in short supply in the blood of leukemics. In 1963, Dr. Sidney Farber announced that his associates at Children's Hospital had injected the stored platelets into children threatened with hemorrhage, that the infusion many times had prevented fatal hemorrhage and that the procedure had afforded physicians time to administer antileukemia drugs which often gave another remission. This may have lengthened the short life spans of leukemic children. The platelets—unfortunately available at very few research centers—had no bad side effects.

Drugs come and go. Extracts of the decorative plant, periwinkle, are found to give a ten-week remission to leukemic children resistant to other therapies. A dozen drugs have been discarded, usually as too toxic, after extensive clinical trials. Urethane (or urethan), used for years to treat multiple myeloma, was reported in 1963 to have yielded an average survival of seven months; placebo-treated patients, however, lived thirteen months. NCI investigators find that a new drug, MeGAG, helps two-thirds of the patients with acute myelocytic leukemia; others contend it is extremely toxic and of no help. And some preparations, long-abandoned, have been revived; Dr. Joseph E. Sokal of Roswell Park has reported that colcemide, a derivative of the antigout plant extract, colchicine, which was discarded after extensive testing against solid cancers, has given excellent results in chronic myelocytic leukemia.

Amid the turbulent testing of potential antileukemia preparations and the enthusiasm and skepticism accompanying it, it is obvious that present treatment leaves much to be desired. In the best research and medical centers, current therapy gives complete (and temporary) remissions to only 35 per cent of children and partial remissions to 25–30 per cent. Between 10 and 20 per cent of adults are given substantial help. Every treatment has serious side effects, although in experienced hands these can be controlled to a degree. While the well-to-do can afford the best and those with meager funds are given the best in some large public institutions, others find the financing of treatment burdensome; the financial load is lessened only by the brief survival of most leukemics. One rough estimate is that in a private hospital specializing in cancer treatment it costs at least $5,000 to support very good but conventional treatment of a child during a losing bout with leukemia. Another rough estimate is that each bed in a government leukemic ward costs about $72 a day, or $25,200 a year, for routine treatment alone; special research procedures cost another $25,000 (with parents supplying about one-third of the platelets used). Good experimental treatment of leukemia is often far beyond the average family's resources. The best is available only in a few research centers, and at crushing cost to families which can and must pay for an additional few months of life for the patient.

The outlook for the future treatment of the disease is good or bad, according to one's point of view.

On the pessimistic side, some have questioned the soundness of the drug-testing system. Only some of the preparations which prove of value in humans have had any effect on the mouse tumors on which they are tried in the routine search for antileukemic compounds. And it is a matter of chagrin and concern to some observers that promising leads of the past are forgotten and others of the present often are ignored, as the technology of testing more and more encroaches on the science of investigation.

On the optimistic side, it seems almost certain that a few of the enormous number of candidate compounds now under test will turn out to be of some value. The present system cannot help but yield new drugs, new combinations of drugs and radiation, more effective dosage schedules and new methods of administering treatment which will add at least a little time and a little comfort to the survival of future patients. NCI investigators have reported that, whereas one of the better antileukemia drugs alone will give a complete remission (lasting 40–90 days) to 21–57 per cent of children, a combination of four drugs (methotrexate, prednisone, vincristine and 6-mercaptopurine) yields lengthy remissions (90–150 days) to about 85 per cent of the patients.

A number of clues to the nature of leukemia someday may suggest new treatments. Some of them reflect differences not only between leukemia and normal tissues but also between leukemia and other cancers.

Scientists at Jefferson Medical School many years ago found evidence that the body has two distinct blood-making systems—the lymphatic organs and bone marrow—and they work on a reciprocal basis. When one is impaired, the other increases its production. The scientists reported that they had isolated from human urine two substances which they called myelokentric acid and lymphokentric acid. These acids stimulated, respectively, the marrow and the lymphatic blood-forming systems. In their crude state, the acids were given to leukemic patients, and there was a strong suggestion of benefit in some cases. Then they were forgotten.

More recently Dr. Avery Sandberg of Roswell Park has discovered evidence that there are profound chemical differences between the cell genes (DNA) in leukemic and normal humans. While normal cell genes contain more guanine than thymine, the reverse is true in leukemia. Dr. Sandberg also has detected an imbalance of two (DNase) enzymes in leukemic urine; the extent of the imbalance correlates closely with the condition of the patient. Some feel that DNase prevents the leukemic cell from maturing and aging. Dr. David Rothstein of Albert Einstein Medical College in Philadelphia has found that the chemical differences extend to the cell's protein-producing machinery (RNA); the thymus RNA in leukemic mice contains 20 per cent more than normal guanine and cytosine.

Various scientists have uncovered a series of interesting properties of blood. They include the observations, for instance, that normal rabbit serum contains something which cures mouse lymphosarcoma; that leukemic guinea-pig serum has something which destroys normal spleen cells; and that normal human serum breaks up mouse solid-cancer cells (but, so far as is known, not mouse leukemic cells).

Some of the leukemic cell's defenses against drugs have been mapped. Dr. Frank M. Huennekens of the University of California in La Jolla has shown that leukemic cells have an abundant supply of an enzyme (dihydrofolate reductase) which detoxifies antifolic acid drugs. Dr. Dougherty at Utah has shown that leukemic cells transform the leukemia-destructive hormone, cortisol, into another hormone, cortisone, which helps preserve the cells' youth and malignant vigor.

Oxygen concentrations appear to play a role in leukemia. At the University of Saskatchewan, scientists exposed leukemia-susceptible pregnant mice to low oxygen (the equivalent of 25,000 feet altitude) for five hours; their offspring had fewer and later leukemias than expected. Dr. Benjamin Siegel of the University of Oregon retarded the course of virus-caused leukemia by keeping the mice periodically under pressurized oxygen.

VA studies have shown that, while adrenal stress hormones stimulate metastases in solid cancer and shorten the lives of patients, they enable men with acute leukemia to survive twice as long as those not given the hormones.

Even the age factor is erased; while solid cancers progress fastest in the young, treated and untreated adults with acute leukemia often die sooner than the young—the older the faster.

With an increasing number of preparations now showing activity against various viruses, it is to be hoped that human leukemia may be traced to a virus or some other infectious and controllable agent. That this hope may have substance is indicated in rapidly accumulating evidence of the transmissible nature of leukemia. If all reports prove true and significant, it could be that human leukemia is due, not only to one virus or several of them, but to other infectious agents as well.

It will be remembered that Dr. Heath discovered that there had been an excess of children who developed rheumatic heart disease during the Niles outbreak. Dr. Samuel K. McIlvanie of Spokane, Washington, who treated many of the leukemics from the Lewiston, Idaho, area, found that, along with the leukemia, there had been a concurrently high incidence of viral hepatitis, streptococcal infection, and rheumatic heart disease. The twenty-four leukemia cases included sixteen children. All were from a rural area demarcated by Lewiston, Idaho (pop. 22,371), and adjoining Clarkston, Washington (pop. 6,209). Peak years for leukemia were 1955 and 1957. Peak years for hepatitis were 1954 and 1958, and the outbreak of streptococcal infection and rheumatic heart disease occurred during the last half of the 1950–60 decade. Other factors were investigated. Pesticides had been used in the area; some water supplies had been polluted by debris; two patients had a leukemic relative in the family; and four had had contacts with leukemia prior to becoming ill. Perhaps most significant of all, however, was the existence of concurrent infectious diseases. Dr. McIlvanie feels that leukemia's cause has not been proved.

Equally intriguing relationships have been explored by Dr. Denis Burkitt in an East African "lymphoma belt." The lymphomas, endemic among children one to fifteen, are not found among native adults, but adults moving into the area from the outside are subject to them, raising the possibility that native adults had been exposed and had developed immunity to the disease. The disease resembles a dozen different tumors affecting the jaw, thyroid, testis, ovary, or many other sites, notably excepting the spleen and several peripheral lymphatic organs. The disease occurs only below an altitude of 5,000 feet at the equator, 3,000 feet in Nyasaland (1,000 miles to the south), and 1,000 feet 2,000 miles south of the equator. It was found only where the temperature does not go below 60° and where there is ample rainfall and vegetation—and mosquitoes. A bone disease prevalent in those areas has been traced to a mosquito-borne virus. Whether lymphoma is related to the bone disease virus is not known.

Several scientists have reported finding viruslike particles in human leukemia.

Dr. Joseph L. Melnick and his wife, Dr. Matilda Benyesh-Melnick, at Baylor, have found apparently identical particles in the lymph nodes, blood, and marrow of 80 per cent of children with leukemia (all over two years old), in several youngsters with infectious mononucleosis, and in 10 per cent of young babies (half of them under one year) with neither disease. In tissue culture, the viruses brought a malignant-appearing change to human marrow cells. The altered cells have been injected into monkeys in efforts to produce leukemia.

Dr. C. L. Burger, then at Oak Ridge and now in Chambersburg, Pennsylvania, spun viruslike particles of two types out of the plasma of eight leukemics. Dr. W. Ray Bryan at NCI has recovered from the blood of 30 per cent of the acute leukemics he has examined a tadpole-shaped virus which causes mouse leukemia, and he also has found it in the blood of an appreciable number of their parents and siblings as well. The virus infected human embryonic cells in tissue culture, and, when the cells were injected into mice and monkeys, it caused leukemia in the mice and blood changes, possibly preleukemic, in the monkeys. Dr. James T. Grace, Jr., at Roswell Park has recovered from the blood of 80 per cent of his human leukemia patients virus particles which closely resemble those which cause leukemia in both mice and rats. Dr. DeCarvalho, in Cleveland has reported finding antibodies against a presumed leukemic agent which exists in leukemic children while in remission (but not in those in an active phase of the disease) and in 92 per cent of normal people. This finding would indicate that the leukemic agent is extremely common, affects most people, and induces antibodies against it in all but leukemics in an active stage of their disease.

Several years ago, Dr. William Dameshek of Boston published his opinion that leukemia might be a matter of autoimmunity. Autoimmunity, we have seen, means being immune against oneself. In autoimmunity of the kidney, for instance, the system produces antibodies which destroy kidney cells and impair the function of that organ. The Boston hematologist felt that there well may be many causes of leukemia—viruses, radiation and chemicals—and that by some process these leukemogens cause antibody-producing cells to proliferate. Some of the leukemia antibodies, he believed, attack normal cells and structures of the body. In support of his argument, he mentioned that in chronic lymphatic leukemia antibodies attack normal red blood cells, and that in multiple myeloma large quantities of a peculiar gamma globulin, possibly representing perverted antibodies, are found in the blood or urine. The most effective agents against leukemia, he said, also suppress immunity; they include radiation, nitrogen mustard, 6-mercaptopurine, thioguanine and stress hormones produced by the adrenal cortex. Research developments tend to validate Dr. Dameshek's hypotheses.

Dr. Donald R. Korst of the University of Michigan has produced evidence in laboratory animals that the gamma globulin antibodies of multiple myeloma are lethal. He worked with mice who spontaneously developed multiple myeloma comparable to the incurable disease which kills 3,000 Americans annually by attacking various organs and punching out bones until they break under slight stress. Dr. Korst found that Cytoxan, or cyclophosphamide, an anticancer drug resembling nitrogen mustard, knocked out the myeloma cells, suppressed antibody production, and cured or slowed the disease in mice. Cytoxan now is being tested in humans with multiple myeloma in the hope it will selectively destroy the deadly antibody-producing myeloma cells.

Antibody production in lymph-cell diseases is disturbed in all directions: some patients have a pronounced deficit of gamma globulin; some, as in multiple myeloma, have an excess of abnormal gamma globulin; and some seem to have normal amounts of gamma globulin, but the antibodies fail to attack some invading viruses and infectious organisms. Many leukemics eventually become immunologically helpless, and the viruses of chicken pox and shingles, several types of fungi and other micro-organisms take up residence in the victim, grow with impunity and kill rapidly. At Duke University, autopsies revealed that 4 per cent of the leukemia and lymphoma patients had fatal fungal infections; the organisms entered through respiratory channels and attacked lungs and brain, mostly, but also liver, kidney, and stomach. The postmortem examinations of leukemic patients showed numerous other infections of a less serious nature. The onset of most of the infections had occurred during drug treatment—evidently, the immunity-suppressing action of the drugs superimposed on the leukemic's weakened immunity had encouraged the infections.

Dr. Noel J. Collins of the National Children's Hospital, Dublin, has commented on the apparent relationship between leukemia and infections. He has said that, in the absence of microscopic examination of cells, the blood picture of leukemia still is confused with that of whooping cough and infectious mononucleosis, that malarial parasites sometimes are found in the leukemic marrow and spleen and that leukemia sometimes coexists with tuberculosis. While no one has established cause and effect, Dr. Collins has speculated that this sequence of events takes place: (1) the antigens (foreign molecules) on an infectious agent stimulate the production of antibodies and then the proliferation of antibody-producing cells; (2) if the antigens persist, even though the infectious agent be destroyed, the antibody-producing cells overgrow; and (3) in a state of immunologic exhaustion, new lymphatic cells lose their "identity proteins" and grow without restraint, as do bacteria when they have lost their "identity proteins."

If Dr. Collins is right, leukemia could be a case of cure-and-overcure —stemming from a sort of allergic condition. Long after the infectious virus has been disposed of, or after the last bacterium is dead and its decomposed remains transported with wastes out of the body, an antigen may persist. The antigen is the ghost of the now-dead organism which once bore it. It continues to haunt the system and keep it in a state of alarm, until immune mechanisms are worn out.

This could be an explanation: The virus which caused the original infection could have deposited a molecule or two of its nucleic acid in a normal cell. The nucleic-acid residue became either part of the cell's genes (DNA) or protein-producing machinery (RNA); and, hidden and protected deep within the fortress of the cell, it continued to produce antigenic proteins. The antigenic proteins were expelled from the cell (if they had remained on the cell surface, antibodies would have destroyed them and the cell); and their constant production kept the immune system active unto exhaustion . . . and leukemia.

In the absence of a virus, similar effects could have been achieved by (1) the cell's taking up the nucleic acid of a destroyed bacterium or fungus and incorporating it in its own nucleic acids, or (2) alterations in cell nucleic acids wrought by radiation or carcinogenic chemicals.

The cure-and-overcure is comparable to curing Communism with Fascism.

In keeping with this idea, it is also possible that leukemia is not a cancer at all, but rather, the effect of a cure-and-overcure of cancer, as well as of infections and nucleic acid changes within the cell. This speculation is supported by recent observations of Drs. Robert and Annabelle Liebelt of Baylor and Leon Dmochowski and John A. Sykes of M. D. Anderson Hospital. This group transplanted a liver cancer into seven young mice. It grew in four mice and withered away in three. Eight months later three of the mice with the liver cancer and the three who had rejected the cancer came down with stem-cell leukemia.

The Texas scientists then removed the liver cancer which had grown in one of the mice and transplanted bits of it to sixteen other mice. The transplants took and grew in only three of the sixteen mice; these three with liver cancer did not develop leukemia but eventually they died of the liver cancer. Of the remaining thirteen mice who had overcome liver cancer, however, every single one developed leukemia between 137 and 316 days after the transplant.

Once again, the liver tumor was transplanted, and this time it grew into liver cancers in all the mice. None of them developed leukemia.

On the fourth time the tumor was transplanted, it took in all the mice. The scientists surgically removed the cancer from four of these mice; and all four were cured of liver cancer—but all four developed leukemia and died of it. All the rest of the mice in this experiment were allowed to retain their liver cancers, and none of them became leukemic.

If these results can be extrapolated to humans, leukemia could be due to the system's efforts to (1) cure a viral or bacterial infection or a solid cancer, (2) correct a congenital defect due to the poisoning and mutation of certain embryonic cells, or (3) destroy a cell bearing the nucleic acid of a strange species or a carcinogen-altered nucleic acid and protein.

Some support for speculation that leukemia may overcome the effects of solid tumors comes from work by Drs. Eric and Ruth Ponder, pathologists, at Nassau Hospital, Mineola, N.Y. The Ponders first found that mouse *breast-cancer* tissue contained two distinct antibodies or antibody-like substances. Tagged with fluorescent dyes and traced, one substance was observed to make red blood cells clump together; the other substance ruptured red blood cells. The two activities depleted the breast-cancerous mice's red cells and made them anemic.

In two different strains of *leukemic* mice, the Ponders observed a completely different fault in immunity. In these animals, scavenger cells (phagocytes) gorged themselves on red cells in the leukemic mice's spleens, making the animals anemic. This act of cellular cannibalism did not begin in leukemia-susceptible mice until the animals were obviously sick with leukemia. The question is: In leukemia, did the scavenger cells attempt to remove red cells contaminated by a virus or by nucleic acid from a solid cancer? Were the phagocytic cells themselves infected by the virus or cancerous nucleic acid they had ingested?

While solid cancers thrive when the antibody-producing RES is blocked, at least one lymphoma is cured by the blockage. Drs. A. Lazar and D. Childress of the University of Chicago injected an RES-blocking agent into rats with a transplanted (Murphy-Sturm) lymphosarcoma which ordinarily kills 77 per cent of the animals. When they blocked the RES by injecting methylcellulose before the transplant, 96 per cent were cured (the transplant grew normally for 11 days and then withered away); 82 per cent were cured when the methylcellulose was given one day after transplant and 67 per cent when they waited eight days to block the RES.

The principles of cure-and-overcure—if such they can be called—could apply equally to mouse and man. A slender bridge of evidence has been established by a few groups who have sought for a denominator common to both humans and experimental animals.

Dr. Steven O. Schwartz of the Hektoen Institute, Cook County Hospital in Chicago, in a dramatic series of experiments has shown that there may be some kind of kinship between the leukemias of man and mouse. He injected mice with cell-free filtrates of the brains of humans who had died of leukemia. Susceptible mice died rapidly, and even some leukemia-resistant mice developed the disease. These results were taken to indicate that a human leukemia virus caused leukemia in mice.

Other groups also have induced animal cancers with human material; Dr. James T. Grace, Jr., of Roswell Park found that children's leukemic tissues contain a potent inducer of mouse breast cancer; this would be a case where human overcure becomes, in mice, a case of undercure. The breast cancers may have kept leukemia from developing. The replicating cancer antigen (possibly nucleic acid, nucleoprotein, or protein) which had induced the leukemia in the children may have infected the mouse breast cells.

Dr. Schwartz has injected the material from human leukemia brains into healthy prisoner-volunteers at Cook County Prison. The volunteers reacted against the material as they would against an ordinary vaccine. They did not develop leukemia at that time—nor, so far as anyone has reported, in the six or seven years since the inoculations. Instead, their blood developed antibodies which rapidly counteracted the leukemia-inducing material. Second injections induced vigorous immune reactions.

When mice were injected with the prisoners' serum, along with the leukemia-inducing material (a supposed virus) from leukemic mice or leukemic human brains, they did not develop leukemia. The human antiserum destroyed the leukemia inducer and prevented leukemia.

Dr. Schwartz made three different kinds of blood tests for immune response to his leukemic material. All leukemic mice and leukemic humans were negative. Patients with Hodgkin's disease in remission and with infectious mononucleosis were positive. Dr. Schwartz then tested blood samples from himself, other doctors, laboratory aides, and hospital personnel who handled leukemic mice or leukemic humans. The samples showed that some of them had been exposed to the leukemia-inducing material; these healthy humans had produced antibodies against it. It is noteworthy that Dr. Schwartz first became interested in leukemia viruses when, within a short time, one of his male lab technicians and his female secretary came down with leukemia and died of it.

Dr. Schwartz was called into the investigation of the Niles cluster of leukemic children. Blood samples from the leukemics themselves showed that they were immunologically impotent against the leukemic, possibly virus, material—their blood did not react against it. One-third of the members of the leukemics' families had antibodies against the material, however.

Until a virus is isolated, one is free to speculate that leukemia may be caused by a stray bit of strange nucleic acid—viral, bacterial, altered normal, or otherwise. In the Niles outbreak, the nucleic acid could come from bacteria which caused rheumatic heart disease in some children. In curing themselves of this infection, other children's systems could have been flooded with nucleic acid and other debris from the destroyed bacteria. Taken up by normal cells, the nucleic acid could transform the cells; the transformed normal cells then might produce and release a stream of antigens (and possibly antibodies as well) which would exhaust the immune system (and possibly attack normal cells). This could be the genesis of leukemia.

In the cancer maze, the paths that do not lead up blind alleys often end up in circles. If leukemia should represent a case of cure-and-overcure of cancer, a full 360 degrees would have been attained:

Carcinogens cause runting (they suppress growth).

Cancer cures and overcures runting (cancer is growth).

Leukemia cures and overcures cancer.

Lethal radiation cures and overcures leukemia.

Marrow cures and overcures lethal radiation diseases.

Marrow causes runt disease.

And we're back where we started from.

CHAPTER 22

THE COMMON DENOMINATOR

About forty years ago the German biochemist Dr. Otto Warburg propounded a theory which has influenced every serious student of cancer down to the present. He offered a definition of the chemical differences between normal and cancer cells.

Dr. Warburg said that a carcinogen acts by destroying the mechanisms by which the normal cell produces energy. In the normal human and animal system, hydrogen atoms are shuttled back and forth between reacting molecules, ultimately combining with free oxygen in which fats and sugars are burned down to yield energy and carbon dioxide. In destroying this oxidation, or respiration, system, carcinogens kill a great many cells. Occasionally, however, Dr. Warburg contended, a cell escapes this death by suffocation; deprived of its ability to live by oxygen, the cell turns back the clock a few billion years to revert to the inefficient fermentation type of chemistry by which some microbes live. Cells which survive in this manner become independent of the controls exercised by the body; they become cancer cells.

Dr. Sidney Weinhouse of Temple University spent a substantial part of his brilliant career in biochemistry showing that the Warburg hypothesis, valuable as it is, has serious flaws. He proved that tumors do not necessarily abandon oxidation for fermentation, and when they do it is only to varying degrees. He argued that oxidation and fermentation need not be entirely independent processes, that the end product of fermentation (lactic acid) does not necessarily represent a completely defective respiration (muscle, during exercise, produces much lactic acid) and that many non-cancerous human and animal cells supplement oxidation with the fermentive kind of energy production. Dr. Weinhouse proposed no substitute for the Warburg theory; he merely said that the cancer cells' peculiar permeability to sugar could account for its chemistry.

"Let us theorize, by all means," Dr. Weinhouse said, "but let us temper our enthusiasm for any one theory by the realization that it will doubtless be so oversimplified as to appear incredibly naive to future generations of biochemists."

Dozens of theories—biological, biochemical and philosophical—and thousands of clues have been proposed as an explanation of cancer. Carcinogens, it has been said by various respected sources, act as irritants, as mutation-inducers, as immunity suppressors, as inciters of autoimmune reactions, as cell protein deleters, as liver damagers.

In recent years, a major effort in cancer research has been to discover a common denominator—a characteristic which applies to all cancers and not to normal cells. A common denominator, some assert, would establish the kinship of all cancers and might make possible a universal drug or vaccine which would prevent or cure all cancers. The search for a common denominator has involved ions, atoms, molecules, cell particles, various body systems and such imponderables as life, aging, and death.

The burden of evidence indicates that there is a common denominator in cancer. It is a permanent alteration in the cell's nucleic acids. Directly or indirectly, all carcinogens seem to change the DNA of the cell genes and the RNA which produces enzymes and other proteins. As metabolism is now understood, it makes no difference whether the change originates in DNA, in RNA, in one of the countless precursor chemicals which eventually comprise nucleic acids or, indeed, in the products of DNA and RNA. Metabolism, it now is becoming clear, proceeds in chemical cycles; a reproducible fault or change in a phase of one cycle is likely to be reflected in the entire next cycle, and, if it is at all workable, will be built into the future metabolism of the cell. It becomes an inheritable trait and will persist until another agent or accident again alters the particular gene which controls it.

Alterations in nucleic acids may not be the lowest common denominator. As 9 is a common denominator of 27 and 54 (3 is the lowest), nucleic acid changes are the lowest common denominator so far found in cancer. It is now known that carcinogens change nucleic acids in many ways; ethionine joins with A, or adenine, to form an unnatural s-adenosylethionine in causing liver cancer; dimethylnitrosamine transforms G or guanine, into 7-methylguanine; beta-propiolactone also reacts with guanine; radiation not only opens the carbon ring in guanine but also interferes with the breakdown of RNA by inactivating the enzyme, RNase; 2-acetyla-minofluorene binds to ribosomal RNA and protein; polyoma virus causes breaks in chromosomes which put the genes in a strange new juxtaposition, and other viruses add their own nucleic acid to that of the cell's. Dr. Leonard S. Lerman of the University of Colorado has shown in exquisite detail how some mutagens—acridine dye molecules, specifically—could become wedged between two coils of the DNA molecule.

The method by which ultraviolet light damages cells has implications of still another chemical course leading to cancer. Dr. Paul Howard-Flanders of Yale discovered that ultraviolet damages the thymine on the paired DNA helix. Certain enzymes skillfully snip the damaged segments off the DNA and knit the severed ends of the molecule to repair the deletion. The process leaves an apparently shortened DNA, but a serviceable one. Ultraviolet also affects the RNA. Drs. L. Grossman, J. Ono, and R. G. Wilson of Brandeis found that the rays added a molecule of water to the U, or uracil, segment of RNA. This drastically altered protein synthesis by the changed segment; the watered U behaved like a C, or cytosine, in triplet coding. The reverse, too, was true; irradiated C behaved like U. The process could be reversed and the damage undone with a modest amount of heat, which detached the extra water molecule from the RNA segment. This may explain why severe sunburn skin effects can be modified by a fairly hot shower.

Often a mutagen or carcinogen (they can be one and the same) causes dramatic nucleic acid changes which become visible under the microscope. Leukemogenic doses of X rays have been found to add an extra chromosome to mouse spleen cells and cause gross damage to another chromosome. Some cancer viruses have somewhat similar effects; polyoma seems to fracture one of a pair of daughter chromosomes in a dividing cell; and the chromosome healing process results in the carrier cell's becoming malignant.

Carcinogens may arise within the cell itself. Any number of missteps on the cell's tangled chemical assembly line, where countless reactions constantly take place with almost the speed of light, can lead to the synthesis of an imperfect RNA or DNA nucleotide. Indole, one of the seventy normal breakdown products of the amino acid, tryptophan, induces rat-liver cancer; the tryptophan end product, which is the vitamin, niacin, is part of the mechanism which shuttles electrons in the oxidation of fats and sugars. Cancers seem to have much less of this shuttling apparatus than do normal cells.

The business end of a virus is its nucleic acid. A distorted cellular nucleic acid can behave like a *de novo* or endogenous virus. It alters the cell that creates it and changes other cells which later are infected with it.

The biochemical control of cancer appears to rest squarely in the rapidly dissipating secrets of DNA and RNA.

The chemical common denominator sets off an awesome train of events in the cell and in the body. Oddly enough, carcinogens suppress growth; the carcinogen-treated host and its tissues die a little—many cells being killed and others losing their capacity to multiply—before the strange new cancer cells start to proliferate. The defensive cells of the RES, or immune system, are paralyzed, first by the carcinogen and then by the products of the growing cancer.

Cancer cells, once established, expand by dissolving the glue which sticks the cells together and by invading areas occupied by normal cells. They kill normal cells which stand in their way by competing with them for available food, and probably by poisoning them. They excrete an enzyme which melts away the body's natural barriers to cell and tissue expansion. They sacrifice the enzyme systems which enable them to serve the body, and they develop those which permit them to multiply. Somehow, they manage an amoeboid locomotion, which is denied to all body cells except white blood cells, scavenger cells, germ cells and fiber-spinning cells. And they have far-reaching effects on virtually every tissue in the body; one scientist has reported that the effects of a breast-cancer-inducing chemical, taken orally, register almost immediately on the character of breast cells, and that a well-established tumor brings "distant malignancy-associated changes," to cells in every organ and tissue in the body.

Eventually, the diminishing food taken in by the host fails to satisfy the needs of the growing cancers. At this point, the cancers start feeding on the substance of the host, and the chemistry of the host is that of starvation and slow death.

The cancer cells, repelling normal cells and one another, bore their way into lymphatic channels and blood vessels where they are borne by body fluids to new and distant sites, at which points they establish colonies, or metastases. It is possible that nucleic acids from disintegrating cancer cells may infect normal cells, much as a virus would, and in this way also establish metastases. Dr. Vincent Groupé of Rutgers has observed this sort of infection in a virus-caused turkey cancer.

All these properties are products of the common denominator, the nucleic acid changes which transform the cell into a free agent in a hostile system—a savage cell.

Is there a purpose behind all these awesome events? There seems to be —the most basic purpose of all: survival. All men—and all organisms, are mortal. Cancer represents a rebellion against the mortal system—the weaknesses, the diseases, the aging process, which lead only to extinction.

On the death of the host, normal cells divide once and no more; the tumor cells in the dead host continue to divide for many hours.

A highly malignant tumor was removed fifteen years ago from a humble Baltimore woman. Cultured in laboratory dishes, it grew with amazing, almost frightening, vigor. By the ounce and by the pound, this astoundingly proliferating piece of flesh continues to grow in hundreds of laboratories throughout the world. The donor is long dead. But through her tumor—its growth unchecked, its vigor undiminished as it undergoes thousands of experiments—she has achieved immortality of the eternally growing flesh.

CHAPTER 23

CANCER DETECTION AND DIAGNOSIS

Early in 1963 Dr. Sidney Farber reported that he and Dr. Alfred B. Handler at the Children's Cancer Research Foundation had discovered a strange phenomenon: when they injected the blood of cancerous humans or animals into fertilized chicken eggs, the embryos died or the chicks hatched with striking deformities. Normal blood did not have these remarkable effects.

The scientists carefully refrained from calling this a blood test for cancer—nothing, not even the claim of a new cancer cure, is as explosive within science as the suggestion of a practical blood test for cancer. Scores of scientists of great and small stature through the years had felt the merciless lash of their peers for proposing a procedure for the easy detection of cancer. To be sure, most of the tests were utterly useless. The harshest critics disregarded the clearly stated limitations of the tests, and some of them grossly exaggerated the discoverers' claims.

Scientists are sensitive about cancer blood tests because, of all the rewards of research, few if any would be as rich in honors and in satisfaction as the finding of a simple and reliable test for cancer's presence. If early cancers could be detected by an easy office procedure, relatively few ever would reach the incurable stage.

At this writing, the Farber-Handler technique has been applied to several hundred patients with cancer, with noncancerous diseases and with no detectable disease. With high fidelity, blood or plasma from patients and animals with metastasizing cancer kills or cripples 7–9-day-old chick embryos, while blood and plasma from those with nonmetastasizing tumors and numerous other conditions do not. If the results hold up under further testing, and if others can reproduce them, a milestone in cancer control will have been achieved.

Meanwhile, Dr. Anthony J. Sbarra and others at Tufts have discovered that something, probably a protein, in the blood of acute and chronic lymphatic leukemics blocks bacterial (*B. subtilis*) growth. When yeast extract or trypticase soy is added to the cultures, the block is removed, bacterial respiratory activity is increased, and the cells again multiply in lymphatic leukemic serum. These studies not only offer hope for a test for these leukemias, but they also present an intriguing problem as to what the soy factor (if it ever is isolated and identified) might do as a leukemia drug.

Eleanor J. Macdonald and Dr. Herbert Lombard of Harvard a generation ago undertook a careful statistical analysis of cancer in Massachusetts. The study became the format of the classical Connecticut registry, which Miss Macdonald and Dr. Matthew Griswold established a few years later. The investigators made careful records of the number of patients, the kinds of cancer they had and how long they had survived. The Connecticut study became the basic reference and guide for epidemiologists throughout the United States and the world. It enabled physicians to predict with rough accuracy the outlook of patients with various types of tumors, and it became a measuring stick for those in experimental treatment to gauge the merit of their approach.

In 1963 Miss Macdonald completed another intensive study. Now at M. D. Anderson Hospital, University of Texas, Houston, she published statistics detailing the incidence and survival rates of cancer in El Paso County during the seventeen-year period 1944–61. Almost one-half of the 314,000 residents of this border area were Latin Americans (Mexicans), giving the survey an ethnic flavor as well as a cross section of socioeconomic levels. The study provided a wealth of information on cancer susceptibilities and survival. One of the paramount points was that early detection, diagnosis, and treatment are a life-and-death matter in many kinds of cancer.

Excluding skin cancer, which is highly curable for the most part, 80.9 per cent of all patients with early cancer survived one year, 54.6 per cent five years, 47.3 per cent ten years, and 42.7 per cent fifteen years. Comparable figures for those reporting advanced symptoms were 35.1 per cent one year, 11.7 per cent five years, 8.0 per cent ten years, and 7.1 per cent fifteen years.

As in most other diseases, women with cancer proved more durable than men with cancer—about 15–25 per cent longer-lived on the average.

One of several reasons for their ability to beat cancer was the fact that they were more inclined than men to report symptoms to doctors while the disease was still in an early and curable stage.

The Macdonald El Paso study showed, as have many others, that the better educated people, with some awareness of the need to nip cancer early, and the better-off people, with the means to finance proper treatment, are more successful in combating cancer than are the poor and uneducated. Non-Latins, whether male or female or with early or advanced cancer, were between 30 and 50 per cent more successful in surviving five, ten or fifteen years than were Latin Americans with comparable cancers. The moral from this portion of the report appears to be that good care pays off.

The study showed that non-Latins had a higher incidence of cancers of the breast, skin, mouth, bowel, bladder, prostate, ovary, and body of the uterus, while Latin Americans were more prone to most other cancers, particularly those of the stomach, uterine cervix, liver, gall bladder, and bile duct.

Cancer death rates dropped in El Paso during the course of the study. They fell on an average of 1.36 per 100,000 population per year, with the sharpest decline taking place since 1954. By contrast, cancer rates elsewhere have continued their rise. Some of the El Paso decline may be attributed to the study itself—the collaborating medical profession in the county was keenly aware of the fact that it was playing a key role in an important epidemiological survey and emphasized early detection, prevention, and prompt treatment. One of the surprising features was that breast-cancer survival lengthened by about 30 per cent; breast-cancer mortality generally has remained at a plateau for decades.

Curability and early detection were synonymous to a high degree in cancers of some sites. Early breast-cancer cases outsurvived late cases 3 to 1; in cancer of the intestines it was 8 to 1; thyroid, 2 to 1; rectum, 5 to 1; prostate, 3 to 1; body and cervix of the uterus, 2½ to 1; ovary, 6 to 1; mouth and pharynx, 3 or 4 to 1.

In skin cancer (excluding melanoma), survival was relatively high—88.3 per cent at five years, 79.7 at ten years, and 77.2 at fifteen years, with basal-cell cancers being much more curable than squamous-cell cancers. Melanoma proved to be about 40 per cent curable—a high rate when one takes into account the argument by a few specialists that true melanoma is incurable.

Some cancers proved to be hopelessly advanced when first detected. Five-year survivals amounted to 9.4 per cent in cancer of the central nervous system, 4.1 for men and 2.4 for women with lung cancer, 8.8 stomach, 2.8 liver, 5.9 for all leukemias on an average, and 7.7 for various cancers of the blood-forming cells.

For a majority of cancers, early detection paid off handsomely. This applied primarily to tumors which were accessible—which could be seen or felt or which could be investigated in a routine examination.

Memorial Cancer Center in New York has made several studies of delay in detecting advanced cancer. In 1948 investigators found that in only 32.5 per cent of the advanced cases entering Memorial had there been no element of delay; the disease was hopelessly advanced by the time anyone could suspect its presence. In the rest, patients were at fault in 31.2 per cent of the cases, physicians in 23.4 per cent, and both in 12.9 per cent. Delay diminished and operability increased progressively as public education programs made people increasingly cancer-conscious.

In the 1948 study, physicians who had cancer were as dilatory in having their own cancers diagnosed as were lay patients; the doctors they consulted were almost as slow, on an average, as those consulted by lay patients.

The Memorial study showed that patients refrained from going to the doctor for several reasons. Some reasons were emotional—the patients feared the doctors would ridicule them; they were afraid of treatment; and they just did not want to hear whatever bad news the examination would bring. Some remained away for economic reasons—they felt they would be unable to pay for treatment; they couldn't stand the double burden of at least temporary joblessness and medical bills; they dreaded the prospect of being a burden on their families and friends. And some felt they had cancer and that it was incurable.

The doctors' faults also were varied. Some, themselves unable to diagnose the case, failed to refer it to others who could. Some gave up when there was no immediate response to the right treatment; some gave no advice and no treatment; and some, misdiagnosing the case, gave the wrong advice and the wrong treatment.

About 80 per cent of the commonest cancers can be detected by a first-class examination in the doctor's office. Not all of them, however, will be curable when found—some lung cancers grow for thirty or forty years before symptoms reveal their presence, and occasionally breast and other cancers no larger than the head of a pin have metastasized widely when they first are found. Nevertheless, as things stand at this writing, the best assurance of beating cancer lies in having a thorough physical examination periodically by a competent doctor or, better still, group of doctors including a general physician, internist, surgeon, gynecologist, radiologist and, in the background, pathologist. A good registered nurse and secretary are indispensable to a large detection practice.

Dr. Emerson Day of the Strang Clinic, New York, feels that a good detection examination includes taking of a careful health (personal and family) history; a thoughtful searching for physical complaints; blood, urine, and feces analysis; uterine smear test; visual examination of every accessible surface and organ; careful investigation of the mouth, naso-pharynx, larynx, vagina, cervix, and lower colon; palpation of lymph nodes, thyroid, breasts, prostate, uterus, ovaries, and testes. Some take X rays of liver, intestines, stomach, gall bladder, lungs, kidneys, and bone. Dr. Day suggests that long-term cigarette smokers should have chest X rays and sputum tests twice a year. Exposures to carcinogens and possible pre-dispositions to various cancers should be taken into account, Dr. Day feels. A good examination can hardly be done in less than one hour. It usually takes from two to four hours in a detection clinic, and the cost ranges, roughly, from about $25 to more than $100.

About 1.5 per cent of those who are examined at a cancer-detection center turn out to have cancer, most often skin cancer. About 10 per cent have precancerous conditions. The thorough examination brings to light more or less serious noncancerous problems needing medical atten-tion in about two-thirds of the patients.

The advice to have two checkups a year is very good—and very im-practical. If every physician in the United States spent forty hours a week, fifty weeks a year, giving one-hour checkups, each person could be accom-modated twice a year. This would leave little time, however, for other medical work. Teaching and research institutions are best equipped to give mass detection examinations, but these frequently do not find favor with county medical societies.

The American Cancer Society, in a long-term campaign of public ed-ucation, has publicized "seven danger signals" in the hope that patients having any of them for more than two weeks will consult their physician. They are: (1) unusual bleeding or discharge; (2) a lump or thickening in the breast or elsewhere; (3) a sore that does not heal; (4) change in bowel or bladder habits; (5) hoarseness or cough; (6) indigestion or difficulty in swallowing and (7) change in a wart or mole.

In its professional education program, the Society has listed "seven tragic diagnostic mistakes." These are made by doctors who (1) fail to diagnose oral cancer on the assumption that it is a canker sore; (2) believe the lump in the breast is benign without bothering to biopsy; (3) assume that symptoms are due to a benign gastric or duodenal ulcer without further studies; (4) fail to recognize that an old inguinal hernia which suddenly becomes symptomatic may be associated with cancer of the prostate or colon; (5) treat undiagnosed uterine bleeding with hormones; (6) ignore the fact that bleeding piles may mask rectal cancer; and (7) treat anemia without recognizing that cancer may be causing it.

It is important that both doctors and patients exercise a measure of common sense in regarding symptoms which in a great majority of cases turn out to be something relatively minor. In enrolling 1,100,000 presumably healthy adults in a six-year prospective study designed to determine who gets cancer, the Cancer Society found that 62.2 per cent of the men and 54.9 per cent of the women had one or more possible cancer complaints (cough, indigestion, hoarseness and frequent urination, in that order, were the most common). With increasing age, the number of symptoms increased in men and decreased in women. Only 11.9 per cent of the men and 17.6 per cent of the women had taken their complaints to the doctor.

Despite the feeling by many physicians that most of the patients who come to them with complaints of cancer are hypochondriacs, several retrospective studies show that the patient's own feelings often are the most reliable index of the presence of cancer. The feelings frequently antedate actual diagnosis by a year or more. This was indicated clearly by an American Cancer Society survey in Toledo, Ohio, where patients' complaints —with no detectable disease—turned out to represent cancer in a sobering percentage of cases. Other studies have shown that between 20 and 40 per cent of breast-cancer patients are misdiagnosed by the first physician who sees them. Errors are made in the other direction too: investigators at Montefiore Hospital in New York, on a careful check of its terminal patients, once discovered that eighteen who had been sent there to die had either no cancer at all or readily curable cancers.

Dr. Perk Lee Davis of Paoli, Pennsylvania, World War II Chief of Cancer Wards at Walter Reed Hospital and now a cancer consultant for the Navy and a member of the Pennsylvania State Cancer Commission, has observed that "patients' vague, seemingly neurotic complaints" sometimes are signs of unsuspected cancers.

> Cancer and leukemia patients often have numerous and vague complaints, the kind we impatiently refer to as an "organ recital." Or they may have only one really strange complaint, maybe a rectal discomfort they cannot describe, or a headache that is somehow different, or a "funny, itchy feeling." Such complaints are easily dismissed with a shrug, or a referral to a psychiatrist. Too often, in fact, that is just what happens. Many a cancer patient has come to me on referral from a psychiatrist who realized, after fruitless sessions, that the patient's symptoms could not be explained by his mental status. These patients, and many others, could have been helped much earlier (and possibly have been cured) if their physicians had taken their vague, early complaints seriously.

Dr. Davis has listed as conditions which should be suspected of cancer when they do not clear up within a reasonable time following treatment: itching, generalized or local lesions which mimic scabies, tuberculosis,

meningococcemia or fungus infections, and skin sensitivity to detergents
(leukemia, Hodgkin's or other cancer); headache (particularly a "different kind of headache"—leukemia or brain tumor); bone and joint pain,
with or without chills and fever (multiple myeloma, leukemia, or bone
sarcoma); weakness and fatigue; cough and hoarseness; blood in the urine
or difficult urination, tender kidneys or back pain; change in bowel function, rectal fullness, enlarged liver or spleen; bruising, or small hemorrhages under the skin.

Several studies have indicated the value of women's examining their
own breasts periodically. In one group of 700 women who did so, eight
discovered cancers during a ten-year period. The cancers were small,
early and, it can only be hoped, curable.

Dr. Helen Olendorff Curth of Columbia University says that when
she finds a person with malignant (but not benign) acanthosis nigricans, "I
can state with certainty that he has or soon will have cancer." This disease is marked by pigmented growths of thickened skin, often in the armpit and around the beltline. Dr. Curth has reported a score or more of such
cases, all of which were associated with cancers of the glandular tissue
of the stomach, lung, pancreas, esophagus, ovary, uterus, cervix, prostate,
breast, liver, and lymph nodes.

Hidden stomach cancer often reveals itself in a peculiar form of pernicious anemia, marked by a lack of a stomach secretion called intrinsic
factor. Stomach-cancer patients also lack gastric hydrochloric acid, and
a variable percentage also have stomach ulcers, possibly a forerunner of
their cancer. Duodenal ulcers are not related to cancer.

Dr. Edward H. Reinhard of Washington University has pointed out
that cancer often affects nerve tissues, resulting in degeneration of the
brain cortex, interference with sensory functions, and neuromuscular disorders. Its effects on connective tissue and bone are shown in clubbing
and other bone disturbances, and such skin conditions as dermatomyositis,
scleroderma, and acanthosis nigricans. Blood-vessel effects are registered
in migratory thrombophlebitis and nonbacterial thrombotic endocarditis,
and blood effects include anemia, polycythemia, leukemoid reactions,
eosinophilia, fibrinolytic purpura and cryofibrinogenemia. The disturbed
body chemistry includes the carcinoid syndrome, urinary irregularities,
a high or a low blood sugar, and high calcium and adrenal hormones.

Radiation has been used in many forms to detect various internal kinds
of cancer. The techniques have been successful in reducing cancer mortality
to only a slight degree.

A total of 1,867,201 persons in Los Angeles County—almost 60 per
cent of the population over fifteen years old—were given chest X rays in
a 1950 campaign against tuberculosis. Five years later, Dr. Lewis W.

Guiss of the University of Southern California and his associates decided to see what had become of 3,500 people in the series who had been marked as "lung tumor suspects." In 1959, he presented his findings. Of the 3,500 suspects, 211 were known to have developed lung cancer and died of it during the five or six years since their chest X rays were made. Of the rest, 620 were lost to follow-up, 358 had died of noncancerous diseases, and 179 of other-than-lung cancers. A total of 2,132, or 60.9 per cent of the suspects, were alive, although some of them, of course, might still develop lung cancer, in keeping with the national average. Dr. Guiss concluded that patients operated upon before the appearance of lung-cancer symptoms had three times the chance of cure of patients with symptoms. All in all, these results would hardly persuade the average "suspect" to undergo surgery; on an average, the chances of a suspect's having lung cancer appear slim and the chances of a cure are a good deal slimmer.

Dr. Guiss found that even the skilled radiologist who read the chest films was prone to error, and so were two noted radiologist reviewers. In calling certain films negative or positive for cancer, they were wrong almost as often as right. They missed many of those who were only a few months as well as a few years away from death by lung cancer.

Dr. L. Henry Garland of Stanford University, a radiologist of long experience, has written that two expert readers missed 9 per cent of chest X rays positive for disease, three readers of moderate training missed about 25 per cent, and two physician-readers of little experience missed 44 per cent. He has said that an X-ray reader is apt to change his mind once in every five positive cases.

There are many explanations for the lack of reliability of X rays, the commonest one being that the films must be considered in context with the patient's history, symptoms, and other diagnostic findings. Under these conditions, it is certain that the interpretation of films would have been 100 per cent accurate in the case of patients dying of lung cancer when the X rays were made and perhaps more correct on other patients.

No physician and no informed layman will deny that diagnostic X rays often serve a splendid purpose generally in guiding the physician in treating the patient. Obviously, however, conventional X-ray pictures have added little to the deplorable cure rates for lymphomas and cancers of the lung, liver, pancreas, stomach, and other difficult-to-diagnose and difficult-to-cure malignancies.

Hope lies in the unconventional detection media—in techniques which possibly were developed and ignored or abandoned long ago, in new and ingenious approaches and perhaps in methods not yet discovered.

Happily, the unconventional techniques keep cropping up. A few of them seem to have merit.

Dr. Shields L. Warren of Boston in 1930 published a paper in the *American Journal of Roentgenology* in which he asserted that X rays would show up a cancer in the human breast. His batting average—detecting 50 of 58 breast cancers—was high. Radiologists in Europe and South America became intrigued with the Warren observation and tested it. In the right hands and under the right conditions, X rays did indeed show up cancer of the female breast. Dr. J. Gershon-Cohen of Philadelphia's Albert Einstein Medical Center found X-ray diagnosis of breast cancer of value, and in a long, uphill and not-too-successful campaign from 1937 on urged its adoption; of twenty-three breast cancers he uncovered by X rays, seventeen were localized. Dr. Raul A. Leborgne of Montevideo, Uruguay, in 1953 outlined a successful X-ray technique, and urged that it be applied periodically to women with a family history of breast cancer.

Dr. Gilbert Fletcher of M. D. Anderson Hospital, whose ingenious innovations have helped raise the radiation cure rates of several kinds of cancer, in 1956 called the attention of his associate, Dr. Robert L. Egan, to European reports of considerable success in radiological diagnosis of breast cancer and suggested that he look into them. Dr. Egan developed a technique which he called mammography, and in one series of 1,000 patients with breast lumps he correctly identified 238 of the 240 which turned out to be breast cancer, including 19 unsuspected breast cancers missed by conventional means. After considerable testing of voltages, screens, films and emulsions, he settled on low kilovoltage, high milliamperage, and fine-grain film.

At this point no one concedes that mammography, which is a detection measure—and a fairly expensive one—will take the place of examination of suspect tissues under the microscope, the regular diagnostic procedure. Nevertheless, the technique will be of enormous value if others can reproduce Dr. Gershon-Cohen's or Dr. Egan's results. It might eliminate the still-common practice of preoperative biopsy—removing a sample of the suspect tissue for microscopic examination—a procedure which some contend may spread the cancer. It also should give the patient a good idea as to whether she will come off the operating table minus a breast and adjoining tissues. Under ordinary procedures, neither the patient nor the surgeon knows at the start of an operation whether breast amputation will be necessary; the decision is made shortly after the start of the operation when the lump is removed and, during a ten-minute halt, examined under the microscope and identified as malignant or benign by the pathologist. When diagnosed, 60 per cent of the breast cancers have metastasized, and 50 per cent are incurable.

An extremely simple technique for the preoperative screening of breast lumps was devised about fifteen years ago by Leo C. Massopust, Sr., a veteran medical photographer and artist at Marquette University. With ordinary photographing equipment plus an infrared filter and film, he makes pictures of cancer-suspect breasts. The infrared rays in ordinary light bring out structures two millimeters beneath the skin surface; the pictures show the superficial veins of the breast. If the veins are sinous and engorged, they are deemed to raise suspicion of the presence of cancer. This simple, cheap and rapid procedure—as many as twenty-five patients can be filmed in an hour—identified 60 of 64 cancers in a series of 1,000 patients; there were no false positives.

Dr. Owen H. Wangensteen and his associates at the University of Minnesota have experimented with several techniques for the detection of hard-to-find cancers. They have injected radioactive phosphorous into patients with stomach disorders, lowered a deflated balloon coated with a photo-sensitive emulsion into the stomach, inflated the balloon (which made "pictures" of radioactivity concentrations in the tissues), deflated the balloon, and withdrawn it. By the "pictures" on the balloon, they were able to determine in a good percentage of cases which stomachs harbored cancers; the phosphorous concentrated in the hyperactive cancer tissues. Similar pictures made by placing a sensitive film over the breasts of radioactive phospherous-injected patients enabled the group to identify thirty-one cases of breast cancer, with two false positives and no false negatives. They also have found that cancer takes up about 25 per cent more radioactive iron than do normal tissues or benign tumors.

It often is difficult for the surgeon to find brain cancer; there sometimes is little to distinguish normal from cancer tissues. In 1948, Dr. George E. Moore, then at the University of Minnesota and now at Roswell Park, hit upon a method: he injected the patient before operation with a dye, fluorescein, which concentrated in the tumor and glowed under ultraviolet light. Tumors on the surface of the brain were easily seen. He then injected a fluorescein molecule containing two radioactive iodine atoms into the patient. By running a small Geiger counter over the brain, it now became possible not only to see the superficial tumor but also to detect radioactivity from tumors buried under the surface of the brain. In 1961, a group at Argonne Cancer Research Hospital reported that octoiodofluorescein, a molecule containing eight radioactive iodine atoms, enabled them to detect the position of brain tumors without even opening the skull in more than 70 per cent of the cases. Radioactive mercury has also been useful in scanning.

Drs. Gordon L. Brownell, physicist, William H. Sweet, neurosurgeon, and others at Massachusetts General Hospital have experimented with many radioactive compounds which might determine the location of brain tumors prior to surgery. Arsenic has proved most satisfactory and now is used routinely in patients showing symptoms of dizziness, fainting, stumbling, and sudden changes in smell, vision and other senses. With high fidelity, the test indicates not only the location but the general size and shape of brain tumors. Twin counters, scanning the head line by line, draw a picture of the brain and its tumor content.

When a surgeon begins an operation for cancer, his primary concern is for the spread of the tumor. Accurate knowledge would enable him to excise all the cancer-tainted tissue—or, if the malignancy is too widespread, spare the patient the operation. Dr. Harry W. Fischer and others at the University of Iowa have developed a system of contrast lymphography which in some cases gives them a very good idea, preoperatively, of how much tissue to remove. They inject an opaque dye into lymphatic vessels serving the tumor and then make X-ray pictures of the area. In many cases, the procedure has shown where cancer has spread to nodes.

At the University of Rochester, Dr. Gordon L. Spar and others have found that rabbit antibodies against human fibrin concentrate in tumors. Impregnated with radioactive iodine, these antibodies have guided physicians to human brain tumors. The Rochester group now is determining whether these radioactive antibodies will be of use in detecting and even treating other cancers.

Back in 1923 a Greek immigrant, Dr. George N. Papanicolaou, or "Pap" for short, undertook to examine under the microscope a large number of samples of fluid from the vaginas of healthy women and women with a variety of vaginal symptoms. The tests, at Woman's Hospital of New York City, were to determine whether the fluid contents changed during the menstrual cycle.

Dr. Pap found remarkable changes in the cells shed into this fluid during the estrogen and the progesterone phases of the monthly cycle, in pregnancy, in various infections, and in other conditions. The most striking cell changes of all were found in women harboring cancers of the uterine cervix. Early cancers, including tumors so small that they could not be seen with the naked eye, profusely shed cells with large, deep-staining nuclei, which made them conspicuous among all other cells.

For five years Dr. Pap at Woman's Hospital and at Cornell University Medical College pursued these studies. Convinced that this form of cytology offered a superior method of detecting early uterine cancers, he published a preliminary note in one of the journals. "Then I sat back and waited for the response from scientists and physicians," he once recalled. "I was certain there would be great curiosity. Few mentioned my paper. Later—much later—when the clinical implications were discussed, there was a good deal of skepticism."

For many more years Dr. Pap continued his studies, improving and simplifying his techniques and obtaining ever-mounting percentages of correct positive and negative diagnoses. Eventually Drs. Joe V. Meigs, Ruth M. Graham, and Maurice Fremont-Smith at Harvard Medical School ran the Pap test on their patients and duplicated his results. In 1943 the Harvard group reported that they had obtained substantially the same impressive percentages as Dr. Pap, and endorsed the technique as a vast improvement over all the methods then used to find early cervical cancer. They predicted success for it on other sites as well, including the lung. Even this report—and several confirmatory accounts which appeared during the next three years—failed to rouse great clinical interest in the procedure. In 1947 a popular magazine carried a story on Pap smears which sent women everywhere to their doctors demanding the test. The technique no longer could be ignored.

For a few years physicians told their inquiring or demanding patients that (1) they didn't know anything about the reported test and could not perform it, or (2) the accounts were sensational and erroneous. At the same time a number of pathologists attempted hastily and awkwardly to do the test and failed; some proclaimed it of no use, inaccurate, difficult to do, expensive, and impractical. Many contended only tissue samples— not smears—were helpful.

Eventually, the smear technique, as proposed by Dr. Pap and as modified by numerous investigators, was accredited as a procedure with a great life-saving potential. Dr. Charles S. Cameron, then with the American Cancer Society and now Dean of the Hahnemann Medical School, Philadelphia, and Dr. Emerson Day, then in charge of the detection center at Memorial Cancer Center, New York, asserted that if all women older than twenty or thirty years would have a smear test made at regular intervals, deaths from cervical cancer soon would reach the vanishing point. Careful and conscientious investigators in research institutions, one by one, began obtaining and reporting very good results.

Apathy and opposition to cytological techniques did not subside completely when the Pap smear was endorsed as a cancer-detection measure.

Some contended that smears were so difficult to take they never would become a regular office procedure. Others said the expense would be prohibitive for most patients. Other scientists showed that women could take their own smears with good efficiency and at low cost. Dr. Abraham Oppenheim headed a study for the New York City Health Department, in which do-it-yourself kits (consisting essentially of a 6-inch cotton-tipped applicator, a little collodion and 95 per cent alcohol solution) were given out to 500 Harlem Hospital outpatients. The women (50 per cent of whom had not been graduated from eighth grade) were given oral or written instructions in how to use the kits and preaddressed containers in which to mail specimens to the Health Department. Guided only by written instructions, women sent in smears which were satisfactory in 85 per cent of the cases;

all but 5 per cent of the smears submitted by women given oral instruction were satisfactory. The kits cost about one cent each, and processing
and reading them cost between $1.25 and $1.75. Other populations in
various parts of New York City also were tested with equally good results.

Dr. Herbert E. Nieburgs of Mount Sinai Hospital, acting for the New
York City Health Department and aided by volunteer workers of the American Cancer Society, distributed a 15-cent do-it-yourself kit to women in
Floyd County, Georgia. It contained a specially-designed tampon; after
being worn for from six to twelve hours, it was placed in a box containing
two slides which automatically were smeared with the tampon vaginal
contents. The slides were mailed to the laboratory in New York, where they
were wetted with water (causing the dried cells to swell), fixed, stained,
and read. An average of 0.62 per cent of the slides contained cells suspicious of cancer. Women yielding the positive slides were given a biopsy
and examined closely.

Dr. Ludwig von Bertalanffy of Los Angeles has shown, despite considerable skepticism, that a dye called acridine orange stains DNA green
and RNA red and that a high suspicion of cancer can be detected even by
the average amateur after a few days of instruction. The flaming fluores-
cence of cells under the microscope has reduced the time needed to search
smears for telltale cancer cells down to from three to six minutes. The
physician or his technician can master this routine phase of clinical
cytology.

True cytology, however, is an art and a science, and its practitioners are
artists and scientists of varying degrees of proficiency. Cytology is a vast
field, and as its potential broadens it is becoming more and more compart-
mentalized.

Dr. George L. Wied of the University of Chicago can determine from
vaginal smears the hormonal status of a woman, pregnancy a few days after
its occurrence, the prevalence of various bacteria, and the presence of
cancer. Drs. John and Ruth Graham, now at Roswell Park, have predicted
with a high degree of accuracy whether patients with cervical cancers would
respond better to radiation or to surgery; the predictions were based on the
response of the patients' normal cells to radiation and the kind and quantity
of cells present in a smear.

Dr. Papanicolaou (who died in 1962), the Doctors Graham, and many
others have devised dozens of techniques for the cytological detection of
cancers of many sites. Lung cancer has been detected from sputum and
bronchial washings; stomach cancer from stomach washings and aspira-
tions; lung and heart cancers from fluids which collect in the sacs containing these organs; bowel cancers from cells in feces; cancers of the kidney,
ureter, bladder, and the massaged prostate from cells in the urine; breast

cancer from cells in breast secretions; and brain cancers and metastases in brain and spinal fluids.

A great deal of money and time has been invested in efforts to develop color-translating and automation systems for the detection of cancer cells in smears. So far, nothing of practical value has come of this. Airborne Instruments Laboratory in Mineola, New York, has developed a high-speed scanning device which adapts television techniques in converting the microscopic image of cells into electrical signals. Some of the automatic decisions are made in five-millionths of a second, others in one-ten-thousandth of a second—giving a potential analysis of 30,000 cells a second. The instrument does only what a human can do, but with infinitely more speed and precision. One great drawback is that the human never can be sure that it is a cancer cell; many cells which resemble cancer are found in normal situations and in benign tumors, and even the most careful human judge occasionally will call the condition cancer when it isn't.

Shortly before he died in 1958, Dr. Nathan Chandler Foot, a Cornell Medical College pathologist of considerable note, delivered a technical article to the editor of the journal, Cancer, and said, "This will be my last paper. I have joined the club. I have prostatic cancer and am inoperable." A realist, he was resigned to his death, which occured a short time later. At autopsy, Dr. Foot's pathologist-successors found that he had no cancer at all.

Dr. Foot, in diagnosing his own condition, had overlooked the basic tenet of his speciality: it is cancer only when microscopic examination proves it is.

Thousands of patients have been "cured" of cancers they never had, because reputable physicians and surgeons (as well, of course, as countless quacks) have diagnosed the disease by means other than microscopic examination. The "cures" often entailed amputation of a child's leg on the suspicion of bone sarcoma, excision of the breast or uterus of a young woman, the removal of a lung or stomach from a man.

In some kinds of cancer, overdiagnosis (calling it cancer when it isn't) is more to be deplored than underdiagnosis. Dr. Eugene Pendergrass, the University of Pennsylvania radiologist, has urged conservatism (no treatment or radiotherapy rather than surgery where there is doubt) in treating childhood bone sarcoma; he has said that biopsy alone, without a detailed history of the patient and diagnostic X rays, sometimes can be confusing. He has stated that the cure rate for these cancers (excluding misdiagnosed benign bone tumors) seldom exceeds 5–10 per cent. Dr. E. J. Van Scott of NCI has pointed out that it is unrealistic to advocate removal of pigmented nevi (moles) for fear that they may become cancerous; he found in an examination of 735 individuals of all ages that they had, on an average, between sixteen and thirty nevi each somewhere on the skin and that 26.5 per cent of the people had a least one nevus on the palm or sole of the foot, where they are most subject to irritation and, some feel, most likely to become malignant.

The expert on whether or not a lump or sore is maligant is the pathologist—the "doctor's doctor." Pathologists, after qualifying as physicians, spend an extra four years in residency acquainting themselves with the characteristics of various diseases, and spend the rest of their professional lives learning, teaching, correcting their own and physicians' mistakes (often in postmortem studies) and making judgments, on the correctness of which hang the well-being, the limbs, and the lives of patients.

Beyond the superlative and exacting basic training required of all pathologists, there is a wide range of abilities. A few become, in effect, a "pathologist's pathologist"; gifted men like Drs. Arthur Purdy Stout of Columbia University, Lauren V. Ackerman of Washington University, and Fred W. Stewart of Memorial spend a generous portion of their time conducting seminars for other pathologists, studying others' slides and rendering opinions on them, and consulting on difficult-to-diagnose cases. Their diagnostic errors in cancer are less than 3 per cent. Most good tumor pathologists would be happy if their errors did not exceed 5 per cent. At one famous hospital, a study of sixty primary cancers of the liver showed that forty-two were diagnosed only at autopsy.

Dr. Stout has written:

There is a certain small percentage of tumors for which an exact diagnosis is extremely difficult, and even if the pathologist has had a wide experience with microscopic tumor interpretation and is both a keen and interested observer, he can make mistakes. Errors of this sort can lead to disaster sometimes; they may cause the unnecessary loss of a breast or an extremity or, per contra, they can be responsible for the failure to perform a lifesaving radical operation. This writer has made errors of both sorts in the past and has seen them made by others.

Dr. Stewart, lecturing physicians, said:

A pathologist cannot describe something to the nonexperienced individual and leave him with any notion of the groundwork for recognition of the precancerous state. To acquire this information, one must know lesion behavior from personal experience and that of others, and not merely the histological appearance of tissues and cells. Lesions that even resemble cancer may well not be precancerous. Rather innocent-looking processes, on the other hand, may have serious import.

Drs. Harold A. Kaminetzky and Elizabeth A. McGrew, cytologists at the University of Illinois, have found that application of an agent (like podophyllin) which prevents cell division produces cells which are difficult to distinguish from cancer cells; they expressed the opinion that similar agents, possibly produced by trichomonas or other organisms which commonly infect the vagina, may lead to false diagnoses of cancer of the cervix—and, in the hands of the inexpert, unnecessary surgery or radiation.

Nonpathologist misdiagnoses are by no means confined to the average physician whose knowledge of pathology is necessarily superficial. Some of them stem from noted surgeons and others with a remarkable record of curing cancer. Dr. Stout has written that he has "been pained to discover that some authors are willing to seek notoriety by publishing case reports of tumors obviously misdiagnosed, with the diagnosis based upon the interpretation of an anonymous pathologist."

"Once such erroneous publications appear in print and are recorded in countless abstract lists all over the world, the error has gained the status of fact," he said. "It will be quoted in future books and publications and continue to mislead the medical public for generations to come." Pathologists specializing in other areas can err in cancer, Dr. Stout said. "Nationally known names are not a guarantee of accuracy in tumor interpretation, for the individual's reputation may depend upon work in other fields."

A standard guide for the pathology of tumors is the fascicles of the *Atlas of Tumor Pathology,* published by the Armed Forces Institute of Pathology. The percentage of deviations in general practice from this diagnostic yardstick has not been computed, but a few studies indicate that it probably is substantial. In fact, there are no completely reliable estimates of cancer misdiagnoses; at least, none has been published. One recent review of 7,146 so-called cancer deaths for the Province of Saskatchewan has given a rough idea, however. In this case, confirmed and unconfirmed causes of death, as cited on the meager evidence of death certificates, and failure to certify cancers recorded with the provincial Cancer Commission were used as the basis of calculations. Overdiagnoses of cancer were estimated at 11.4 per cent and underdiagnoses at 14 per cent. It is a sobering thought that more than one in ten patients are subject to unnecessary mutilation or may be deprived of the possibility of cure by the doctor who diagnoses the case. In percentages, the most commonly overdiagnosed cancers were of the stomach (256.5), bronchus, trachea, and lung (134.6), pancreas (120.3) and large intestine (117.6). Most commonly underdiagnosed were cancers of the skin (125.6), mouth (117.6), prostate (107.4), and breast (91.6). From these findings, the investigators from the Allan Blair Memorial Clinic of Regina and the National Cancer Institute of Canada concluded that "death certificate diagnoses are insufficiently accurate to permit their use as a reliable indication of the incidence of cancer." Death-certificate data, nevertheless, is the basis for official estimates of cancer in the United States.

In cancer, the patient seldom sees the pathologist. But on the skill of this man behind the scenes often depends the correct diagnosis and treatment of the disease. When diagnosis is made without the aid of a skilled pathologist, the patient's chances for proper medical treatment are greatly diminished.

Back in 1945, an official of New York's Hospital for Joint Diseases received a note stating that the writer, a Viennese handwriting expert, Alfred Kanfer, could diagnose cancer from handwriting. Would the director give the writer a chance to demonstrate?

At this particular period, there were numerous reports of new blood tests, urine tests, and sundry other tests for cancer, all of them under vigorous and highly successful challenge. A handwriting test was something new, however; and the official, in a moment of curiosity, invited Mr. Kanfer to visit. Despite several articles by the expert in reputable European medical and scientific journals, this stood to be the most preposterous test of them all—the cancer test to end cancer tests. So the hospital official believed.

The handwriting expert was shy, quiet, knowledgeable, and intensely serious as he explained his system. The official gave the expert 150 handwriting samples—100 from well people and patients with noncancerous diseases and 50 from cancer patients.

The tests took some doing. There were careful examinations of samples under a strong lens, numerous calculations, and finally the decision—in the form of a grade. Of the fifty samples from cancer patients, forty-five were marked + 10 to + 20 and positive, and five were marked + 5 to + 9 and suspicious. Of the 100 noncancer samples, ninety were scored from zero to − 12 and were negative, and the other ten scored + 1 to + 9 and were graded suspicious.

The official was appalled by the uncanny accuracy of the test. Moreover, he was now involved. Staff members were invited to listen. The expert explained that over many years of study of handwriting specimens of cancer patients, he had devised a system with 740 criteria indicating negative or positive. Later he reduced these criteria successively to 55 and then to 48—18 representing negative and 30 positive. Judgments were made on the way letters were formed, the tension of the pen, the smooth or abrupt transition from letter to letter. Considered positive were the sharp angular and overextended writing of letters like *n, m, u,* and *w;* the irregularity of height, width, spacing, and slants of small letters; erratic changes of light pressure on upstrokes and heavy pressure on downstrokes and connecting strokes; sudden alterations in tension and rigidity; the lack of sharpness and continuity of edges of letters and the uneven distribution of ink within a stroke; and the failure to make certain letters as round and oval as they should be. In favor of negative diagnoses were such characteristics as gradual changes in width and the regularity of strokes; the nice looping of the *o, a,* and other rounded letters; the evenness of curves in *m, n, u,* and *w;* and, under the microscope, the regular and solid edges of letters.

A cancer test is not very useful if only one man can do it. Mr. Kanfer gave the official and three of his staff a brief instruction in running the test and had them perform it. Two of the staff did almost as well as the expert. The test was reproducible.

No honorable man at this point could tell the expert to take his handwriting test elsewhere. Yet no man who hoped to hold his status in the medical profession could let it be known that he was seriously interested in a handwriting test for cancer. At the same time, no responsible investigator would ignore anything of value in the detection of cancer. The official had integrity. The hospital began long-term experiments in "graphodiagnosis."

The American Cancer Society was asked for financial support, and, out of curiosity, an investigator looked into the test. The investigator found that the test indicated cancer with good fidelity—so good that the agency quietly granted funds for "neuromuscular coordination" studies in cancer.

One investigator decided that "graphodiagnosis" was really a test for old age rather than cancer. The fact that it had proved more reliable in young than old patients did not influence his opinion. The test worked well in some studies, but was disappointing in others. In one series, it achieved an accuracy of 80–90 per cent in negative determinations and 80–85 per cent in positive diagnoses—with some seemingly false positives eventually turning out to register otherwise undetectable and unsuspected cancers. A large insurance company has begun studying the system.

Announcements of new blood and other tests for cancer are not as frequent as they used to be. Most of those who introduced tests in the past have taken their licking and retired from this phase of investigation. Those who now feel they may have discovered something of value in detecting cancer usually are reluctant to say so; they are not inviting abuse. Public health agencies are not aggressively seeking a test.

Several blood tests in the past have registered positive for a high percentage of patients with serious cancers—the kind that are hardest to detect. They were based on an excess or deficiency in the blood of enzymes or their inhibitors, antigens or antibodies, polysaccharides or glycoproteins, and other debris from decaying tumor and injured normal tissue, coagulating proteins, albumins, globulins, vitamins, trace metals, amino acids, fats, lipids, cell poisons, red-cell destroyers, and numerous other chemicals of known and unknown identity. Other tests have been based upon the presence of compounds in urine. Of considerable interest at this writing is the finding by Dr. Edward D. McLaughlin of NCI of a blood fraction which he calls MF10. When this fraction is extracted from human serum and injected into mice bearing transplanted cancers, it slows or arrests cancer growth. The amount of MF10 present can be measured by the inhibition of the cancers' growth. In the blood of healthy people or patients with noncancerous diseases, MF10 measured 72 to 168 units (per 100 milliliters of serum); in patients possibly cured of cancer for from fourteen months to seven years, 16 to 56 units; in patients with untreated cancer, 8 to 52 units; and, in patients with recurrent or metastatic cancer, 4 to 52 units.

Several dozen techniques and instruments for identifying and measuring the purported cancer chemicals have been employed. They determined color changes under heat and cold, optical rotation, muddiness, clotting time, magnetic properties, current-voltage curves, and migration of particles or red cells within an electric field or on filter paper or down a column of starch. The reactants showed up under infrared or were fluorescent in ultraviolet light; they satisfied the dietary requirements of mutant bacteria or reflected starvation in the patient.

A few tests, generally accepted, give strong or weak hints as to the presence of specific cancers—blood in the urine for genitourinary cancer, blood in feces for gastrointestinal cancer, abnormal cells for leukemia and Hodgkin's disease, serum acid phosphatase for prostatic cancer, Bence-Jones protein for multiple myeloma, serum akaline phosphatase for bone cancer, gonadotropin hormone for choriocarcinoma and a few others.

There is as yet, however, no recognized screening test for cancer. While some of the tests, in the hands of their originators, have detected 90 or 95 or higher per cent of the proved cancers, numerous objections have been raised. Some of the objections have proved completely valid; others are disputed with some bitterness.

Critics have contended that some tests are not reproducible—the claimed results cannot be obtained by others. Test defenders have answered that those who checked the tests were incompetent, hostile, or subjective (they were developing their own tests) and their methods faulty.

Critics have said that a practical test must detect at least 90 per cent of all cancers that can be found by other methods (including exploratory surgery and radiation) and give less than 5 per cent false positives. Defenders have answered that if similar requirements were imposed, we would not have a satisfactory test for syphilis and numerous other detectable diseases. They point out that the Wassermann test is useful—but by no means specific—for syphilis.

Critics have said that some tests which do show cancer with acceptable fidelity also register positive for late pregnancy, tuberculosis, pneumonia, arthritis, cirrhosis, recent injuries or surgery, temperatures over 100 degrees, and numerous acute infections. Defenders contend that almost all these conditions are self-evident or readily diagnosable and can be distinguished easily from cancer. They say some seemingly false positives eventually proved to be true positives—the cancers could not be confirmed by other methods at the time.

Critics have said that tests must show very early cancers, latent cancers, inactive cancers, and recurrent cancers as well as advanced cancers. Defenders say that any test which shows up cancers earlier than they now are found is worthwhile.

Critics have said that tests which show the presence of cancer but not its site would serve only to confuse the doctor and depress the patient. Defenders say that ignorance of cancer is not bliss; it is important to learn that cancer is present and then, knowing or suspecting it is there, search for it.

Within the last decade of quickening investigation, numerous techniques of exquisite sensitivity for chemical, biological, and physical determinations have been developed. It is possible that some of them may be able to find—and possibly even to define—the critical differences between normal and cancerous systems and serve as a practical detection or diagnostic test for cancer.

One of the current developments in biophysics, for instance, is in the field of thermography—the measurement of heat emanating from various body sites. Dr. R. Bowling Barnes of the Barnes Engineering Company, Stanford, Connecticut, has developed a system of photographing the infrared aura of the skin, which may vary by several microns in wavelength and by many degrees in temperature from site to site and under different internal and environmental conditions. He has predicted that thermography will have considerable diagnostic value in many disease states. Drs. R. N. Lawson and M. S. Chughtai of McGill University and Dr. Gershon-Cohen have made thermograms of women suspected of having breast cancer and have located the cancers by elevated temperatures of the skin above them; the heat, they have shown, is produced by the stepped-up metabolism of the tumor, rather than by an increased flow of blood to the area. Inflammation also registers.

The Farber finding that cancer contains something which kills chick embryos or makes monsters of them stands to be a biological detection tool of enormous importance, if preliminary results hold up under continued testing.

Though no universal chemical test for cancer has yet emerged, numerous sensitive new methods have been developed for the determination of enzyme, antigen, antibody, and other molecules, and it is thoroughly conceivable that someday some of them will detect any cancer patterns which may exist. They will do this, however, only if scientists have a test in mind and will perfect it over the opposition of the inevitable critics and cynics.

CHAPTER 24

SURGERY

Of all the experimental animals, man is the most complicated, the most unpredictable and, for these reasons, the least satisfactory from the scientific point of view. In medicine, it is hard to distinguish miracle from mirage, and sometimes it is difficult to determine from the human data whether certain procedures do more good than harm.

Despite these and numerous other considerations, a few points are crystal clear, and they should not be lost sight of in considering the philosophical differences, the controversies over techniques, and the abuses which abound in the field of surgery. A great many cancers are readily curable by surgery; most of them are in the curable stage for a limited period—only until they have begun to spread far from the original tumor. People with cancer symptoms should consult a competent physician at the earliest possible moment, and, if surgery is suggested, should seek the services of the best man available for their particular tumor. More than one million Americans have been cured of cancer, a majority of them by surgery, and with improving techniques and talents the surgical cures of cancer are rising steadily. Patients can save themselves, and usually they can do it only by prompt and intelligent action.

Dr. I. S. Ravdin, Professor of Surgery at the University of Pennsylvania, recounted for a group of science writers in 1962 the numerous and comparatively commonplace advantages which enable surgeons each year to perform unprecedented and often incredible feats of skill and daring with the scalpel. They are helped by talented assistants, blood banks to replace lost blood, a variety of anesthetics, antibiotics, strict antisepsis, tissue replacements, information on the patient's physical and chemical status before, during, and following surgery and scores of other contributions by physicists, engineers, biologists, and biochemists.

Dr. Ravdin said:

No aspect of surgery has benefited more than that concerned with malignant disease. The limitations of surgery in malignant disease now depend, in large part, on the technical ability of the surgeon and the boundaries of his conscience. It has become possible to do extensive dissections of the lymph nodes of one or both sides of the neck, to remove the larynx, a lung, the entire stomach or one lobe of the liver. One can remove large portions of, or the entire, large bowel or the urinary bladder. Some operations in reality are "subtotal eviscerations."

In spite of all the technical advances, we don't know why some malignant lesions grow so slowly that one wonders whether they are truly malignant, while others spread like a fire on the prairie.

The truth is, we know very little about the over-all biological characteristics of malignant lesions.

The best surgeons are subject to episodes of alternating pleasant surprise and chagrin as about 15 per cent of their prognoses prove wrong. The patient given six months to live may survive in comfort for five, ten or more years; the one they assured of being out of the woods sometimes is dead of the disease in a few months. With cancer, the professional certainty of cure or death is only a little more reliable than the experts' predictions on the weather, an election, or a horse race. On very rare occasions, without any treatment whatsoever, a patient with advanced cancer will be completely cured; for these spontaneous cures, there are many explanations, none of them very satisfactory. To the very best physicians, they represent an ultimate proof that while there's life, there's hope.

As would be expected in any rapidly developing, constantly changing area of intellectual and technical endeavor, the field of surgery is a battleground. New ideas are challenged vigorously; time-honored convention is questioned, and the giants wrestle with one another and with all comers, particularly presumptuous upstarts from the relatively recent specialty of radiotherapy. New fashions often have a short life—in some cases, not short enough. The regular use of antibiotics to prevent infection of surgical wounds, once hailed as a major advance, now is regarded as questionable; a review of 3,000 major orthopedic procedures at Chicago's Wesley Memorial Hospital showed the infection rate was twice as high when prophylactic antibiotics were used as when they weren't.

Some of the top-level disputes are a source of dismay to the general run of surgeons and confusion to other practitioners. By and large, however, the struggles are yielding improved methods of treatment for cancer. Cure rates are improving; and where cure is impossible, more and more patients are surviving in comfort.

One of the thorniest issues centers around the adage that early cancer is curable while late cancer is incurable. This flat rule contradicts the occasional experience of every cancer surgeon who has removed an enormous malignant tumor that has been growing a decade or more and cured the patient, or who has removed an entire organ containing a pimple-sized cancer only to find that the patient is dead of the disease within a few months.

Dr. Ian Macdonald of the University of Southern California, an articulate surgeon of large experience and considerable skill, for more than fifteen years has insisted that "biological predeterminism," rather than the size of the tumor, the time it has been growing, and its site, shapes the destiny of the patient and should serve as a guide to surgeons. He contends that even some exceedingly small cancers with a tendency to shed cells from their inception will have sealed the patient's doom by the time they are first noticed; in these cases, he believes, extensive curative-type surgery may well be futile, meddlesome, mutilating, and life-shortening. He feels that, on the other hand, some large cancers which have been growing for a long time but which do not readily shed cells (metastasize) should be regarded and treated as curable. Many of the factors governing "biological predeterminism" are vague. The experienced cancer pathologist, however, usually can distinguish between the fast and slow metastasizing tumors.

Dr. Macdonald's concept covers many of the more serious cancers, notably of the stomach and breast. To buttress his arguments, he cites statistics which indicate that early cancers often have proved more deadly than late cancers. Of more than 6,400 cases of stomach cancer at the Mayo Clinic, for instance, patients with symptoms which had lasted three or four years had cancers 60 per cent more resectable (removable) and had almost double the five-year survival rate of patients whose symptoms had lasted less than three months.

Critics have called "biological predeterminism" a philosophy of premeditated failure, unwarranted fatalism, pessimism, hopelessness, frustration and mysticism, confusing, illogical, and tragically harmful. They have compared it to the preantibiotic-era spirit of resignation which held that the death of millions from infectious disease represented "God's will." Many have objected to any discussion of biological predeterminism, because, as one critic put it, "should this concept become widely known and accepted, the already deeply rooted pessimism prevalent among general practitioners regarding the value of the surgical approach in cancer of the stomach will be reinforced."

Dr. Macdonald has denied that his theory is in agreement with "those deft but dour wizards of biometry (longevity statistics) who suggest that cancer of the breast is uninfluenced by treatment." He has attacked "the protagonists of surgical super-radicalism who represent 'the-triumph-of-hope-over-experience' philosophy in tirades decrying any recognition of the biologic facts of neoplastic life." He has admitted that "the concept is inherently fatalistic, but no more than the neoplastic processes it attempts to describe."

Dr. Macdonald's most vigorous dissent is reserved for those who would silence discussion of the subject.

I prefer a belief in the propriety of free discussion of medical, scientific and technical developments, philosophic or practical, within the medical community at large in a free society. The pessimism owes its deeply rooted status to nothing more than the true end results of surgical treatment. In fact, the family physician, as well as the internist, is more apt to have an accurate impression of the ravages of gastric cancer than is the surgeon.

He said the general practitioner often refers to the surgeon only the apparently operable cases, while internists take care of patients from the time they leave the hospital following surgery until their deaths. This leaves the surgeon seeing only selected patients for short periods of their illness.

Dr. Macdonald defends and employs conventional procedures—radical mastectomy, adrenalectomy, and pelvic exenteration. He emphasizes that he is arguing for realism, not the abandonment of useful surgical measures.

Several of the foremost surgeons, while perhaps not subscribing to the doctrine of predeterminism as such, have compiled biological and clinical data to support contentions that extensive surgery in some cases does more harm than good. Others of equal eminence hold to the principle that in many incurable cancers, surgery may help to decrease pain, increase the feeling of well-being and in some cases enable patients to live normal lives for many years with their cancers under complete control. Occasionally a procedure intended to be purely palliative will cause remaining cancer to disappear surprisingly, unpredictably, and for prolonged periods.

Animal experiments are of limited help in solving the mysteries of man's response to trauma, surgical and otherwise.

Most experiments have shown that injuries do not induce cancer, but, by and large, speed the growth of existing cancers. Such deliberate trauma as the reopening of cancer wounds, burns, needle puncture of the liver bearing early cancers, and contrived emotional upsets have accelerated spontaneous, transplanted, and chemically-induced cancers in several animal species.

In one series of mice being treated with carcinogens, however, the trauma of electrical shock inhibited the development of cancer.

Scientists at the National Cancer Institute have tested the effects of removing various types of tumors from mice. Drs. William E. Schatten and William M. Kramer reported that when they transplanted rapidly spreading (metastasizing) cancers to the legs of mice and three weeks later removed the cancerous leg or the original transplant, latent metastases elsewhere in the body came to life and grew rapidly. They were convinced that the removal of the cancer, not the stress of surgery, was responsible for this; when they amputated a noncancerous leg of the cancer-bearing animals, the relatively few cancer colonies remained quiescent. Another NCI group headed by Dr. Alfred S. Ketcham found in experiments with five different mouse tumors that removal of the original cancers permitted the established metastases to grow rapidly but inhibited the development of new metastases. When Dr. A. D. Gulledge of Baylor University removed the primary breast cancers from mice, the animals developed an average of four metastatic cancers, whereas in animals retaining their original cancers an average of only 1.2 metastases appeared.

A University of Illinois group headed by Drs. Gerald O. McDonald and Warren H. Cole entered an exhibit at the 1960 annual meeting of the American Medical Society describing an elaborate series of controlled experiments to determine what role, if any, surgical stress might play in the course of cancer. Their motives they explained in this way:

> Most surgeons have encountered the patient whose cancer grows rapidly following operation, resulting in death within a few weeks. Since no two tumors behave in the same manner, we have no proof of the validity of a possible decrease in resistance of the patient to his cancer cells following operation. However, because of the great clinical importance of this possibility, we have tested this hypothesis utilizing the laboratory animal [rat] and 256 Walker carcino-sarcoma.

The McDonald-Cole studies involved injecting previously stressed animals with a graded series of strong and weak tumor cells capable of causing cancer with predictable frequency in anywhere from 30 to 100 per cent of the test animals. They investigated the possible part played by two commonly used anesthetics and the "deep freeze" anesthetic technique called hypothermia; they simulated the surgery given to humans with abdominal cancers; and, as another form of stress, they gave some of the animals the liver poison, carbon tetrachloride.

All the stresses—operative, liver poison, hypothermia and both the chemical anesthetics (nembutal and other)—decreased the animals' resistance to injected cancer cells. As compared with unstressed controls, operative stress increased the tumor takes anywhere from 50 to 450 per cent, carbon tetrachloride by 300 per cent, nembutal 330 per cent, ether 75 per cent and hypothermia 30 per cent, and when anesthetic was added, 60 per cent. The decreased resistance to cancer lasted two or three days after the stress. By removing glands and administering hormones, the scientists determined that neither the pituitary, adrenals, nor, at least to a significant degree, the thyroid influenced the stress-stimulation of cancer. They felt that this stress was different from the hormone-governed stress described by Dr. Hans Selye of Montreal.

There are many kinds of trauma and stress, several explanations for each of them, and actually very little sound information on the mechanisms by which any of them operate. The extreme consequences of all of them are shock; but even here there are at least two broad categories—primary shock which induces an immediate collapse in response to psychic blows or physical injuries, and secondary shock which usually occurs a few hours after an injury. Whether ordinary stresses and shocks are involved in the lowering of resistance to cancer or whether the phenomenon is due to entirely different mechanisms is unknown. An occasionally voiced clinical impression is that cancer patients to varying degrees are less able to withstand operations than are patients with noncancerous diseases; but there is no way of knowing whether this fault, if indeed it actually exists, plays a role in the surgical dissemination of cancer.

Drs. Mark A. Hayes, Ira S. Goldenberg, and others at the Yale Department of Surgery for many years have studied the mechanisms and control of surgical shock. They have sought to learn what enables some patients to survive extensive operations requiring many hours, while a few, particularly some cancer patients, may go into surgical shock several times during a procedure which takes only an hour or two. In surgical shock there is a sudden, profound fall in blood pressure, the skin turns deathly pale and cold, the body temperature and metabolic rate drop, breathing becomes shallow, and the pulse small and rapid. Usually the surgeon has only a few minutes in which to restore the patient, to fill the chambers of the vigorously beating but incompletely filled heart, and restart the blood flow through the stalling arteries and engorged distant vessels into the empty great veins. The Yale scientists have found that the thyroid gland plays a leading role in surgical shock; as nearly as they have been able to trace it, the gland produces, under the anxiety of the preoperative period, vast amounts of its hormone, releases it in a "thyroid storm" into an already overactive metabolic system, ending, like the one-hoss shay, in a general breakdown of many overstressed nervous, muscular, circulatory, and chemical systems. The scientists feel that in shock, adrenal hormones, which normally moderate the action of thyroid hormones, are incapable of restoring the needed balance. It may be that the stress of surgery exhausts the thyroid. Surgeons at Walter Reed Hospital also have reported finding postoperative hypothyroidism in many patients.

Cytologists at various research centers have observed strange and often conflicting surgical phenomena in some animals and some humans. A few minutes after the start of an extensive operation, cancer cells may disappear suddenly from the bloodstream. For weeks following surgery, the circulation is free of these cells. This occurs regardless of whether or not tumors are removed. In recurrence, the cancer cells begin to emerge from their secret hiding places and repopulate the bloodstream. It is speculative as to whether the surgical mechanism, whatever it may be, enables the hiding cancer cells to establish new colonies.

In other cases, however, the opposite occurs. Showers of cancer cells are released into the bloodstream not only during operation but also during the removal of specimens for microscopic examination, or merely when lumps are felt.

The Illinois group, under Dr. Cole, has searched the bloodstreams of 108 patients who underwent surgery for various forms of cancer. In 48 per cent of the cases, cancer cells were present before, during, or following their operations. In 17 per cent of the patients circulating cancer cells could be found only during the operation.

Dr. Cole, as a result of his observations, has laid down a set of precautions to help guard against the surgical spread of the cancer. They include the avoidance of unnecessary preoperative washing and manual exploration (palpation) of the tumorous area, extreme care not to cut through the tumor or to handle it more than necessary, the early tying off of blood vessels and lymphatic channels through which dislodged cancer cells might escape, and the careful removal of the tumor and all tissues which might be tainted by cancer. These and other measures to prevent cancer in suture lines, reduced local recurrences of colon cancer from 9.9 per cent to zero. Surgical instruments and gloves often are contaminated with loose cancer cells; and suture threads have implanted cancer cells in the patient's tissues.

Many studies indicate that in 25 to 60 per cent of patients, cancer cells are left in the operative field. Investigators have learned this by swabbing out the area at the end of an operation and examining the washings under a microscope. There is conflicting evidence of the dangers of these loose cells; one study at NCI, conducted by Dr. Arthur W. Hilberg, showed that cancer recurred in almost one-half the operated patients harboring detectable malignant cells; at Roswell Park the recurrence rate was 9 per cent; another NCI group headed by Dr. Marvin S. Arons found that there was no correlation at all between the postoperative presence of cancer cells and local recurrence, distant metastases, or survival. Dr. Cole's series reflected great differences, small differences, and no differences in recurrence among patients found with and without cancer cells following surgery; much depended on the type of cancer. Generally, however, twice as many incurable as curable patients showed circulating cancer cells. Evidently the patient's own immunity often destroys cancer cells left following surgery.

Controversy over techniques has extended to most of the common sites of cancer, and much of it hinges on how extensive an operation should be. In a curious turnabout in terminology, surgeons who favor radical (extensive) operations are considered conservative, while those favoring conservative operations are considered radical. In both instances, the surgeons have in mind curing cancer; the difference is in the amount of tissue wagered on the cure. Protagonists of radical operations feel that it is best to remove not only the cancer but all the nearby tissue to which the cancer may have spread; their opponents feel that the less tissue removed the less likely cancer cells are to be dislodged and the more comfortable the patient will be.

Both conservative and radical surgeons offer highly persuasive sets of statistics to support their arguments. The statistics, however, are seldom comparable. One set may be based upon every patient seen, whether explored or not, whether or not the cancer was removed, and whether the patient died of cancer, of an accident, or of heart disease; other statistics may deal only with patients carefully selected for operation because of their apparently excellent chances of cure. If one examines closely enough the cases operated upon by a surgeon enjoying an extraordinarily high cure rate, he is almost certain to find that the surgeon has refused to operate on many patients with only a fair-to-middling chance of cure. The cure rates by other surgeons of equal skill may be low because of the number of long-shot gambles they take in trying to cure patients of doubtful curability.

And then, of course, there is the enormous range of competence in the art of surgery; it is almost comparable, in other forms of art, to the spectrum of skills between a Michelangelo and a housepainter.

One cancer which is the center of numerous controversies is that of the female breast. Differences of opinion begin with diagnostic procedures. Many authorities agree that it is inadvisable to take a preoperation biopsy —that is, to insert a needle which removes a sample of the lump for microscopic study—because this, they say, is likely to scatter cancer cells into the circulation. Some have raised the question of whether even the removal of some suspect tissue at the start of an operation may not spread cancer cells dangerously; they recommended removal of the entire suspect lump and the tissue surrounding it.

The next question is how extensive the operation should be. Almost all American surgeons perform a radical mastectomy—that is, they remove not only the breast but also surrounding lymphatic tissues as far as the armpit, parts of the chest wall and other sites of potential spread. A few contend that simple mastectomy, principally the removal of the breast, is equally curative and much less disabling. And a few others assert that simple mastectomy followed by radiotherapy to the points of spread yields the best results of all. Because of differences of statistical evaluation, there are no absolute answers to these problems.

Dr. Hugh Auchincloss, Jr., of the Columbia Presbyterian Hospital, New York, had the unique privilege of reviewing in 1960 the records of 152 cases of breast cancer which had been treated by his late father between 1935 and 1947. The cure rate was about the same as that achieved by other fine surgeons—56.6 per cent had survived five years and 38.8 per cent ten years. With the perspective of a decade or two, the younger Dr. Auchincloss traced the destinies of patients who, at operation, had a good or a bad outlook. Those who did well had cancers which (1) were discovered and removed early, (2) did not metastasize rapidly, and (3) did not underlie the ringlike tissue surrounding the nipple. Some of the cases were a desperate gamble; they were too far gone for surgery and the patients would have been better off without it. On the other hand, nineteen patients whose disease had spread to lymph nodes in the armpit were well and without cancer ten years or more after surgery. The pathologist had called some of these cases hopeless, but, happily, he was unduly pessimistic.

Of those who lived without cancer recurrence for many years, including those with an original bleak prognosis, Dr. Auchincloss, Jr., said:

> I am not impressed by those who say that a woman never gets over the loss of a breast and that the effects of a mastectomy may be devastating and long-lasting. It is true that some have a harder time adjusting than others, and a great deal may depend on the age of the patient, her occupation, her social and marital status, and, above all, on the sympathetic understanding of the surgeon. If this understanding approach is available, and if it is supported by a husband or other members of the family, I have yet to see the patient who does not in the end achieve a satisfactory adjustment.

While he decried discrimination in selection of patients to the degree that an occasional one with advanced but curable disease might be denied an operation, he added:

> The performance of ill-advised radical mastectomy in an obviously very advanced case can work just as much harm as the opposite extreme. When it fails and metastases appear early in the postoperative period, it only serves to confirm the impression in the mind of the patient and her friends of the futility of operation and, in the end, works a disservice to the patient and surgeon alike. It is inevitable that some patients, perhaps quite a few, will be subjected to noncura-

tive operations in order to avoid denying operation to the occasional patient who might have been cured.

Despite all the disputes and the accumulating data on cancer of the breast, very little progress has been made in curing it during the last three decades. Surgery is the overwhelming choice of treatment. The most reliable statistics indicate that, with at best a few percentage points improvement, apparently localized breast cancer has been and is about 75 per cent curable and all stages of it about 50 per cent. Less than 1 per cent of the victims are men.

Among other cancer sites for which surgery usually is the treatment are the salivary gland, stomach, bowel and rectum, ovary, prostate, testis, kidney, bladder, and thyroid. Surgery almost invariably is used to treat melanoma and in about three cases out of four to treat skin cancers. When the tumors appear to be localized, surgery is the preferred treatment for cancers of the body of the uterus. Substantial rises in surgical cure rates have been reported during the last two decades for skin cancer, for cancers of the large intestine and rectum and for early cancers of the lung, uterine cervix (more often treated by radiation than surgery), and stomach; less impressive improvement has been registered in other surgically-treated tumors.

Ingenious new treatments appear to have raised the cure rates for some cancers; but usually these are practiced only by certain groups and, consequently, the improvement is not reflected in over-all statistics. The techniques sometimes are so complicated that they remain more or less the exclusive property of the surgeons who invented them, or they entail additional care, training, study, and facilities which conventional surgeons are unwilling to understake. Many balk at extremely radical operations.

The "second look" operation devised by Dr. Owen H. Wangensteen and his group at the University of Minnesota may have cured about 10 per cent of patients who otherwise would have died of stomach-cancer recurrence and possibly 25 per cent of patients with recurrent bowel cancer. This surgery involves careful removal of all tissues to which, according to their considerable observations, these cancers are likely to spread and, an exploratory six months after the initial surgery, to make certain that unsuspected cancer colonies have not formed. Patients have had as many as six "second looks" before the final one showed them free from residual or metastatic cancers.

Another University of Minnesota surgeon, Dr. John McKelvey, for many years has published data indicating that cancer of the vulva, the entrance to the vagina, responds well to curative surgery in eight or nine cases out of ten. Many surgeons, considering the usually advanced years of these patients and believing this kind of cancer is difficult or impossible to cure, do not operate.

Dr. Alton Ochsner of New Orleans often will perform a radical operation on lung cancer patients whom most other surgeons would let go; three-fourths of his lung operations are for palliative purposes only. He justifies the procedure by statistics—in his skilled hands, operative mortality is low and survival in comfort seems to be lengthened. Inferior surgery, however, leaves the patient crippled and may shorten survival.

A sizable series of lung cancers treated at the University of Pennsylvania Medical School indicates what happens, statistically, when a good and aggressive Department of Surgery, with due regard to the evils of unnecessary surgery, still refuses to give up easily. Of 764 lung cancer patients seen there (344 of them more than five years earlier) 56 per cent were explored, 34 per cent received conservative surgery (the removal of the affected lung lobe), and of resected patients, 26.7 per cent (or 9 per cent of the 344 operated on five or more years earlier) were alive when the report was compiled. The key to survival in these cases rested on whether cancer had invaded their blood vessels—when it had, only 6 per cent survived five years; when it hadn't, 75 per cent survived.

A dozen years ago Dr. Alexander Brunschwig of the Memorial Cancer Center in New York demonstrated that "subtotal evisceration" of the human pelvis could be accomplished with reasonable operative mortality. This involved removing the rectum, much of the colon, the urinary bladder, part of the ureters, all the internal reproductive organs, the pelvic floor and wall, the lymph nodes, and many blood vessels. The patients usually were on their feet two days after surgery. The operation was designed for patients whose cancers had spread through much of the pelvis but not beyond. The procedure, appears to have extended the life span of some patients with pelvic-spread cancers and has cured a few. For cervical cancer patients who for one reason or another will not chance radiotherapy, which has established itself as the preferred treatment in most centers, radical surgery offers a cure rate of 87 per cent, if the disease is seemingly confined to the cervix. At Washington University about one-half the patients whose colon cancers were treated in this manner were surviving, at last report, for from thirteen to thirty-four months following surgery.

That radical surgery is not always the best treatment is indicated in a report by Dr. Benjamin F. Rush, Jr., who traced the fate of 91 stomach cancer patients who had their entire stomachs removed and 117 who lost only part of their stomachs between 1940 and 1951 at Johns Hopkins Hospital. Only 9 per cent of the "nutritional cripples" who lost all their stomachs survived five years, as compared with 25 per cent of those who lost only part of it.

An extremely difficult operation enables the few surgeons who do it to remove up to 80 per cent of the human liver, a favorite resting place for metastatic cells from other sites. Dr. George T. Pack of Memorial Cancer Center, a pioneer in this surgery, which until recently was considered impossible, has removed one or another of the three lobes in a variety of patients and feels he has extended the life span of some of them. The liver regenerates to some degree.

A "chemosurgical" technique designed more than two decades ago by Dr. Frederick E. Mohs of the University of Wisconsin has had sparse adoption, despite its 5 to 18 per cent increase in the cure rate for cancers of the skin and other accessible sites, including superficial melanomas. It is a simple procedure, in most cases involving little more time, pain, and risk than having a tooth filled. It must be done with meticulous microscopic examination of tissue, however. The procedure essentially consists of: (1) a local anesthetic to the tumor area; (2) scalpel excision of all of the visible tumor; (3) application of dichloracetic acid to stop the bleeding promptly; (4) the spreading of a zinc chloride paste which forms a solid crust over the entire bed of the excised tumor; and (5) immediate freezing, slicing, and microscopic examination of the removed tumor. On the following day, the underside of the crust on the tumor bed is mapped off into sections, removed and carefully scanned under the microscope for residual cancer cells. If cancer cells are found, that specific area of the tumor bed is attacked with cell-destroying chemicals, the paste is reapplied to the tumor bed and, on the next visit, this crust in turn is examined for cancer cells. The procedure is repeated until the crust no longer shows cancer cells. Most patients are cured in two office visits, but occasionally many visits are needed to track down and destroy the thin, sinuous, tunneling tentacles of cancer. The technique makes it possible to destroy all the cancer cells with a high degree of certainty, good healing, and cosmetic effects. Normal tissue need not be sacrificed. In more than 5,000 cancers, one-third of them unsuccessfully treated by earlier surgery or radiation, Dr. Mohs has effected these cure rates: basal-cell, 98.7 per cent; squamous-cell, 90.9 per cent; lip cancers (squamous), 93.2 per cent; and melanoma of the skin, 41.2 per cent. While skin tumors account for only 1.5 per cent of cancer deaths, these tumors can be painful and horribly mutilating if let go.

Two now-standard procedures which are not regarded as curative have restored for long periods the health of thousands of hopelessly advanced cancer patients. The first involves the removal of the testes and administration of female sex hormones to men with prostatic cancer. The second calls for the removal of the adrenal glands from women with metastatic breast cancer. The operations have dispelled pain, restored appetite and the feeling of well-being, and sent many of these patients back to work and normal life. The operations are effective in all breast and prostatic cancers whose growth is dependent upon hormones produced by the glands.

Removing the pituitary, the master gland, also helps about 40 per cent of the patients with hormone-controlled breast cancer who are beyond other aid.

Deaths on the operating table have decreased a great deal and they continue to go down; stomach removals which a few decades ago used to cost the life of one in every three or four patients now claim 5 per cent or fewer when done by skilled surgeons. Surgical shock has come under considerable control. Older people, if they are in fair physical shape, can undergo surgery almost as well as younger people.

A great deal has been learned about the alterations in body chemistry following operations—the water intoxication which induces convulsions, the changes in nitrogen and carbohydrate balance, the elevation of sugar in blood and urine, the decreased glucose tolerance, the increase in urinary potassium and retention of sodium and chloride, and the hormones and enzymes responsible for these vast changes. By anticipating the changes and by learning the limits of fluid and glucose to be given patients to cope with kidney shutdown and other disturbances, postoperative disasters more and more are being overcome.

The substitution of plastics and tissue transplants for damaged organs is in its infancy, but a few scientists already have shown that this field will be one of the more exciting chapters in medical history. The human trachea has been replaced by a heavy mesh plastic—durable, strong, rigid, nonwettable and pliable enough to serve successfully. A segment of the small intestine or colon has been transplanted as a substitute bladder, or a part of the esophagus. In experimental animals and a few humans, heart valves have been replaced with plastic devices; the great artery leading from the heart has been repaired, and the aortic arch has been replaced.

The principle that with increasing cold, body chemistry slows progressively—about 50 per cent with every ten-degree drop in blood temperature until at 75 degrees the heart comes to a complete standstill—is opening new horizons of treatment.

A new chapter in the history of medicine may have been started by such surgeons as Dr. Claude R. Hitchcock of Minneapolis General Hospital and Dr. William McDermott of Massachusetts General Hospital. Dr. Hitchcock has removed one kidney or one lung from baboons, refrigerated it or circulated drug-laden blood through the isolated organ and then, as long as eight hours later, restored it in perfectly functional condition to the donor. Dr. McDermott has had equal success in isolating or removing, treating, and restoring the entire liver of other experimental animals. At the University of Oregon Medical School, Dr. Stanley W. Jacob has removed the heart from one dog, refrigerated it (under enormous pressure to prevent ice formation), placed it in another dog, and found that it beat normally for several hours. These experiments represent the curtain-raising studies which someday in the not-too-distant future may permit the vigorous treatment and repair of organs outside the body and the replacement of worn-out human organs with those supplied by a living or dead donor. To make transplants possible, geneticists even now are solving the secrets of tissue compatibility; with increasing frequency they are able to make tissues from one species grow and function in a totally unrelated animal. At this writing, primate organs are being transplanted to humans—in some cases with temporary success.

Visions of future marvels of surgery are of slight comfort to hundreds of thousands of hopeless, helpless patients now ill with advanced cancers. Some of them are unable to obtain the type of surgery first performed on January 29, 1881, when Dr. Christian Albert Theodor Billroth at the University of Vienna removed part of the cancerous stomach and three contaminated lymph nodes from Frau Theresa Heller. (The patient survived this classical operation in good shape but died of her cancer four months later.) While some of the best medicine in the world is practiced in the United States, the shortage of good doctors—and particularly of first-class surgeons—is such that many patients, wittingly or unwittingly, fall into the hands of shoddy substitutes.

The American College of Surgeons, the professional society of 25,000 rigorously trained and highly qualified surgeons, has vigorously campaigned against numerous abuses by general practitioners and specialists in nonsurgical medical fields, especially poor surgery and unnecessary operations.

Dr. Robert S. Myers, executive director of the American College of Surgeons, reported in 1961 that one-half the operations performed in American hospitals were being done by unqualified doctors; that is, the physicians lacked sufficient training to qualify for certification by the American Board of Surgery, the American College of Surgeons, or the American College of Obstetrics and Gynecology. One survey indicated that 30 per cent of the physicians who operate in hospitals are neither full-time nor part-time surgeons. Unqualified surgery is most commonly found in smaller hospitals and least often in the large ones, Dr. Myers said. The American Academy of General Practice has taken strong issue with Dr. Myers' remarks.

Numerous studies in the past have shown that many operations are unnecessary. As recently as 1961, Dr. Ray E. Trussell, New York City's Hospital Commissioner, reported that an investigation of medical care given teamsters' families showed that more than 50 per cent of Cesarean sections and one-third of the hysterectomies (removals of the uterus) reviewed were unnecessary.

CHAPTER 25

RADIOTHERAPY

Of the million living Americans cured of cancer, one-half have been treated with radiation, either exclusively or in combination with surgery and/or drugs.

The number of radiation cures of cancer is increasing steadily—in some research centers and against some cancers, spectacularly. The reasons for this are many. Radiologists gradually are winning a greater, however grudging, share of recognition and cooperation from surgeons, who are variously their academic superiors, critics, competitors, collaborators, enemies, and friends; they have achieved sufficient status in most university and hospital treatment centers to be assigned more and more of the curable cases; powerful new devices in treatment centers now make it possible to deliver lethal doses to any part of the body; and radiotherapists have learned a great deal—much of it by trial and error—about the most effective quality and quantity of radiation for various types of tumors. They also have learned much about the protection of the patient and his healthy tissues. It has been demonstrated too often that there is not much point in curing a cancer, if, in the process, one cripples the patient and leaves him in greater pain and distress than ever.

As in other fields of medicine, the choice of physician is important. A few aging champions of conventional, 250,000-volt (250-kilovolt) X-ray machines, after a long and losing crusade to persuade their colleagues that multimillion-voltage equipment has virtually no advantages over their 250,000-volt devices, have retired to a second line of defense: it is far better to be treated by a competent radiologist with 250-kv equipment than an incompetent with a linear accelerator or betatron. While some

317

may find merit in this argument, it is equally true that the best bet for a cancer cure rests with the most skilled and experienced radiotherapist commanding the most efficient equipment, 250-kv and otherwise. Except for the simplest and most curable cancers and those beyond anything but palliation, the general physician with an antique X-ray machine and sketchy knowledge of radiotherapy is hardly the man to treat a complicated malignancy.

A great many radiological techniques, some of them new and some of them recently adopted after years of proven worth in experimental centers, are enhancing the patients' chances of cure.

"Multiportal" methods, in which beams are fired at a tumor from several angles rather than one, concentrate radiation on the cancer while sparing normal tissues.

Supervoltage machines are searching out and destroying deep tumors with minimal effects on the patient's skin and other intervening tissues. During the last decade, this equipment has become more and more available to large and medium-sized treatment centers everywhere. Few small hospitals have it, because their patient load does not justify the cost and they lack skilled people to maintain and operate it. With a general and growing shortage of doctors in many areas, most patients must accept whatever treatment is available or offered.

Perhaps one of the most important, yet least acclaimed, advances in radiotherapy has been the gradual establishment of dosages for various tumor types. These still-continuing plodding studies are of paramount importance to the patient; too small a dose means the eventual recurrence of cancer, while too large a dose may not only fail to cure the cancer but may burden the patient with complications as serious as the cancer. Correct dosages usually can be determined only after long, carefully controlled series of studies, because cures do not become apparent for many years and some complications are equally long in developing.

Among the considerations in dosage are the type of beam or isotope used, the geometrical pattern of implanted radon or other isotopes (to concentrate hot spots on the tumor and cold spots on the sensitive normal structures), and the rate of isotope decay or the duration and frequency of irradiation.

In various research centers, several types and sources of rays are being applied experimentally against cancers and their different effects evaluated. About thirty different kinds of atomic particles are known or postulated, and an increasing number of them are being used medically. They are of different masses and charges; and for every particle there appears to be an antiparticle of equal mass and opposite charge. Most numerous are the tiny electrons, which orbit around atomic nuclei as planets do around the sun; they have a negative charge and a mass of one. Protons have a positive charge and mass of 1836 (i.e., 1,836 times as massive as the electron), neutrons no charge and a mass of 1839, deuterons (a combined proton-neutron) a single positive charge and a mass of 3671, alpha particles (double proton-neutron) with a double positive charge and mass of 7296, and X rays and gamma rays with no mass and no charge but a speed almost that of light. In relative size, the particles vary from B-B's to bowling balls; if their energy is the same, their speed varies inversely with their mass. Einstein summed it up in the equation $E = mc^2$, with E representing ergs of energy, m grams of mass and c the speed of light in centimeters. As particles slow down they gain in mass. While bowling balls travel slowly, they strike with shattering force. Big bull-in-a-china-shop neutrons, with no charge, plow their way through the microcosmic heavens of molecules until they strike and split an atomic nuclear sun, producing an explosion of charged splinters. X rays, with pure energy and no mass but great speed, also penetrate matter deeply until they are absorbed by or paired with atoms and, in turn, dislodge electrons from their atomic orbits.

The denser the tissues, the more effectively X rays are stopped. Because of this it is possible to register on diagnostic film the shadows which represent successive tissues as X rays pass through air and water and the solid substance of bone, fat, and flesh, silhouetting organs, injuries, erosions, breaks, bulges, and dents.

One of the great virtues of radiation is that quite often it rescues a cancer patient after it has become apparent that surgery has failed. The same can be said of surgery; when radiation has done all it can do and it is not enough, the surgeon may be able to remove the remaining cancer and effect a cure. Radiation may do away with cancers which are too widespread for the surgeon to remove but still confined to an area lending itself to radiation, or it may destroy cancer cells dislodged into the lymphatics or bloodstream during surgery. By the same token, the surgeon sometimes can remove the dead and decaying (necrotic) masses of cancer following radiation.

Some cancers can be treated equally well by either surgery or radiation. Others respond more readily and more surely to radiation than surgery. Still others are resistant to radiation; and if the surgeon cannot remove them, the patients are regarded as beyond cure.

While there is considerable difference of opinion as to the preferability of surgery or radiation for many tumor types, a few cancers are generally recognized as being resistant to radiation and indicated for surgery. These include malignant melanomas, sarcomas, teratomas, and adeno-carcinomas of the digestive tract.

Many cancers beyond surgical help are sensitive to radiation, and while some of them may be incurable they, nevertheless, may wither away for variable periods following treatment. These include leukemias and leukemiclike diseases, seminoma, neuroblastoma, Wilms's tumor, ovarian embryonal carcinoma, medulloblastoma and cancers of the nasopharynx, oropharynx, tongue, uterine cervix, vagina, and (inoperable) breast.

Where there is a choice of surgery or radiation, the general advantages of radiation are that properly conducted treatment is less maiming and disfiguring, usually requires less hospitalization, involves less strain and trauma and eliminates the risk of spreading cancer at operation.

Thirty years ago indulgent surgeons at the University of California Medical School permitted radiologists to treat early cancer of the movable portion of the vocal cords. After ten and twenty years, the surgical and radiological cure rates achieved by surgery and by radiation were compared and found identical—about 80 per cent in both cases. Radiotherapy had the big advantage, however, of leaving the patient with his natural voice, whereas surgery left him mute or faced with the prospect of learning to speak with an artificial voice. Here and in several other well-staffed institutions, radiotherapy has become the preferred treatment for laryngeal cancer, except in cases where the disease has spread beyond the vocal cords and must be removed surgically.

Modern equipment and skillful techniques in radiotherapy have raised the cancer cure rates perceptibly, and they have helped increase the useful and pain-free life spans of many hopelessly advanced patients. Some feel that the maximum cancer-curing potential of radiation will come closer to realization in the near future, as physicists, radiotherapists, surgeons, pathologists, and physicians learn to work more as a team than as individuals. A start is being made in combining radiation, surgery, drugs, and other procedures in various kinds of cancer, and the preliminary results show greatly increased cure rates.

High-voltage equipment under skilled management has increased radiation cures of cancers by substantial percentages, although perhaps most tumors which are resistant to conventional X rays continue to resist high-voltage radiation. In the right hands, the more powerful radiation is showing no greater—and in some cases far fewer—bad side effects than conventional X rays. The bad effects, largely avoidable by expert treatment, include the destruction of mucous linings of the digestive tract, bladder ulceration, bone injury, marrow destruction, skin burns, cataracts, sterility, lung fibrosis, blood-vessel scarring, hemorrhage, loss of hair and other damage, immediate and delayed, transient and permanent. Some of the minor effects of radiation sickness, such as nausea, have been reported controlled by tranquilizers and even by hypnotic suggestion.

The modest predictions of responsible pioneers in the field of supervoltage radiation, such as Dr. John Trump of M.I.T., Dr. Gilbert Fletcher of M. D. Anderson Hospital, University of Texas, Dr. Robert Stone of the University of California and Dr. Henry S. Kaplan of Stanford, have been more than justified in the performance of the equipment they helped build. Among their predictions, which have come to pass, were the following: supervoltage radiation would effectively attack radiation-sensitive tumors almost anywhere in the body; the rifle-bullet-type rays would spare skin and intervening tissues more than the shotgun-type conventional radiation and concentrate their destruction on the tumor; cure rates would rise slightly, but the principal benefits would be in reducing exposure of the patient to unwanted radiation. They warned that great care would have to be taken to direct the powerful beams so that they would not penetrate and injure vital structures.

Some radiotherapists feel that supervoltage radiation is far superior to conventional radiation in 70 or 80 per cent of cancer patients. Dr. Franz Buschke of the University of California has said the two are as comparable as a new Chrysler and a Model T Ford.

By now many different kinds of apparatus are used in supervoltage radiotherapy: various models of the 2-mev (million electron volt) Van de Graaf machine developed at M.I.T., 2-mev cobalt bombs first used in London, Ontario, and other Canadian treatment centers, 6-mev linear accelerators (an inexpensive modification of the billion-ev equipment) developed at Stanford University, the 5–50-mev microwave linear accelerator at Argonne and the University of Chicago, the 6-bev Cambridge electron accelerator, several supervoltage machines including the 100-mev synchrotron and 20-mev cyclotron at the University of California, the proton beam of the 160-mev Harvard Cyclotron, the 26-mev betatron at the University of Illinois, and specially built reactors at Brookhaven and Cambridge permitting neutron capture. All these and many other types of apparatus are being used against human cancers. Most of the clinical work still is in the experimental stage, but some of it is being rewarded with more than occasional gratifying remissions.

These devices subject cancers to bombardment by widely assorted rays with precision, accuracy and broadly variable diameters. The Stanford linear accelerator propels electrons shot through gold to endow them with high energy up to a speed of 185,000 miles a second, almost that of light, in the first foot of a 6-foot tube and allows them to slow down slightly and gain mass for the remaining 5 feet. The Harvard cyclotron produces protons, which are hydrogen atoms stripped of their electrons; at one-half the speed of light these small, heavy particles can be sent to great tissue depths where they smash atoms and produce explosive radiation. The Brookhaven equipment produces heavy, uncharged neutrons with effective penetrating power up to more than 2 inches; when they strike boron atoms which have been given the patient and which concentrate to a small extent in brain tumors, the boron disintegrates into helium and lithium, which irradiate nearby cells. The synchrotron produces X rays or high-speed electrons. Other machines also can produce highly variable radiation.

Various beams are useful not only in cancer but in other conditions as well. They can be used to destroy small structures like the globus pallidus of the brain; this procedure, also done by surgery and with ultrasonic beams, has benefited some patients with the shaking palsy known as Parkinsonism. The betatron and other high-voltage equipment have been used in efforts to obliterate the pituitary, the moderately radioresistant "master gland" at the base of the brain.

Dr. Arthur Arnold at the University of Illinois noted a decade ago that while the pituitary withstood assault by the betatron rays, the hypothalamus directly above it was destroyed by the rays. The hypothalamus, which is a switchboard connecting the brain with the pituitary and the body's major glands, could be knocked out, thus achieving many of the hormone-suppressing effects sought in removing or destroying the pituitary. Dr. Arnold also observed that while betatron rays seemed to be successful in destroying some brain tumors, the patients often suffered a strange relapse—they lost their sense of balance, walked wide-legged, and eventually lapsed into somnolence and death. Autopsy showed dead (necrotic) tumor tissue brought about the severe intoxication. This observation led to another rescue procedure: several weeks after irradiation for brain tumors, patients underwent an operation in which the necrotic tumor tissue was removed. If the brain stem was undamaged, the patients lived.

Dr. Fletcher has published figures from his own and other leading institutions throughout the world showing large increases in five-year survival rates for many kinds of cancer treated by modern methods of radiotherapy, sometimes in combination with surgery. During the twenty years from 1940 to 1960, these survival rates rose to this degree: for cancers of the oral cavity, from 25–30 per cent to 50–60 per cent; oropharynx (base of the tongue, tonsillar region, pharyngeal walls), from 15 to 30–40 per cent; nasopharynx, from 15 to 35 per cent; supraglottic region of the larynx, from 15–20 to 50 per cent; pyriform sinus and hypopharynx, from 5–10 to 30 per cent; squamous-cell carcinoma of the uterine cervix, from 25–30 to 60 per cent; and infiltrative tumors of the urinary bladder, 10–15 to 30–35 per cent.

These attractive cure rates are achieved only where modern equipment is available to radiotherapists who know how best to use it. Part-time radiologists using 1940 methods and 1940 equipment are still achieving, at best, 1940 cure rates; and they are doing it at considerable risk of injury to their patients.

Radiotherapy achieves unusually good results against some specific cancers only in one or a few centers where new techniques have proved successful. Retinoblastoma seems to be highly curable by supervoltage radiation at Stanford; the treatment leaves considerable vision in the irradiated eyes. Early laryngeal cancer is 85–90 per cent curable, and without impairing speech, at M. D. Anderson Hospital; supervoltage treatment, as practiced by Dr. T. A. Watson and associates in Saskatoon gives at least some cures—15 per cent or better—in cancer of the upper two-thirds of the esophagus.

Horror-struck scientists, following the bombing of Hiroshima and Nagasaki, still felt their work with atomic energy would be vindicated.

They made two predictions: (1) The great many isotopes which now could be produced would enable them to understand and control the complicated chemistry of life; and (2) some of the isotopes would lead to the cure of various kinds of cancer.

Their first prediction is coming true in handsome fashion. With radioactive tracers, biochemists have made enormous strides in analyzing the roles of countless compounds in microbial, plant and animal metabolism. They have done much to unravel the processes of photosynthesis, understand the diffusion of soil foods and fertilizers into weeds and useful plants, trace the movement of moisture through the earth, detect the piracy of land phosphorus, learn the behavior of pests and then concoct poisons for them, determine the age of the earth and its products, decode the chemical cryptograms of low and high forms of life and mutate plants and animals so that they can render a greater service to man.

The second prediction, that isotopes would lead to the conquest of cancer, has not come to pass. Radioactive isotopes, while they have enabled scientists to learn a great deal about the chemistry of cancers, so far have had very limited impact on the cancer cure rate.

Nevertheless, atomic energy has supplied research centers with a great new arsenal of isotopes against cancer in humans. A few of them are of demonstrated worth in curing cancer; others are in the area which separates genius from gadgetry. The true potential of isotopes still is unknown; relatively few have been tested. There are 985 known isotopes—some of them with a life so short their existence is virtually theoretical; it is measured in trillionths of a second. There are 282 stable isotopes and 645 radioactive ones, with half-lives ranging from a moment to millenia. About five out of six radioactive isotopes have a half-life of less than 100 days.

Some isotopes emit radiations so soft and of such short range that only very small areas are affected; tritium incorporated into amino acridine dyes concentrates in cell genes and its radiations, with a half-life of 12.5 years, do not penetrate the cell's nuclear wall. Other isotopes emit radiations which travel enormous distances through air or penetrate deep into dense tissues.

One of the most commonly used isotopes is cobalt-60, which has a convenient half-life of 5.3 years, emits radiation similar to that of radium but with only 10 per cent of radium's nuisance (beta) rays and can be applied in several ways—it is used as a substitute for X-ray machines and radium, or as a needle stuck into tumors (with no danger of spilling, as long-lived radon occasionally does); it can be incorporated into plastic casts placed over tumors or in other devices which are applied and withdrawn at will. As a by-product of reactor use, it can be cooked to any strength in atomic ovens, and when it decays, it can be recooked. Chunks of it the size of a small stack of silver dollars are used as a bomb in teletherapy—enclosed in an 18-inch lead or 10-inch tungsten safe, a series of push-button operations move it out of a concrete wall into position over the patient, open the safe door, permit the pent up 2-mev rays to pour through a nozzle at the tumor target and then close the safe and move it back into the concrete wall. Newer models are much more maneuverable and portable. Cobalt-60 has been called, with more or less truth, a "poor man's radium" because of its great availability, its price (virtually no more than transportation costs from reactors as compared with $6,000 or so a gram for radium), and its ubiquity—many clinical installations now have cobalt bombs and other isotope devices.

Radioactive iodine, iodine-131, has proved of clinical usefulness in about 10 per cent of cases of thyroid cancer. The normal thyroid gland quickly takes up almost all the iodine in the circulation and incorporates it into thyroid hormone. In hormone-producing thyroid cancers, the patient drinks a "radioactive cocktail," the iodine-131 is taken up by the gland and also by its tumors wherever they may be in the body, and the tissues are destroyed by the powerful radiations. Because iodine-131 rays are detectable by counters, hormone-producing colonies of thyroid cancers (metastases) which take up the radioactive materials can be located wherever they are in the body. Sometimes they can be destroyed by the radiation itself; in other instances, the surgeon can remove them. Iodine-131 treatment of thyroid cancers in youngsters has achieved a high cure rate at the University of Iowa Medical School and a few other centers. It is unfortunate that all thyroid cancers are not functional; most do not produce thyroid hormone, do not take up iodine (or iodine-131) and cannot be detected and destroyed. And perhaps it is much more unfortunate that other cancers do not show an avidity for a specific radioactive element comparable to that of hormone-producing thyroid tumors.

Radioactive potassium, or potassium-32, concentrates in all growing cells; and this property limits its usefulness in cancer therapy. Besides irradiating the multiplying cancer cells, it destroys the normally fast-growing cells of the digestive tract lining and bone marrow. Potassium-32 however has proved a boon in the control of polycythemia vera, a condition in which red blood cells multiply without much restraint, thicken the blood stream, and sometimes clog smaller arteries, bringing death by strokes and heart attacks. By depressing the blood-forming tissues, potassium-32 controls this disease for almost unlimited periods. While few consider polycythemia vera as being cancer, it sometimes develops into leukemia. To a degree, potassium-32 has proved helpful in controlling chronic leukemia.

Sometimes cancer produces many tiny tumors which dot the inside wall of the belly cavity or the pleural sac containing the lungs. In these cases, much fluid collects, to the discomfort and distress of the patient. Suspensions of radioactive gold dust, or colloidal gold, have suppressed the growth of the cancers and gotten rid of the fluid. Gold-198 with a half-life of 2.7 days, has been incorporated into nylon thread and sewn through tumors which the surgeon was unable to remove; its rapidly decaying energy, at its peak, is equal to that of a 412,000 volt X-ray machine.

The radio-resistant, pea-size pituitary gland at the base of the brain has been destroyed effectively with implants of a half-dozen or so tiny beads of a radioactive rare earth, yttrium-90. The rays penetrate less than one centimeter into soft tissue and have a half life of 2.54 days.

Small rubber balloons have been guided into such organs as the uterus and bladder and then filled with fluids containing flakes of radioactive cobalt, bromine-82 (35-hour half-life) or sodium-24 (14.9 hours) to irradiate tumors in these organs. The technique has the virtue of simplicity; the balloons can be filled and drained periodically to give any dose to the tumorous organ. This method is being tested in postsurgical management of cancers of such accessible organs as the rectum.

Sulfur-35, with a half-life of 87 days (but which is metabolized out of the system in much less time) has been used against cancers of cartilage in a few patients. The cartilage bed takes up the sulfur and incorporates it into its products.

Many other isotopes are being or have been tested for anticancer effect —tantalum wires stuck into tumors, zinc-69 in plaster casts, deuterium combined with porphyrins and injected into the bloodstream, europium and cesium in teletherapy, and intravenous calcium-47 against bone-destroying cancers.

Innumerable experiments remain to be done.

Improvement in radiation treatment, such as it has been, is due to brilliant work by many scientists. Physicists have built laminated phantoms, replicas of the human body, with light and dense structures representing the bones and organs; photographic film registered the radiation doses reaching each synthetic organ and tissue. Anatomists have helped plot the angles at which rays would have least effect on sensitive organs. Rotating chairs and pendulous couches have been built and radiation sources have been made movable in engineering efforts to devise the safest and most precise multiportal deliveries. Biologists have contributed their observations on the effects of radiation on living systems. Biochemists have tried to make tumors more sensitive and normal tissues more resistant to radiation.

With all these educated efforts, a large element of trial and error still has been necessary. And the errors are costly; sometimes they show up only after considerable time has elapsed and great damage is done. In pelvic irradiation, an overdose or improperly planted radon seeds have produced fistulas, ulcers and necrosis of bowel segments and the urinary system; the milder injuries are self-healing, but major damage is permanent and deadly. It has been found that when kidneys are included in the field of deep abdominal radiation, kidney disease and hypertension may develop; of fifty-four patients so treated and traced many years later, twenty had developed acute nephritis; benign hypertension was found in six and, ultimately, late malignant hypertension in fifteen. A number of scientists have sought ways to determine in advance of treatment which patients might be harmed by radiation.

Drs. John and Ruth Graham more than fifteen years ago began testing all cervical cancer patients at Massachusetts General Hospital for their sensitivity to X rays. They gave each a small test dose to the normal vaginal cells and decided from the percentage of cells killed by the rays whether the patient and her tumor would respond to X rays. On these decisions, radiation-sensitive patients were referred to the radiotherapist, and radiation-resistant patients went to surgery. Those treated with this discrimination enjoyed about twice the five-year survival rate of patients randomly given either radiation or surgery.

Dr. Ruth Guttmann of Columbia University's Francis Delafield Hospital has employed supervoltage radiation with remarkable results against lung cancers too advanced for surgical removal. She has doubled the life expectancy of these patients, rid them of many symptoms and discomforts and enabled some to return to active lives. Seven per cent of her "hopeless" cases survived more than five years. All similar untreated cases died within eighteen months.

Dr. Guttmann reviewed the histories of 100 advanced breast-cancer patients who, because the disease had spread well beyond the breast, were given high-voltage radiation (200 r to all affected nodes daily for a total dose of 5,000 r over five weeks) rather than surgery. Of these, 34 out of 67, or 50 per cent, were alive at five years, 21 out of 48 at six years, and 13 out of 32 at seven years. The percentages were highly encouraging in view of the fact that the patients, with metastases, edema, and inflammatory disease, were inoperable when first seen. Their survival for five years equaled that of other series-metastatic and nonmetastatic—given conventional surgery.

Dr. Ian Macdonald of the University of Southern California has reported these observations in a large series of breast cancer patients: in one-third, the cancers grow slowly, and even late diagnosis and treatment often bring a cure; in one-third, the tumors spread like wildfire and, regardless of the size of the lesion, when first seen these patients are incurable; the other third have cancer somewhere between the fast- and slow-growing, and here time is of the essence—they are curable only if treated early. He has found, as did the Grahams in cervical cancer, that radiosensitive patients often will not respond well to surgery. He believes in sparing radiosensitive patients the mutilation and trauma of surgery and maintaining them as well as possible with radiation and hormones.

It is an adage in medicine that Hodgkin's disease, a leukemiclike condition of the lymphatic system, is incurable. While it sometimes can be controlled with radiation for ten years and longer, it is regarded as uniformly fatal—usually within three years. To this fatalistic attitude, Dr. Kaplan of Stanford University takes exception. He believes the disease is curable and is being cured. He tested a hypothesis advanced two decades earlier by a Swiss radiologist, Dr. René Gilbert, who felt that, if early Hodgkin's disease were treated vigorously with high doses, it would yield to radiation. With the consent of the Hodgkin's patients, Dr. Kaplan and Dr. Malcolm A. Bagshaw gave fifteen of them between two and ten times the normal dose, to their swollen glands and points of potential spread of the disease. Dr. Kaplan reported on ten years of his experiments. Of the fifteen patients, eleven were alive and well—one for ten years, two for more than six years, and eight for from twenty-four to fifty-five months. There had been four failures, or recurrences of the disease; of these, one patient was alive but with Hodgkin's more than two years, one had died with no evidence of the disease after six years, and two others died of Hodgkin's disease in shorter periods. The failures were given less radiation than the successful cases at a time when he was still seeking the optimal dosage. Dr. Kaplan felt the results would have been more impressive if he had used the same high doses on all the patients, between 3,500 and 4,000 r from the 6-mev linear accelerator spread out over a period of three or four weeks. The accelerator was not available for the earliest cases, including three of the four failures. The average Hodgkin's patient has a 25 per cent chance of living five years. Of a control group of nine patients treated by conventional means in the Kaplan series, all but one had died when he reported.

Numerous other successes may be in the making for other kinds and sites of cancer treated by the accelerator. The results will be known as various centers report years hence. Prostatic cancer, generally considered refractory to radiation, has cleared up completely in some patients. Improved results have been achieved against head and neck sites. Treatment of some cancers has been improved by lymphangiography—the injection into lymphatic channels of opaque substances which, under X rays, enable the physician to locate metastases.

Therapeutic radiation ordinarily does not destroy cancer cells directly; only the very highest dose will kill a cell outright. Radiation somehow alters the cell so that it cannot reproduce. The irradiated cell ages, dies, and leaves no progeny.

Radiation has several effects; some of them may be more important in therapy than its direct action on cells.

It has been commonly supposed, for instance, that tumors which at first are sensitive to X rays and will shrink up after a vigorous irradiation, eventually become resistant to the X rays and thrive despite them. Scientists at the University of Minnesota found in experiments with transplantable mouse cancers that it's the patient, not the tumor, that becomes radioresistant. They irradiated mouse tumors until they became radiation-resistant; then they transplanted the cancers to new hosts. In new mice the cancers were once again sensitive to X rays. The scientists then ran another series of experiments. They removed the tumor, irradiated the tumor bed, and then retransplanted the radiation-sensitive cancer to that site; the tumor grew slower than it otherwise would but it proved to be radio-resistant. Something in the tumor bed apparently had great influence on the cancer's response to X rays.

Some scientists state that injury to blood vessels in the tumor bed make the cancer radioresistant.

There are several mechanisms by which radiation induces cancer. Some animal cancers—notably of the lung, liver, and breast—seem to be caused by the direct effect of rays on the site of these cancers. Some are due to a hormonal mechanism—when radiation sterilizes the ovaries, for instance, the increased production of ovary-stimulating hormone by the pituitary apparently leads to the malignant overgrowth of the ovaries. A mysterious, possibly immune, mechanism is involved in radiation-caused leukemia; if the thymus gland is removed first and the mouse is given a large dose of radiation, the animal will not develop leukemia, but if the thymus is left in the animal, or if a thymus is transplanted to the animal after radiation, it will develop leukemia.

Radiation can and does have contradictory effects. The biological response immediately following radiation often will be reversed completely a few weeks later. The situation could be explained as a compensatory or rebound phenomenon in which a damaged metabolic system not only returns to normal but, temporarily, goes far beyond normal in readjusting.

Radiation has a remarkable ability to suppress immunity. Following a large dose of X rays to the entire body, animals and humans become highly susceptible to many infections, and they may die of something as simple as the common cold. It has been shown in animal experiments, on the other hand, that sometimes a light dose of radiation suppresses an infection.

X rays are so powerful in knocking out immunity that it often proves possible to transplant organs, tissues and cells from foreign strains and species to irradiated animals. In its puzzling dual role, however, radiation also has an opposite effect: rats made tolerant at birth to mouse or cow red blood cells lost their tolerance after being exposed to 550 r.

Dr. Kaplan has both produced and cured leukemia in mice with X rays. He produced leukemia as a long-latent disease by spraying the animals with X rays. If, fifty days later, however, he gave the animals a second, large, dose of X rays, 80 per cent of them did not die of leukemia; if he delayed giving the second dose for 100 days, 50 per cent did not die of leukemia.

Some investigators have reported that radiation has a cumulative effect in inducing cancer. German scientists have indicated in their work on rats that there is a critical dosage for the induction of cancers; the dose can be given in a few days or over a period of many months, but when the limits are reached, cancer becomes almost inevitable. Other experiments have shown that radiation or chemical carcinogens given over a long time are more potent than those delivered over a short period.

The reverse also is true. Sometimes X rays do as ultraviolet rays do—just as gradual small doses of sunshine induce a tan which protects against acute sunburn, so do small prior doses of various other kinds of radiation sometimes protect against the lethal and carcinogenic effects of later large doses. Dr. Philip Miller of the University of Chicago has reported that a small prior dose of X rays induced "acquired radioresistance" in mice and greatly reduced the mortality from later doses. Others have increased with small prior exposures the mid-lethal dose in mice from 487 to 617 r (the "immunizing" exposure had to be not less than three weeks prior to the challenging dose); and still others with a small daily dose (0.6 r) over two or three months lowered mouse mortalities considerably from later lethal doses. Dr. Miller and his group found that 75 r over four weeks significantly reduced mouse mortalities from an intestinal organism called pseudomonas, which induces a fatal blood infection.

Future advances in radiotherapy may well come from a better understanding of the effects of ionizing and other radiation on specific molecules. In these areas are explanations of the mutations, infections, aging and death promoted by radiation. Any wisp of new knowledge might suggest a more effective way of delivering radiation, treating cancer and dealing with other diseases.

The basic mechanism of ionizing radiation probably is in the formation of free radicals—atomic fragments with unpaired electrons and an unquenchable zest to join up with particles, atoms, and molecules. High-energy particles split small molecules, and when they strike a large, carbon-containing molecule, electrons are shaken loose from their orbits. This produces a momentary chain reaction; the free radicals which are formed fly about within the molecule and between molecules until they find and bind to a mate.

In some cases, energized molecules bind one another; many small ones pile up, forming large molecules. This is called polymerization. X rays polymerize substances when they produce plastics, vulcanize rubber or change oil from a fluid to a gummy or solid state. Polymerization may be the means by which radiation ages cells; free radicals may weld molecules into large and unwieldy ones.

Radiation, in keeping with its contrary nature, also depolymerizes substances; that is, it breaks large molecules into small ones. In this case substances become more soluble, more fluid, and less sticky.

The cell and the body are vast reservoirs of water, and water is a prime target of radiation. Water (H_2O, two atoms of hydrogen joined to one of oxygen), can become an exploding arsenal under the force of rays; it is transformed to yield a variety of stable and negatively and positively charged products: H, H_2, H_3, OH, OH_2, O_2, O_3, H_3O, HO_2, and H_2O_2. The release of electron-seeking and electron-giving radicals from water profoundly alters many molecules inside and around cells.

The most vital and vulnerable targets for the rain of radiation-released free radicals probably are:

1. DNA, deoxyribonucleic acid, the long, segmented, two-stranded molecules which comprise chromosomes and genes. The segments may be changed or, knocked apart, they may come together, healed, in strange sequences to alter the function of genes.

2. RNA, or ribonucleic acid—long, segmented but usually single-stranded molecules, which form the assembly lines on which cells build ten thousand different kinds of protein molecules.

3. Protein, long, necklacelike molecules (the batterylike beads are of twenty different kinds of amino acids) which coil and curl into balls; the beads are joined by bonds between hydrogen atoms, and when

the necklace is coiled, adjacent beads on the coils are stuck together by the sulfur atom of one to the hydrogen atom of another; this is called a sulfhydryl, or SH, linkage. When rays free the hydrogen atoms and break hydrogen bonds, sulfur-to-sulfur bonds may form to link adjacent amino acid beads previously joined by SH bonds, and the hydrogen bonds may disappear; this breaks the necklace or changes the sequence of beads and alters the character and function of the protein molecule.

Suggestive evidence has been produced to indicate that rays may damage cells through all three of these mechanisms, and by others as well.

British scientists in a preliminary report have indicated that a 250-r dose of radiation to the human spine produces abnormal chromosomes in almost one-third of the irradiated marrow cells; some of the changed cells resemble those in leukemia. New York University scientists have shown that radicals freed from irradiated water inactivate a key enzyme, ribonuclease or RNase, which normally breaks RNA into its segments. Others have shown that under X rays, bundles of cell enzymes, called mitochondria, which serve as the cell's power houses, shrink up.

Radiation also changes the immediate environment of the cell. In a two-way reaction, it (1) depolymerizes, or melts, the cement sticking cells together, and (2) in collagen diseases, like arthritis, it makes tissues tough, leathery, and rigid by increasing the deposition of gelatinous collagen in which cells are embedded.

Theoretically at least, radiation injures numerous substances besides those inside, on and around cells. Among the many proteins which appear to be affected are antibodies which combat infectious agents, molecules which transport oxygen, hormones and other substances, tissue-softening enzymes which make flesh permeable, mucin which greases the digestive tract, digestive enzymes which break food down into useful particles, the elastic material in tendons and the keratin of hair and nails.

Radiation, according to some experiments, produces fatigue much as muscular dystrophy does. In dystrophy, muscles fail to convert a liver-produced, energy-generating chemical called creatine to creatinine; the unchanged and unused creatine is excreted in urine. Irradiated patients also excrete large amounts of unchanged creatine.

Other forms of radiation, such as light, electromagnetism, and heat, seem to achieve ultimate results similar to those of X rays. The radiations probably act in different ways, however. Heat may change protein structure by removing water from the cell and possibly from some of the amino acids, thus eliminating the hydrogen bonds which link one amino acid to another. If enough heat is applied, the protein molecule is denatured; the long, spiraling strings unfold and amino-acid links come undone.

Light, like X rays, seems to relax the sulfur–hydrogen bonds, possibly by being absorbed by sulfur-containing amino acids. At least in milk, light destroys the vitamins, riboflavin, and ascorbic acid. Light also reduces the repulsion between the gene DNA molecules and turns them into a gel. At the University of Chicago and Hahnemann Medical College in Philadelphia, scientists have used a tiny ultraviolet beam in the range of 2,200–3,000 A and with a diameter of only 4/100,000 inch to destroy with superb marksmanship submicroscopic areas of a chromosome and of the eosinophils, or white blood cells—eosinophils appear to be a defense against allergy, infections, and some collagen diseases. The technique eventually may give information on the function of small clusters of molecules within the cell and their vulnerability to rays.

Radiofrequency energy has altered protein molecules; trained upon specific gamma globulin molecules, it has increased their efficiency as antibodies up to a point; then, beyond that point, it completely destroyed their usefulness as an anti-infection force.

Basic studies on barley seeds and insects are suggesting that such factors as temperature, oxygen, water, and light decisively influence X-ray effects. Despite long and intensive studies at Washington State University and atomic energy centers, no clear pattern as yet has emerged; completely contrary effects, in fact, have been reported, depending largely on the concentration of each agent used in the experiment. Oxygen enhances the radiation effect on cells. Water seems to protect against some X-ray effects on cells, perhaps by diluting the oxygen effects; too much moisture, however, washes protective chemicals out of cells. Heat prior to or during radiation seems to increase X-ray effects; after radiation it sets up a state of molecular flux and may help chromosomes and genes recover. Cold during radiation minimizes the damage, but sometimes only temporarily. Ordinary light has revived "X-radiation killed" bacteria; at blood temperature, it acted directly on genes, and at 60°F on something else unknown. Of mice, with cancers implanted in their tails, 19 per cent were cured by X rays at normal temperatures, 47 per cent with X rays at 104° F, 77 per cent when heat was applied an hour before radiation, and 97 per cent when it was applied twenty-four hours after radiation. These are some of the considerations which a few radiologists are seeking to apply to radiotherapy in human cancer. Limited progress has been made.

Perhaps more clear-cut, in mouse tumors, are the effects of electromagnetic fields. As far back as 1948, Dr. J. M. Barnothy, a Hungarian scientist, "cured" transplanted mouse cancers with these radiations. He and his wife, Dr. Madeline Barnothy, now at the University of Illinois College of Pharmacy, have reported these effects of housing mice in magnetic fields of from 3,000 to 6,000 gauss for periods of from one to four weeks: (1) white blood cell counts dropped 33 per cent during the first week, and stayed there for the duration of their residence; the counts rose, ten or twelve days following the mice's removal, to between 50 and 70 per cent above normal; (2) body temperature dropped more than one degree (Fahrenheit) and stayed there for more than one year; (3) food consumption increased slightly, but it decreased in later life; (4) following their removal, the animals were 30 per cent more active than untreated mice; (5) treated mice had a much younger appearance than untreated mice, even through old age; (6) estrus and menstruation stopped during treatment, but the animals were able to become pregnant immediately on its termination; (7) male mice remained sterile for from four to twenty weeks after treatment; (8) at 3,500 gauss, pregnant mice bore offspring which died a few days after birth, and at higher fields the embryos were resorbed by the mother; (9) mice born in the fields or placed there when they were two or three weeks old, experienced about 30 per cent retardation in growth which lasted for months following their removal; (10) mice maintained in a 4,200-gauss field for one month developed spleens which looked like those of mice with leukemic diseases; (11) transplanted breast cancers completely regressed in many cases; and in all cases their spread (metastasis) was prevented; and (12) cell growth slowed, the faster the growth the greater the slowdown.

Radiation studies are still in their infancy. Their potential for curing cancer has barely been tapped.

The problems which stand in the way of improved radiation treatment are more than technical ones, however. Perhaps the most obstructive of all are those inherent in human nature.

First of all there is the matter of evaluating men and their work. Granting that qualified and objective observers in the field of radiation can distinguish between the expert and the fraud, it still is difficult to classify the experts and the leaders. Which are the dreamers? Which are the geniuses? Which are the cynics? Which are the leaf-raking adherents of the "fail safe" philosophy?

In this confusion, new feuds have cropped up before the old ones have completely abated. Some surgeons and some other physicians still are critical of all forms of radiation therapy; supervoltage radiotherapists still must continue to fight a rearguard action against harassment by conventional radiotherapists. The high percentage of inept users of dangerous equipment does not help the cause of radiotherapy.

And now, on the eve of what may prove to be the most spectacular of all innovations in radiotherapy—the introduction of new sources, particularly masers, lasers and electromagnetic effects in the high-voltage radiofrequency range—perhaps the biggest battle of all is shaping up. The handful of men who have begun to explore these fields have met with considerable hostility from many quarters. Even within their own ranks, the experts are at odds on the interpretation of the phenomena produced by their new media.

Countless technical problems beset the small company of scientists in the field. They must seek out the small slivers in the vast expanse of frequencies which will prove specific for their targets. They must test their medium against other radiations. They must distinguish between the several forces exerted—heat, electrical, magnetic, and others—in each effect they produce. They must learn what is safe and what is dangerous about the newfound instruments; the dangerous factors might be applied as new and fearsome weapons of war.

The technical aspects will be worked out in time. The amount of time required depends in part on the human equation. The human equation is unpredictable.

CHAPTER 26

CHEMOTHERAPY

The patient was emaciated, bedridden and in excruciating pain. It was obvious that he was not long for this world.

Then the doctor gave him a small pill. It weighed four grains, was brown and mottled with red spots and tasted bitter. Almost at once, the patient felt better. As the days passed, the patient, on a schedule of four pills a day, began to perk up. His appetite improved, he gained six pounds in two weeks, the morphine dosage was cut to one-fifth what it had been as the pain became weaker and less frequent.

Then came the day when he left his bed and strolled in the late fall sunshine. He told the neighbors he was cured of cancer; and looking at him, with a touch of color back in his cheeks and the light again in his eyes, they believed this was true. Then one night he went to sleep. He never woke up.

The drug—a drug is any substance given for treatment—which had worked this brief miracle was milk sugar. The pills sold for 69 cents a hundred at the cut-rate drug store.

Sugar pills and other pseudodrugs and treatments are called placebos. In Latin, *placebo* means "I shall please."

The man was part of a controlled experiment in which one-half the patients were treated with a new drug and the other half with placebos. It was a double blind experiment; that is, neither the patient nor the physician knew in each case whether the experimental pill or the sugar pill was being used.

The effect of placebos often is substantial; between one-fifth and one-half of patients are relieved of symptoms. In minor illnesses, placebos may give a patient relief during the entire course of his disease; in serious sickness they may keep symptoms to a minimum for a while. Not only can they relieve pain and restore energy, but to a measurable degree, they repair metabolic defects and induce other supposedly objective signs of healing. While placebos help, on an average, about one-third of the patients, they also induce headache, heartburn, cramps, dizziness, drowsiness, blurred vision, nausea, vomiting, and other "side effects" in about 15 per cent of patients—more in women than men and more in the old than the young.

The secret ingredient in these make-believe magic bullets is faith. If the patient has faith in the doctor and faith in the preparation, he stands to improve. A few of the bad "side effects" are due to disease which actually exists but of which the patient is unaware.

In experimental medicine, some physicians invariably seem to obtain better results than others, even when they employ the selfsame preparations in a comparable series of randomly selected patients. It may be that the natural enthusiasm of the skilled practitioner of the art of medicine on the one hand and the coldness of the impersonal "pill peddler" make the difference. The earliest medical literature written in Sanskrit 2,200 years ago and the oral teachings of Ayur-Veda many centuries before that, emphasized the theme: "Treat the patient, not the disease."

Among the modern adages in medicine are: "One should use the new drugs while they still have the power to heal," and "the pink pill is the most important preparation in the doctor's bag."

There are many ways of classifying modern anticancer drugs. Some of the classifications overlap; that is, a single drug may fall into several different categories. Among the classifications are:

HORMONES—gland-secreted (and artificial) "chemical messengers" —which control the growth and function of various kinds of body cells.

ANALOGUES—counterfeit replicas of natural body chemicals or essential molecules in food.

ANTIMETABOLITES—analogues and other substances which block normal cell chemical processes.

ANTIMITOTICS—chemicals which prevent cells from dividing.

ANTIBIOTICS—poisons produced by microorganisms which destroy other microorganisms.

ALKYLATING AGENTS, which react with sensitive atomic groupings of the cells' most vital chemicals and behave as "Trojan-horse" poisons.

RADIOMIMETIC COMPOUNDS, which exert radiationlike effects on cell and host chemistry.

MISCELLANEOUS AGENTS, like viruses, microbes, immunity-stimulating chemicals, and a score of other classes with assorted biological and biochemical effects, known and unknown.

Many modern anticancer drugs have helped patients with one kind of malignancy or another. Sometimes the help is great and long-lasting; the cancers are controlled completely for many years, the patient lives a normal, useful life and perhaps dies painlessly of cancer, another disease or old age. More often the help is limited to a few months; and sometimes the treatment itself may add to the patient's miseries. No close observer is complacent about the progress in chemotherapy.

Nevertheless, a growing number of useful drugs have brought great or small relief to an ever-enlarging circle of cancer patients; one kind of cancer after another has yielded to the palliative effects of one or more preparations. To the average adult with advanced cancer, who comes to realize acutely that all men are mortal, temporary remission is a blessing.

In 1964, about thirty-five drugs were being used clinically in various United States centers against about forty kinds of cancer. Another 160 were being tried on human patients in 150 hospitals. About 50,000 chemicals were being tested routinely in three mouse cancers; of these, according to past averages, fewer than 10 per cent would "pass"—that is, qualify for testing against cancers in rats and other laboratory animals. About one in 1,000 would show sufficient promise to be given to a few hopelessly ill cancer patients prepared to gamble their meager reserves on a substance which tests had indicated might offer them much more help than harm. For each drug that would show definite clinical benefit, somewhere between five and ten million dollars would have been spent in chemotherapy research—the quest for the magic bullet against cancer.

In 1961, the American Cancer Society published a list of commonly used drugs. They were classified as:

1. POLYFUNCTIONAL ALKYLATING AGENTS. These compounds, which add an alkyl (univalent alcohol) group to a molecule, combine with sites of protein, nucleic acid, and other molecules essential to the life of the cell, block the function of these molecules in cell metabolism, and prevent cell growth and division. Monofunctional agents have a single molecular site capable of reacting with cell compounds; polyfunctional have two or more reactive sites. Those with two reactive sites are between 50 and 100 times as effective as those having one reactive site. Nitrogen mustard, the war gas designated as HN2, is the best known alkylating agent. Other mustards, which differ to varying degrees from nitrogen mustard, include the Soviet sarkolysin, the Japanese nitromin, the British chlorambucil (CB 1348 or Leukeran), the German cyclophosphamide

(Cytoxan) and the American antimalaria mustards, chloroquine and quinacrine (Atabrine). The reactive form of mustards contains what is called an ethyleneimine group of atoms; among the compounds built around these groups are TEM (triethylene melamine), which was used in the German textile industry to cross-link and strengthen fibers, and triethylene phosphoramides (TEPA, thio-TEPA and TSPA) synthesized in the United States as potential anticancer drugs by Dr. Moses Crossley of Rutgers University who helped develop chemicals for the textile industry. The British busulfan (Myleran) alkylates by mechanisms different from those of the mustards. Another class of alkylating chemicals, epoxides, are highly useful in the rubber industry because they build up powerful plastics; they are being tested—so far without significant success—against experimental cancers.

2. ANTI-METABOLITES. These are poisons disguised as vitamins, amino acids, nucleotides, or other essential cell chemicals. The elimination, addition, transposition, or substitution of a single atom or a few atoms within the molecule transforms a natural and needed cell chemical into a booby-trap compound; the subtler the difference, the more toxic the antimetabolite often is. Methotrexate is a deliberately-designed bogus form of the vitamin B, folic acid. Another chemical fraud, 6-MP (6-mercaptopurine) has a sulfhydryl group (a sulfur and hydrogen atom) in the position where the natural adenine, or A, molecule contains an amino group (one nitrogen and two hydrogen atoms). Another counterfeit, 5-FU (or 5-fluorouracil) differs from the natural uracil, or U, in having a fluorine atom added and a hydrogen atom deleted. Phthalanilide derivatives block fat synthesis.

3. ISOTOPES. These are off-size versions, usually radioactive, of elements—like phosphorous, iodine, and gold—which are taken up by cells.

4. STEROID HORMONES. These are natural substances produced by the sex glands and adrenals.

5. MISCELLANEOUS DRUGS. These include colchicine, a plant extract, and an altered version of it, demecolcin; urethane, an anesthetic; Fowler's solution, or potassium arsenite; o,p'DDD, a chemical relative of the insecticide DDT, and atinomycin D, an antibiotic.

A catalogue of useful drugs published by the American Cancer Society in April, 1961, is reproduced on pages 340–343.

The list of clinically useful drugs against cancer changes. New ones are added—one year after publication of the foregoing table a few new drugs had found a solid status among anticancer medicines. A plant extract, VLB or vinblastine, had established a place for itself among the preparations which palliate Hodgkin's disease and choriocarcinoma, and a related extract, vincristine, helped leukemic children; progesterone compounds began to make good the fifteen-year-old predictions of the late Dr. Ira T. Nathanson of Harvard Medical School that cancers of the uterine lining might yield to these hormones. Degrees of doubt, meanwhile, developed in some estimations as to the efficacy of a few of the other preparations.

It seems certain that with the passage of time and the better understanding it will bring of the nature of life and of cancer, all the drugs now being used will seem as primitive as transfusions were for pernicious anemia before the advent of vitamin B_{12}, or as 606 was for syphilis before the antibiotic era. Perhaps within the decade, the entire list of present anticancer drugs will become obsolete.

Where will the replacements come from?

They may come from the distant past, the primitive remedies of primitive people—as so many rediscovered drugs have come upon the modern scene. They may come from a more thorough understanding of the roles and interrelationships or hormones, enzymes, DNA, RNA, energy-transferring and energy-transforming compounds which comprise life. They may come from an understanding of the still obscure immunity processes which permit life to survive amid predatory life or from a more complete appreciation of the inexorable trial and error system of evolution by which all organisms and cells seek to improve—often in failure, only rarely with success. They may come from the chance observation of a botanist on a bud or the tedious testing of compounds, or combinations of chemicals or possibly of a resynthesis of life. They may come from chemical or physical forces at present unrecognized.

In all likelihood, however, the keys to the new controls of cancer will be found in the musty, old scientific literature; they will have been unread, ignored, misunderstood, or misinterpreted by one or more generations too much in a hurry to take time to read and to think.

Meanwhile, several million people throughout the world facing death by cancer in the immediate or distant future will do with what is available.

Some put drugs into two categories: (1) those developed by empirical, or trial and error, methods, and (2) those deliberately designed under a biochemical theory.

Down through the ages several thousand empirically-produced preparations have been tested against cancers in animals and humans. They include such bizarre substances as macerated heads of bees and vipers, snake venom, extracts of scorpions, spiders, toads and wasps, dyes, the juices of tumors and fetal organs, narcotics, head-shrinking fluid from the Amazon, unguents of green frogs, crawfish stewed in asses' milk, the

Neoplastic Diseases Responding to Chemotherapy

Diagnoses	Polyfunctional alkylating agents	Antimetabolites	Radioactive isotopes
Leukemia Acute, children		6-MP Amethopterin	
Acute, adults		6-MP Amethopterin	
Chronic myelocytic	Myleran ® HN2	6-MP	Phosphorus-32
Chronic lymphatic	Chlorambucil TEM		Phosphorus-32
Hodgkin's disease	Chlorambucil HN2 TEM		
Lymphosarcoma	Chlorambucil HN2 TEM		
Multiple myeloma			Phosphorus-32 Iodine-131
Polycythemia vera	Myleran ® TEM HN2		Phosphorus-32
Carcinoma of lung	HN2 TEM		
Carcinoma of ovary	TEM HN2	5-FU	
Carcinoma of thyroid			Iodine-131
Carcinoma of breast	TEM HN2		
Carcinoma of prostate			
Wilms' tumor	HN2		
Choriocarcinoma, female	HN2	Amethopterin	
Carcinoma of colon		5-FU	
Carcinoma of adrenal			
Carcinoma of testis	Chlorambucil*	Amethopterin*	
Miscellaneous carcinomas and sarcomas	HN2 TEM Chlorambucil Cyclophosphamide		

*Given in combination

Steroid hormones	Miscellaneous drugs	Results
Adrenal cortical hormones		70% bone marrow improvement; 50% patients live one year or longer.
Adrenal cortical hormones		15–25% improved for several months or longer.
	Demecolcin Urethane Fowler's solution	Patients maintained in good condition during major portion of disease; life occasionally prolonged.
Adrenal cortical hormones		Patients maintained in good condition during major portion of disease; life occasionally prolonged.
Adrenal cortical hormones		Occasional favorable response, but no definite prolongation of life.
Adrenal cortical hormones		Occasional favorable response, but no definite prolongation of life.
Adrenal cortical hormones	Urethane	Symptomatic relief in about 50% of cases, and objective hematological improvement in 15%.
		Prolonged clinical remissions, particularly with P^{32}.
		Brief improvement in about 50% of cases.
		30 to 50% of cases improved for one to three months, sometimes longer.
		Frequently marked improvement in properly selected cases.
Estrogens Androgens Adrenal cortical hormones		20 to 50% improved by hormonal therapy; life may be prolonged in some cases.
Estrogens		80% of cases respond to hormonal therapy; definite prolongation of life.
	Actinomycin D	Temporary regression with 30% pulmonary metastases.
		80% respond, of whom 30% show "permanent" regression.
		15% respond for several months.
	o,p'DDD	Tumor regression and decrease in hyperadrenocorticism in selected cases.
	Actinomycin D*	35% of patients show a favorable and sometimes prolonged response.
Adrenal cortical hormones		In rare instances, favorable responses occur.

Regional Cancer Chemotherapy

Diagnoses	Polyfunctional alkylating agents	Antimetabolites	Radioactive isotopes
Carcinoma in facial areas		Amethopterin + Citrovorum Factor (intraarterial infusion)	
Tumors of the extremities	HN2 (extra-corporeal perfusion)		
Pleural, pericardial and abdominal effusions	HN2 (local instillation into appropriate cavity)		Au^{198} CrP^{32}O^4 (local instillation of drug into appropriate cavity)
Leukemia Involvement central nervous system		Amethopterin (intrathecal injection)	

flesh of gray lizards, suckling pups stewed in urine, serum from the livers of goats, sheep, and pigs, and assorted caustics. Aulus Cornelius Celsus, almost twenty centuries ago, recommended turpentine; and Paracelsus fifteen centuries later echoed his prescription. Benjamin Franklin endorsed two cures with enthusiasm: the application of certain wooden shells to breast cancer and pokeweed for a variety of tumors. In recent centuries, "cancer cures" have included kerosene, gasoline, nicotine, "iron water" from blacksmith's tubs, steel sweat, roasted green frogs, skunk oil, and buckwheat flour mixed with saliva.

While all these preparations probably have disappeared into the mists of time, an ancient one endures. The one that has survived is arsenic, which was mentioned as a drug in the Ebers papyrus of 1500 B.C. A relic of early Indian, Egyptian, and Persian medicine, arsenic has a record of sporadic popularity in Western countries since 1856. It is toxic; it causes human cancer; and it is doubtful whether it ever cured a serious spontaneous cancer in man or beast. The same can be said of almost every drug now being used against human cancer, including the products of brilliant biochemical deduction. Arsenic, however, has been pretty well abandoned in modern chemotherapy except as a control material against which the efficacy of new drugs occasionally is measured; in these instances arsenic with disconcerting frequency proves as effective as some of the highly respected drugs. The relatively few clinicians who use arsenicals against

Steroid hormones	Miscellaneous drugs	Results
		Favorable response of tumors supplied by external carotid artery.
		Response in selected cases.
		About 25 to 50% of patients respond.
		About 80% of children with CNS involvement respond temporarily.

cancer sometimes are viewed with raised eyebrows; the treatment often is regarded as being the exclusive property of quacks.

A great many other compounds also have been tested, more or less empirically, against cancers; and occasionally a rationale for their use is proposed after they have proved effective. In some cases, scientists have pinpointed a specific enzyme which is blocked by the drug; in other cases, the explanation lies in the simple biological observation that the chemical prevents the division of plant or animal cells.

With one exception, male hormone, every drug now commonly used against cancer has been introduced in the last twenty-two years.

Modern chemotherapy of cancer is marked by two revolutionary observations: (1) hormones somehow control the growth of normal tissues and some cancers; and (2) some cancers can be fooled into accepting counterfeit copies (analogues) of natural and essential chemicals and be poisoned by them.

The first principle was exploited originally by Dr. Charles Huggins of the University of Chicago more than two decades ago. From his own and others' animal experiments, he concluded that the growth of cancer of the prostate was stimulated by excessive and uninhibited male hormone and might be suppressed by female hormone. He castrated a patient, bedridden and in pain with advanced cancer of the prostate, and gave him the female hormone, estrogen. The patient went back to work and lived usefully and in comfort for fifteen years, when he died of other causes.

Dr. Sidney Farber of Children's Hospital, Boston, initiated the era of analogues in cancer in 1948. For several years he and his group had investigated the possibility that certain dietary factors might help the host resist the inroads of cancer. Eventually, the B vitamin, folic acid, was given to a few children ill with acute lymphatic leukemia. The vitamin seemed to have some good but fleeting effects on the physical condition of the children, but it became obvious that it also made their cancers grow faster. Dr. Farber obtained from a drug house, Lederle Laboratories Division of American Cyanamid Company, several counterfeits of the folic acid molecule. He tested one on a very sick child and beheld a return to health. The drug was toxic, but, despite this, other children were injected. The gamble was rewarded by a series of remarkable remissions. Some of the children became well enough to return to school and to play, and a few of them, for varying periods, cast off all the symptoms of their disease. In all cases, the remission was temporary. Nevertheless, about one-third of the children were kept alive and in relatively good health, for anywhere from several months to a few years. The drug was called aminopterin.

This success touched off a search for new analogues—not only for false vitamins against childhood leukemia but for fraudulent hormones, amino acids, nucleic acids, and other essential compounds against the entire spectrum of human cancers. This line of research still is the current rage in chemotherapy and has been so for more than a decade.

For many years scientists have sought for an absolute chemical difference between normal cells and cancer cells. They felt that if they could find a chemical which cancer cells would take up and normal cells would reject, they could produce a toxic analogue of the chemical and with perfect selectivity poison cancer cells and spare normal cells.

Dr. Abraham Cantarow and the late Dr. Karl Paschkis of Jefferson Medical School discovered a difference; they found that normal rat liver cells would not take up much of the nucleic acid constituent, U or uracil, whereas liver-cancer cells would. An analogue was not hard to find; a common thyroid suppressant, thiouracil, is a uracil molecule with a sulfur atom attached. When they fed thiouracil to rats along with a chemical which produced liver cancer, the cancers didn't appear; budding cancer cells took it up and were poisoned, while normal liver cells persisted in rejecting it—they made their own uracil from raw materials.

Dr. Charles Heidelberger of the University of Wisconsin drew a blueprint of another uracil analogue which he felt would be highly toxic to cancer cells, and with help from a drug house, Hoffmann-La Roche, synthesized it. As expected from the Paschkis-Cantarow observations, the drug also harmed fast-growing normal cells. But the brilliant biochemical concept cured several kinds of experimental animal cancers without great mortality among the animals. Dr. Heidelberger's clinical colleagues, Drs. Anthony R. Curreri and Fred J. Ansfield, administered the drug to a series of hopelessly advanced patients and found that three, four, or five of each ten derived measurable benefit from it. The drug was 5-FU, fluorouracil, which now is widely used. It is uracil with a fluorine atom where a hydrogen should be.

One objectionable feature of 5-FU, and with virtually all other effective and artificial anticancer preparations as well, is its high toxicity. In most patients the drug has offered little help against cancer unless administered in toxic doses. Nevertheless, an appreciable proportion of patients who undertake the treatment are rewarded with the disappearance of pain, return of appetite and feeling of well-being for many months. A few patients with widespread cancers of the breast, digestive tract, ovary, cervix, and liver have survived so far for more than four years, taking their 5-FU shots once a month. In one controlled series of breast-cancer patients, those taking 5-FU lived an average of more than twenty-nine months; patients not receiving 5-FU died in an average of thirteen months. Drug resistance is slow in developing; the average patient shows no refractoriness to 5-FU for nine months.

Dr. Heidelberger has designed another counterfeit drug which blocks still another phase of nucleic acid formation. It is called 5-FUDR, or 5-fluorodeoxyuridine. In preliminary tests, it has proved superior to 5-FU in a few cancers. It seems to be less toxic than 5-FU.

Biochemists have fashioned hundreds of counterfeits designed to block key cell chemicals. There are now numerous varieties of analogues of the segments of both the RNA and DNA forms of nucleic acid, of the raw material from which they are made and the products which they become in cell chemistry.

They have altered the molecular architecture of amino acids in several ways and with them produced proteins which are alien to nature; microorganisms bearing the functional counterfeits become monstrously grotesque. Most of the known vitamin molecules have been distorted in all dimensions. Sugars, fatty acids, and alcohols have been altered. Analogues-of-analogues and analogues-of-analogues-of-analogues have been fashioned and tested against cancers growing in laboratory dishes and in experimental animals.

Insult has been added to injury in seeking to destroy cancers. Tumor-bearing animals receiving an analogue of an essential food—like vitamin B_{12} or the amino acid, phenylalanine—have been put on diets deficient in the vitamin or amino acid. Dr. Daniel S. Martin of the University of Miami and Dr. Charles A. Nichol of Roswell Park showed that this tactic often increases the anticancer effects of the drug—and also its side effects and lethality.

Many of the analogues are ingenious. One was designed to block fermentation without interfering with oxidation, and this would have proved to be a cancer cure had a theory advanced three decades ago by Prof. Otto Warburg been correct. Warburg contended that cancer cells metabolized much as bacteria and lower organisms do, by fermenting sugar in a long series of chemical steps to lactic acid—whereas the cells of higher animals obtained their energy by respiration (oxidizing sugar to carbon dioxide). Dr. Sidney P. Colowick of Vanderbilt University and Drs. John Papaconstantinou and Edward B. Goldberg of Johns Hopkins University discovered they could completely block fermentation without interfering with oxidation. They confirmed an earlier finding that a counterfeit called oxamic acid ($CH_3 \cdot CO \cdot COOH$) would act like a monkey wrench thrown into the delicate machinery of an enzyme, lactic dehydrogenase, which changes pyruvic acid to lactic acid. Oxamic acid did precisely as the biochemists hoped: fermentation stopped, while respiration was unimpaired. Human cancer cells, growing in laboratory dishes, produced no lactic acid in the presence of the counterfeit; they stopped dividing and eventually died, unless they were revived by the addition of natural pyruvic acid. Unfortunately, Warburg was only partly right; some tumor cells, to a great or small degree, can adapt to a respiration mode of life, and some normal cells have fermenting mechanisms. Oxamic acid, while it dramatically arrested the growth of cancer cells, proved toxic when given to cancerous mice. In the first three humans treated, oxamic acid did no good in one, helped a second, and gave a dramatic remission to a third.

Some clinical success has been reported with a drug which did precisely the opposite of oxamic acid. The drug is called MeGAG, which is short for methylglyoxal-bis-guanyl hydrazone. It inhibits cell respiration and stimulates cell fermentation. MeGAG is one of the more successful of the thousands of compounds explored by a highly imaginative and skillful team, Frederic A. French and the late Dr. B. L. Freedlander of Mount Zion Hospital, San Francisco. With assembly-line techniques and a wide-ranging knowledge of chemistry and biochemistry, the French-Freedlander team have tested hundreds of natural chemicals known to be essential to cell function; they have devised new molecules cunningly contrived to interrupt cancer-cell processes or to potentiate other drugs or physical agents. They have experimented with compounds of completely unknown activity merely on a hunch that they might inhibit cancer. MeGAG was one of these. The most notable effect of MeGAG so far has been against acute myelocytic leukemia—but not other forms of leukemia—which is common in adults and which heretofore has been beyond substantial help by other means. Scientists at Roswell Park have found that MeGAG exerts its effects by interfering with the metabolism of cofactors of the vitamin, folic acid; and they have suppressed the drug's toxicity by giving citrovorum factor, a folic acid product. Others at the National Cancer Institute have hailed the drug's rare, almost unique, action on respiration and glycolysis as a significant step and have predicted that in combination with some of the many fermentation-inhibiting agents, MeGAG will have potent actvity against many cancers.

Phenylalanine is an amino acid which serves as the raw material for the body's manufacture of many important chemicals as well as of proteins. Dr. Karl Dittmer of Florida State University several years ago synthesized an analogue called *b*-3-thienylalanine which was tested on laboratory animals by Dr. Robert W. Wissler of the University of Chicago. The drug, incorporated in a diet which was deficient in phenylalanine, greatly depressed the growth rate of experimental cancers. It had the rare virtue of being relatively nontoxic; it did not harm either the highly sensitive bone marrow or the digestive-tract lining. At this writing, it has not been tried against human cancer.

One of the products of phenylalanine is called DOPA, which is a raw material from which the body manufactures its melanin, or pigment. Analogues have been tested against melanomas, the pigmented cancers, of animals. They didn't work. Apparently melanoma is due to a fault in the melanin-producing cell, not in its melanin production apparatus.

The simplest analogue tested against cancer was deuterium, which is a double-sized hydrogen atom. In high concentrations, it was found, deuterium displaces 30 per cent of cellular hydrogen. It inhibited the growth of mouse cancers but proved toxic.

Many scientists are reshaping natural molecules. They are adding atoms like selenium or sulfur, or azo or alcohol groups to life's essential compounds—purines, pyrimidines, amino acids, vitamins, hormones, sugars, salts, and virtually every substance which the cell uses. A fairly useful drug, DON (6-diazo-5-oxo-L-norleucina), is a heavily-disguised amino acid.

Some of the analogues kill bacteria; some kill embryonic or cancer cells growing in laboratory dishes or chicken eggs; some kill transplanted tumors in mice and cure the animals; some kill cancers in humans, but if used in sufficient strength to eradicate the cancers completely, they might kill the humans as well.

Man has been curing and controlling his diseases for many centuries without the aid of the biochemist. He has drawn on the life about him to heal his hurts, to repair his damaged organs and tissues, to stimulate his tired or failing chemical processes, and to beat off his microbial enemies.

Twenty-seven hundred years before the Christian era, the Chinese treated their asthmas and hay fever with extracts of the plant, mahuang; in 1923, a miracle drug, ephedrine, was discovered—the active principle of mahuang. It has been used for centuries elsewhere against syphilis, pneumonia, and mental troubles. Four thousand years or so ago, Chinese warriors applied dried toad skins to their wounds; the "secret ingredient" was adrenalin, or epinephrine, the hormone produced by the adrenal glands. In the fifth century B.C., the Greek physician or herbalist used routinely 300 different plants in various forms to draw out the poisons of reptiles, heal wounds, relieve inflammation or serve as cathartics, emetics, or diuretics and to control gout, hemorrhage, various aches and pains—and, of course, the common cold. Hundreds of years ago head-hunters of the Amazon and Andes were using solutions of tree bark for chest tightness (now the basis for many cough medicines), vine root as a poison to stun animals and enemies (now used to relax muscles in surgery, childbirth, cerebral palsy, polio and tetanus), and another vine root to prod a reluctant libido (it yields male hormone). In the sixteenth century a German physician, Dr. Leonard Rauwolf, found that jittery East Indians were being toned down with extracts of a snakeroot plant, later called Rauwolfia (the source of several newly-rediscovered tranquilizers).

At least as far back as 1638, primitive people employed chinchona bark against malaria and other microbe-caused fevers; quinine was isolated from it in 1820. A plant called ipecacuanha also has been used against protozoan infections; from this, emetine, the specific for amoebic dysentery, was extracted centuries later.

American Indians have added about fifty botanicals to the remedies still used by doctors: May-apple emetics and cathartics; wild-cherry bark for coughs and as a tonic and sedative; progesterone-containing wild yam and trillium root to overcome the dangers of miscarriage; willow bark as a source of salicin (a chemical relative of aspirin). Incas drew what is now known as cinnamio ester from balsam bark for the healing of chronic inflammatory lesions; and they produced cocaine from the coca bush. (Bolivian and Peruvian Indians also have used coca products for many centuries.) The ancient people of Asia Minor and, later, the Arabs and Egyptians obtained opium, morphine, and codeine from dried poppy juice. Welchmen found that foxglove yielded something—now known to be digitalis—which stimulated the heart; and this was commonly used in Wales long before it was introduced into English medicine in 1785.

Medicine, by and large, is growing much too sophisticated for drugs drawn from roots and leaves and the bark of trees. Only a small percentage of private and public research funds now are spent on this type of empirical enterprise, and some of the old standbys are becoming harder and harder to get. Some Americans find it necessary to patronize a shop on Burton Street, London operated by the Society of Herbalists for such preparations as celery tea for rheumatism and nervousness, lime-blossom tea for indigestion, fatigue and insomnia, wood betony for headaches, balm of Gilead for coughs, and all the other remedies for weak memory, loss of speech, and apoplexy. The Society has only 1,000 members.

The few investigators still searching for nature's healing treasures are being rewarded every now and then with something of value. In recent years it has been reported, for instance, that abalone juice contains something which destroys microbes and another substance which inactivates viruses, and that oysters and clams have yielded material which destroys microbes. A Hugarian reported that of 400 different kinds of plant seeds tested, the coats of thirty-six contained something which kills gram-positive bacteria.

At the University of Wisconsin a few graduate students collected native plants and tested their juices on experimental cancers; their success— in three years and with 1,000 or so extracts, 10 preparations had proved anticancer activity—was such that the operation now has grown considerably. In the Department of Pharmaceutical Chemistry, American and foreign plants are tested, and an effort is being made to isolate the active principle of the promising extracts. The department will try to identify active molecules and synthesize similar substances which might be of medicinal value.

Many plants have yielded substances which destroy cancers growing in laboratory dishes, in animals and, to a degree, in humans.

Dr. J. H. Cutts and others of the University of Western Ontario a few years ago were seeking a plant extract with insulin qualities. They tested an alkaloid extract of periwinkle, the tropical decorative plant which primitive medicine men of the West Indies, South Africa, and the Philippines had found to reduce blood sugar. Tested on mice and rats, periwinkle extracts profoundly lowered the white blood cell (lymphocyte) count. The white count dropped within a day or two and remained depressed for four or five days, when it again rose to higher than normal levels. The preparation also blocked uterine tissues' response to the female hormone, stilbesterol. In animals it showed an amazing ability to inhibit transplanted leukemia and solid cancers and to slow the growth of some spontaneous tumors. Despite serious side effects, two extracts, called vinblastine and vincristine, are being used in an increasing number of humans. Vinblastine has shown powerful but often brief arresting ability against cancer of the human uterus (choriocarcinoma), lung, colon, and stomach, and lymphomas. Vincristine has given remissions lasting about ten weeks to a substantial percentage of patients with several kinds of leukemia and leukemiclike diseases, as well as certain cancers of the ovary, testis, uterine cervix, bladder, and prostate.

Many other plant substances which have been investigated seriously have shown activity against the test-tube, animal, and human cancers. So far, almost without exception, the preparations have proved to be only mildly deterrent to human cancers and severely toxic to the host. Nevertheless, there is a constant hope that one of the many drugs showing promise in animals will prove destructive to human cancers and gentle so far as the patient is concerned.

A bacteria-destroying extract of garlic which limits growth by breaking up sulfhydryl groups in enzymes has extended the life span of cancerous mice tenfold. Extracts of many species of mushrooms have slowed the growth of experimental cancers. A soybean phospholipid mixture which has controlled bleeding in leukemic animals has shown some promise in humans as well. Derivatives of protamine, a small protein abundant in the sperm and sex cells of some fish, have regressed mouse cancers.

Colchicine, which has been used since the sixth century for gout and which, legends have it, was discovered on the Greek Island of Colchis by the enchantress Medea, also has been tested against cancer. Essentially an analogue of the amino acid, phenylalanine, produced by the Autumn crocus, it dissolves the spindle and prevents normal and cancer cells from dividing. In clinical use, it has proved toxic and with brief benefit at best.

Podophyllin is another ancient antimitotic. The plant which yields podophyllin, mandrake or May apple, bears a fancied resemblance to the human form; for centuries it was placed under the pillows of Europeans to correct problems of infertility and unrequited love. An effective cathartic and, in some forms, a narcotic, podophyllin also blocks cell division. Periodically, podophyllin excites one scientist or another by clearing up completely but transiently a superficial cancer. Taken internally, the drug is highly toxic; its anticancer properties, when they are at all demonstrable, are as fickle as the flower is in smoothing out romantic problems or restoring fecundity.

In this biochemical era, to the few investigators who continue to explore her hidden treasures, nature continues to dole out occasional compounds with anticancer activity. Dr. Mary Caldwell of the University of Arizona, who submits annually to screening centers about sixty products of plants collected in Arizona and thirteen Mexican states, in 1962 had discovered three substances of definite anticancer activity and about forty others which may prove of value. Also being tested are such preparations as aristolchoic acid from species which were used by ancient Romans and Greeks as a cancer cure, mistletoe (which at Roswell Park has shown a 73 per cent inhibition of mouse tumors), and algae (which prolong the lives of cancerous mice, when injected along with the transplants).

Often there is a simple or sophisticated rationale behind the testing of various preparations. One of the simplest and starkest is: if the stuff will shrink a head, maybe it will shrink a tumor. Despite the contentions of a few that head-shrinking fluid from the Amazon actually has regressed human cancers, reputable confirmation is lacking.

A productive approach was proposed in 1957 by Dr. S. Meryl Rose, University of Illinois zoologist, who asserted that growth can be limited by its own products and suggested that a search be conducted for tumor products which would control or cure cancer. Dr. Rose has used fluids from seven kinds of adult tissues to suppress the development of similar normal tissues in embryos. He had produced brainless tadpoles by growing them in water containing pieces of mature frog brain and heartless tadpoles by putting a mash of mature heart in their medium.

"Malignant tissues are composed of sickly abnormal cells which die almost as rapidly as they reproduce," Dr. Rose said. "Some of the cancers, the ones which grow through the most tissue, never have more than a few ounces of living tissue. They are never-healing wounds, always growing but never reaching self-limiting size."

Related but divergent views had been expressed a few years earlier by Drs. Hubert S. Loring, M. C. Niu and Victor Twitty of Stanford University. They were investigating the possibility that specialized tissues—like muscle or brain—leak an "organizer" (tentatively identified as nucleic acid) which can be taken up by unspecialized, embryonic cells and transform the latter toward the form and function of the donor cells. In laboratory dishes, they produced evidence that this probably was so—unspecialized, embryonic cells developed the traits of the specialized cells placed in the culture. The two cell types were separated in the medium by a thin membrane through which small "organizing" chemicals could diffuse.

Another principle was pursued by the late Dr. L. V. Heilbrunn of the University of Pennsylvania. He sought for and found a natural substance which arrested the growth and development of immature cells. The most logical place to look for the material, he reasoned, would be in ovaries. Females are born with about 200 or 300 ova—all they ever will have. (This is in contrast to males, who produce sperm prolifically during their entire reproductive period.) Something in the ovaries suppresses the development of the immature eggs until the female reaches puberty, when the ova begin to mature and to divide and are shed, one by one, with each menstrual cycle. The ovarian material isolated in impure form appeared to be a mucopolysaccharide somewhat resembling the anticlotting agent, heparin. By preventing the clotting or gelling of cell structures, which is an essential step in mitosis, the material blocked cell division. When small amounts of extracts of cow ovaries were injected into mice with transplanted tumors, they prevented or cured between 15 and 25 per cent of the cancers; moderate amounts made the cells divide, and large amounts killed the animals. Dr. Heilbrunn reported that urethane, nitrogen mustard and 6-MP (6-mercaptopurine) showed similar anticlotting properties; and he attributed the anticancer effect of these drugs to this quality.

Others, at the University of California, have begun exploring chemicals which prevent the production of sperm. They are called nitrofurans. Because they act upon the sulfhydryl groups in the amino acid, cysteine, the scientists have attempted to increase their activity by administering cysteine along with the nitrofurans.

One of the most powerful anticoagulants in nature is the unidentified substance secreted by the mouth glands of eels; it keeps fish-blood fluid while eels drain them. This material once was studied at Ohio State University for possible anticlotting drug use against such clot-complicating conditions as strokes, coronary thromboses, polycythemia vera and some cancers.

Drs. A. J. Riker and Albert C. Hildebrandt of the University of Wisconsin demonstrated some years ago that crown gall, a plant tumor, could be controlled with "unbalanced rations" of normal nutrients. The scientists added to the ordinary diet of the plant tumor tissues—which were grown in laboratory glassware—extra helpings of natural amino acids, a sugar, a nucleic acid constituent, an alcohol or fatty acid. By these means they were able to arrest the disease growth.

Several other scientists have inhibited the growth of animal cancers by feeding or injecting substances required in the normal processes of growth.

Dr. Wilhelmina Dunning of the University of Miami fed rats a yeast rich in nucleic acid; when she added to the diet chemicals which induce liver cancer, the tumors developed slowly or not at all. Dr. Ernest J. Dornfeld of Oregon State College showed a decade ago that young animal tissues grown in test tubes slow down or stop growing when the ribonucleic acid constituents (adenylic, cytidilic or guanylic, but not uridylic, acid) is added to their medium; whole RNA inhibited the growth rate 65 per cent.

Since shortly after its beginnings, life began to prey upon life. It still does today. Humans are no exception; they feed upon plants and animals over which they have been given dominion.

Of the many weapons possessed by the sane predators—who kill to feed or survive rather than kill to kill—chemicals are by far the most common. Chemical warfare is waged by viruses, by microorganisms, by plants, and by animals of all descriptions. The chemicals are mainly poisons. The poisons often are specifically designed by the predators for their prey.

In 1889, a man named Vuellemin coined a word for this chemical warfare. He called it antibiosis. Several decades later a British scientist revolutionized medicine by application of the antibiosis principle to human health. It started with the chance observation that molds contaminating cultures produced something that killed bacteria. It extends now through the plant and animal kingdoms to the well-known fact that snakes, poison ivy, skunks, wasps, and many other forms of life produce something which protects them against man and other enemies.

In a relatively short time it was found that many kinds of life produced these precious antibiotics—actinomycetes, molds, bacteria, mushrooms, lichens, flowering plants, conifers, and algae among others. The seeds of some plants, like broccoli and cabbage, are rich in antibioticlike substances; material in cauliflower seed, especially from cauliflower of low viability, has inhibited the growth of bacilli, Corynebacterium, sewage bacteria, pseudomonas, and staphylococcus.

The targets of the antibiotics progressively increased; not only bacteria proved vulnerable but also molds, yeasts, algae, protozoa, rickettsiae, large viruses, and bacterial viruses.

Sporadically during the last two decades, antibiotics have been tried against cancer. In recent years, they have been tested routinely along with other types of drugs.

Dr. Ivor Cornman, now of Falls Church, Virginia, in 1944 obtained the refuse of a batch of penicillin—the dirty brown, sticky, "gunk" that manufacturers threw away after they had extracted the active material. He added extracts of it to cultures in which he grew eight different kinds of cancer cells and also normal cells. The results were amazing: the penicillin wastes rapidly destroyed every cancer cell without harm to the normal cells. Five of the twenty extracts he prepared showed anticancer activity. The scientist asked the producers for more of the material. He was told that, in refining penicillin, the particular strain he had used had been lost. All the antibiotics available then and since then have failed to duplicate the test-tube miracle. And all efforts to find the lost strain have come to nought.

Meanwhile, other antibiotics have shown promise, not only in experimental animals but also in humans. Mithramycin has given remissions lasting several months in about 30 per cent of patients with embryonal cancers and to some with metastases to nerve and brain. Streptonigrin has been useful against several kinds of cancer. An antibiotic called Refuin, found by Yeshiva investigators in donkey droppings, has been tested in seventy-eight cancer patients. Thirty-two showed remissions, sixteen of them lasting more than three months.

It took, and still takes, a considerable degree of daring to test unknown substances in humans. Animal results give at best a faint idea of what might happen in humans, and often the promise is so false as to encourage clinical experiments which end in disaster. Despite this, and despite the ever-present possibility of punishment by conservative and retrogressive elements within medicine and liability to lawsuit by patients and their families (a signed application or permission for experimental treatment carries only so much weight), a few brave physicians continue to push forward the frontiers of medicine.

An ever-present problem in chemotherapy is when to give up on a preparation.

One antibiotic which looked promising in test tubes and animal studies was given to a series of hopelessly advanced cancer patients in 1953. A few seemed to show a good response; but as time passed, one after another died, nine of them older patients, seemingly not of their cancers. The physician discovered at autopsy that the antibiotic had damaged the kidneys of the aged patients, and he promptly published a warning to the profession. It was time to give up on this drug.

It was predicted from the start of test tube and animal tests that actinomycin D would be toxic; of the many related antibiotics that had been tested, it did the most damage to normal tissues; it blocked protein and nucleic acid synthesis with startling suddenness. Nevertheless, it inhibited or cured many transplanted animal cancers, including mouse leukemia, melanoma, breast adenocarcinoma and bone sarcoma; it showed similar striking effects against human cancer grown in the hamster cheek pouch. Dr. Sidney Farber cautiously began testing the drug against human tumors seen at Children's Hospital in Boston. At first the results were equivocal: actinomycin D seemed to help one or two youngsters; but in the mild dosages used it had no effect on others. Eventually, however, with slightly elevated doses, it became apparent that some of the patients were receiving definite benefit; the drug was not as toxic as had been feared.

Dr. George Moore at Roswell Park tested actinomycin D on a man dying of stomach cancer; the patient showed an excellent remission but soon died of his disease. The case, however, encouraged further testing. In Dr. Moore's series only two of sixteen patients with stomach cancer were helped by actinomycin D; but the drug proved of definite benefit to anywhere from 25 to 60 per cent of Roswell Park patients with cancers of the breast, colon, kidney, lymphatic tissue, liver, and pancreas. Comparable results were achieved at Memorial Cancer Center in New York. Experiments are continuing with actinomycin D; it has become perhaps the most helpful antibiotic in clinical use against cancer.

A few other antibiotics have been used clinically. Actinomycin F has shown some promise in trials at Memorial Cancer Center, and streptovitacin A, a product of spent beer fermentation, has produced a few temporary remissions, but it is very toxic. Mitomycin has proved of value at Roswell Park.

The role of antibiotics in cancer chemotherapy has only begun to take shape. In test-tube and animal experiments, a lengthening list of new substances are showing some promise.

Lumberjacks in the Bohemian Forest have held for many years that eating mushrooms of the local variety prevented cancer. Dr. Everett S. Beneke of Michigan State University extracted from these giant puffballs a substance called calvacin, which inhibited thirteen of the first twenty-four experimental animal tumors they were tested against. Dr. Armand J. Guarino has isolated from the soil of the University of Michigan another antibiotic, cordycepin, which has cured 20 per cent of mouse cancers without evidence of great toxicity.

With total synthesis of the skeletal antibiotic molecules, it has become possible to design a great many artificial antibiotics—500 variants of penicillin were produced within a few months following synthesis of this substance.

In 1954, a man wandered into the pressroom of the International Cancer Research Congress in São Paulo, Brazil, and announced to science writers that he had a plan for producing antibiotics specific for cancer. His idea was to bury human tumors in soil capable of supporting bacterial growth; the microbes present would develop adaptive enzymes and produce substances which would decompose and destroy the human cancers. Some of the substances, he predicted, would behave as tumor-specific antibiotics when given to cancer patients. The man's name was not on the program, and he was unknown—perhaps not even a qualified scientist. The idea still awaits trial.

Dr. Riojun Kinosita tells with wry humor of his days as the Vice President of the Japanese Medical Society. One of the centuries-old duties he inherited was to hail into court those who peddled panaceas on the temple steps of Nara. In court, chemists testified that the panaceas contained only yeastlike substances. Indulgent judges invariably dismissed the charges. After the value of antibiotics became recognized, the cure-alls were reexamined. They had antibiotic activity . . . and presumably had had antibiotic activity for centuries.

A recurrent and disturbing thought is that valuable clues to the control of cancer may have been lost in the swift sweep of modern science and the increasing difficulty of communications. Scores of leads—some of them sound, others perhaps capricious—have been proposed. Few survive long enough to be tested even against animal cancers. And a great majority of those which do have effect against one or another animal tumors never reach clinical testing. Considering the dearth of good anticancer drugs, no sound idea should be dismissed lightly. A random sample of rationales on which some preparations have been proposed include these:

RNASE. The enzyme may break up the cancer cells' protein factories. RNase has decreased the RNA content and prevented development of ascites cancer cells.

VITAMIN B$_{12}$. Many cancer patients eventually become anemic, and B$_{12}$ controls some kinds of anemia. Dr. Martin Bodian in London has reported that among twenty-eight children with neuroblastoma, B$_{12}$ produced arrest or regression of the disease in fifteen; long-lasting remissions or complete arrest were effected in all children under one year old.

NICOTINAMIDE. This vitamin provides a basic spark of life—it permits shuttling hydrogen ions to activate enzymes and hormones. In cancer, the shuttle is defective. Dr. Freedlander and Mr. French found that high doses of nicotinamide helped prevent or overcome a few induced and spontaneous mouse cancers.

POLYLYSINE. This false protein composed of a monolithic string of a single type of amino acid, lysine, made tumor cells leak their vital chemicals, caused chromosomes to clump and inhibited some mouse cancers.

VITAMIN A. In aging women, massive doses of vitamin A have "rejuvenated" the sometimes precancerous cornified skin of the vagina. In many stomach cancer patients the vitamin A level of the blood is low and cannot be elevated with shots of the vitamin (but certain hormone combinations seem to have some corrective effect on this).

DNASE. Aging cells contain inhibitors of DNase, an enzyme which breaks down DNA; young cells have very little of the inhibitors, leukemic cells none. If a DNase inhibitor can be isolated from the cells of old liver, it might be useful in cancer treatment.

FORCE FEEDING. As cancers increase in size, the host loses weight. One reason is the host loses his appetite. On the theory that their weight and resistance to cancer might be built up, far advanced cancer patients at the University of Rochester were fed by stomach tube. They gained weight; but the extra poundage, composed mostly of water, was dissipated quickly when they no longer could take the force feeding. While the experiment seemed to benefit a few patients, it may have accelerated the disease in others.

CARCINOGENS. Most of the chemicals used to treat cancer also cause cancer. Dr. Alexander Haddow of the Chester Beatty Group in London used polycyclic hydrocarbon carcinogens against rat cancers and found that they inhibited their growth. Dr. Charles Huggins of the University of Chicago, on the same principle, administered the common laboratory carcinogen, 3-methylcholanthrene, to six breast cancer patients who were hopelessly advanced; five of them received benefit for varying periods.

ROCKET FUEL. Hydrazines were found in 1958 to stimulate the central nervous system and combat depression; they block the brain enzyme which destroys adrenalin and other adrenal hormones. Their effects on cancer have not been reported at this writing.

TRANQUILIZERS. Reserpine was reported to inhibit localized mouse leukemia, and reserpine and also chlorpromizine have slowed the course of a transplanted mouse cancer.

ANESTHETICS. They might slow metabolism and kill tumors. Super-heated vapors of ether, chloroform, and trichlorethylene, tested on eighty-four advanced cancer patients, reduced the tumor, increased appetite and controlled hemorrhage in twenty-one. They also cured 37 per cent of mice with transplanted breast cancers.

EXTRACTS OF THE SMALL INTESTINE. Tested because in animals and humans cancer rarely occurs in the small intestines, these extracts did inhibit some mouse cancers.

FATTY ACIDS. Because there is a disturbance of fatty-acid metabolism in many cancers, Ottawa scientists tested sixty-two different fatty acid preparations against transplanted mouse cancers. Of these, thirty-three were active against the cancers in a highly acid medium; four impeded cancer growth at the normal body level of acidity and alkalinity.

The development of an anticancer drug often involves a tortuous intellectual process. In urinary-bladder cancer, for instance, the story might begin with the surprising finding by several surgeons that these tumors require continued stimulation by something in the urine. Many surgeons employ a two-stage operation: In the first stage, they produce an artificial urinary drain directly from the kidneys through the side of the patient, allowing the bypassed bladder to remain idle; a few weeks later they reoperate, removing the cancerous—usually bottom—portion of the bladder and reconstructing the remaining normal urinary system. Not uncommonly, when they reoperate, they find that the cancer has shrunk or disappeared; in the absence of something in urine, it could not survive.

Dr. Eric Boyland of the Chester Beatty group in London set out to learn what it was in the urine that stimulated the growth of bladder cancers in dye workers. If he could find the culprit chemical and eliminate it, he might be able to prevent or cure the cancers. He, as well as many other scientists, found that aniline dyes as such apparently are not carcinogenic.

In body chemistry the dye is altered and one product, called 2-amino-1-naphthol is carcinogenic. In a free state in urine the carcinogen makes the bottom of the bladder cancerous. Dr. Boyland discovered why most animals are protected: the carcinogen became tightly cemented to glucuronides and in this bound state it was innocuous. In man, however, an enzyme called beta-glucuronidase splits the 2-amino-1-naphthol off the glucuronides, thus permitting it to attack the bladder cells.

Dr. Boyland discovered that a relatively simple chemical, 4-saccharolactone, blocked the enzyme and prevented the liberation of the carcinogen. Whether 4-saccharolactone will cure or control human bladder cancer remains to be seen. Some of the patients so treated have shown initial benefit.

Very often cancer treatment is suggested by serendipity. As with the legendary three princes of Serendip, who sought for one thing but, by accident, continued finding other things of great value, alert scientists constantly are encountering new clues to the nature of cancer.

Dr. Kenneth Scott of the University of California for more than fifteen years has followed a serendipitous course. It all started when he injected radioactive iodine into mice bearing transplanted cancers and discovered a surprising thing: instead of concentrating in the thyroid gland, as happens in normal animals and humans, the iodine was diverted; much of it was excreted, and easily measurable amounts settled in areas around the tumor and was incorporated into compounds which rupture chemical storehouses called mast cells. Over the years, Dr. Scott discovered that what he had observed was the rule in cancer, not the exception. Animals and humans with spontaneous cancers showed the same iodine-trapping phenomenon.

Link by link, Dr. Scott has put together a chain of evidence implicating in close and logical relationship such factors as iodine, tumor polypeptides, mast cells and their contents, including histamine and serotonin, hallucinogenic LSD, red-cell permeability, potassium, plasma fluid volume, selenium, sulfur, alpha-2 globulin, renin, kidney angiotensin, the adrenals, and aldosterone.

The Scott studies, which are continuing, offer more and more targets for drugs that might correct a chemical fault which leads to cancer, or which interrupts the chemistry that makes cancer possible. Renin and antibodies to renin are available; angiotensin II has been synthesized, and its analogues now can be made; aldosterone and its blocking agent, spirolactone, are available. Dr. Scott is studying their effect in cancer.

Dr. Irene Corey Diller of the Institute for Cancer Research, Philadelphia, has specialized in exploring little-known byways of biology and cytology in a long and productive career in cancer research. Two decades ago she felt that the spleen might well contain something of value in overcoming cancer. The embryonic spleen produces most or all of the blood cell types, and the adult spleen matures red cells and disposes of them, stores blood, manufactures lymphocytes and, generally, controls the composition of blood. The spleen plays a major role in resistance to infections. Dr. Diller injected cancerous mice with an aqueous extract of cow spleen and found that her preparation had a devastating effect on the tumors, both transplanted and chemically induced. To this day the work has attracted little attention, although this material completely cures a high percentage of experimental mouse tumors. Other scientists also have found activity in spleen extracts; with spleen material they call oncotine, Drs. Casimir Funk and Philip Thomashefsky of New York reported in 1954 that they had reduced the growth of transplanted mouse tumors by more than 40 per cent and enabled the cancerous mice to gain weight. Another spleen extract which they called oncostimuline had the opposite effect—it increased tumor growth and depressed host weight.

Dr. Herbert Hirsch of the University of Minnesota for many years has tested the theory that cancer may be caused by free radicals produced within cells and tissues. He has found that something in normal livers inhibits the formation of the free radicals, while in cancerous livers the inhibitor is lacking. His efforts to isolate and identify the inhibitor, which then could be tested for its ability to suppress the growth of cancer, so far have been unsuccessful; the inhibitor is readily destroyed by X rays and ultraviolet light and may be difficult to obtain in stable form.

Meanwhile, however, Dr. R. A. Holman of the Welch National School of Medicine, has reported suppressing cancer growth in rats by adding to the animals' drinking water a dilute solution of hydrogen peroxide, which is readily broken down into several free radicals; he has said that more than one-half the rats with transplanted cancers were completely cured in from fifteen to sixty days on this system. Two of four cancer patients showed marked improvement when put on dilute hydrogen peroxide, which is a natural substance in the body as well as a common hair-bleaching agent. Several other scientists tried and failed to confirm these results. A group at Tulane University, however, have extended the survival of cancerous mice from sixteen days in untreated controls to ninety days among those injected with hydrogen peroxide.

Some anticancer drugs have been introduced under dramatic conditions —nitrogen mustard, for instance. This was a German poison gas, prepared and stockpiled during World War II for use if and when gases proved expedient. British agents recovered samples of it from a torpedoed vessel, and British doctors noted profound blood changes among exposed sailor-survivors. Samples were sent to London and to Yale University for analysis. The scientists found that nitrogen mustard exerted a highly destructive effect on white blood cells, lymphatic tissue, and bone marrow. Dr. Thomas F. Dougherty, now of the University of Utah, and others at Yale injected a fat old mouse dying of leukemia and witnessed the animal's dramatic recovery. Whispers of a cancer cure spread rapidly around New Haven, and they reached a man dying of acute lymphosarcoma. Because sitting or lying was excruciatingly painful, he was suspended by straps from the ceiling. The pain-ridden patient implored Dr. Dougherty's wife, Dr. Jean Dougherty, a physician, to test the "cancer cure" on him. The patient was given nitrogen mustard, and he went into a remarkable remission. For several weeks, he enjoyed a new lease on pain-free, normal life before resistance to the drug developed and he died of his disease.

Dr. Calvin T. Klopp of George Washington University had established, in dog experiments, the feasibility of intraarterial injections of drugs; but still he hesitated to apply the technique to humans. He knew that many booby traps beset the path of the physician in experimental medicine who tries to apply animal findings to clinical problems. As he still searched his conscience, a patient dying in great pain of a throat cancer entered the cancer clinic. Beyond sedation by the strongest narcotics, the patient begged the physicians to try anything which might relieve his misery— either by controlling the pain or ending it in death. After consultation, the hospital staff agreed that in this case a trial of nitrogen mustard, intra-arterially, was justified. The procedure was carried out; the patient almost immediately rallied, and within a week some of the staff were beginning to wonder whether they had not witnessed the initiation of a new way of curing some kinds of cancer. After this definite, dramatic remission, the patient died of his cancer. His response, however, indicated that further work on this therapeutic approach was warranted. This effect, the first intraarterial use of nitrogen mustard, was never again matched for dramatic recovery from a desperate situation in the Klopp series.

Dr. Herman Hoster of Ohio State University had a double interest in seeking a cure for Hodgkin's disease: (1) As a specialist in this area, he was treating at all times between fifteen and thirty Hodgkin patients, and (2) he himself had the disease. Dr. Hoster, during the dozen years in which his disease was controlled by X rays and, when he became resistant to them, by radiomimetic drugs, expanded his laboratory so that equipment filled the halls and even the washroom of the space assigned to him. Despite almost constant fatigue, he worked day and night trying to determine whether Hodgkin's disease was virus-caused and seeking a means of controlling it. During his last weeks alive, he sat on an inflated inner tube to absorb the small shocks of road bumps as he was driven to his laboratory. He and his clientele were prepared to try any scientifically logical remedy. They had little to lose. On the strength of a report that two World War II soldiers with Hodgkin's disease were spontaneously "cured" when they also developed acute infectious hepatitis, sixteen of Dr. Hoster's Hodgkin patients volunteered to be infected with hepatitis. The first two to come down with hepatitis—as a result of nasal spraying with the virus—showed an excellent remission. The rest of them, including Dr. Hoster himself, received little if any benefit from the dangerous clinical adventure; none died of hepatitis, however.

It is hard to explain why, in so many cases, a new drug or a new procedure brings an exciting result the first time it is used, then produces only sporadic remissions, if any, in subsequent trials. The placebo effect is hardly an adequate explanation. Perhaps it is a matter of sheer chance: when the law of averages provides a highly responsive first patient, the drug or procedure is given extensive testing; when the same law of averages produces nonresponsive patients, the drug or procedure may be abandoned without adequate trials.

Research in cancer has produced many leads toward the control of other diseases—genetic, congenital, infectious, endocrine, and induced by various chemical and physical agents. Cancer research also has borrowed liberally from other investigations in efforts to find a magic bullet for malignancy.

Dr. Ralph Jones, Jr., when he was at the University of Pennsylvania headed up the United States Army team which produced drugs which cure or control malaria. He was investigating the effect of Atabrine-type compounds on normal and cancer cells when the Army called upon him to cope with a serious epidemic confronting troops in the Korean war: malaria was disabling far more men than were canceled out in combat. Dr. Jones and his group synthesized a series of compounds—quinones—which by brilliant chemical deduction they believed would wreck the metabolism of malarial protozoa without great injury to normal cells. The drugs, primaquine and chloroquine, were offered to troops returning by ship from Korea to Seattle. Soldiers on Army transports were ordered to take the drugs; they did, and when they arrived in Seattle there was not a single case of malaria among them. Marines, on Navy transports, were advised by Navy doctors that they could take the drugs or leave them alone (after all, this was an Army-produced preparation); many left them alone, and at the end of the fourteen-day voyage to Seattle, a high percentage of Marines had come down with malaria. This unpremeditated controlled experiment established the great value of the drugs. Dr. Jones has tested many quinones and related and unrelated preparations against cancers; he has combined some of them with mustards and other molecules; and while he has failed so far to produce a specific for any kind of human cancer, several of his own and others' drugs in his hands have had spectacular success in animal tumors and decided palliative effect in some patients.

Among the drugs contributed to experimental cancer chemotherapy are a host of hormones, antituberculosis preparations, vitamins, antibiotics, and many other substances originally designed against other diseases.

From cancer research have come countless preparations dredged out of folk medicines of the distant and forgotten past or conceived by modern biochemists and basic scientists. They include antimicrobials, antivirals, abortives (many drugs conceived for cancer are potent destroyers of embryos during the first two or three months; when they fail in their lethal mission, they produce monsters), immunity-suppressors (for potential organ transplantation and use against such autoimmune conditions as thyroiditis, some forms of arthritis and lupus erythematosis), metal-binding drugs (such as phytic acid which binds calcium in the digestive tract and prevents its entry into the overcalcified system), radiator anti-freeze, sterilizing agents (like nitrofurans for males and antihormones for females), fever suppressants (like steroid metabolites), a compound which controls itches and cures most cases of bursitis (adenosine monophosphate) and dozens of other remedies.

Dr. Jane Wright at New York University has cleared up mycosis fungoides, an ugly and deadly growth of skin and lymphatic tissues, with large doses of methotrexate.

So far, the by-products of cancer research have been more valuable in the treatment of other diseases than of cancer itself.

Someone once suggested that there isn't much point in finding a magic bullet for cancer unless one knows how to aim the gun.

To this end, investigators have sought more effective ways of delivering drugs to the tumorous areas. They have found a few.

More than a decade ago, two research groups almost simultaneously experimented with injections of drugs into arteries serving tumor sites. One group was headed by Dr. Klopp, the other by Drs. Michael B. Shimkin and Howard R. Bierman, then at the Laboratory for Experimental Oncology in San Francisco. Several kinds of drugs, in various experiments, were injected into arteries serving the tumors; and the circulation was dammed up with a tourniquet or clamps for a few minutes while the sick tissues were made to sop up the drug. For internal cancers, long, pliable catheters were snaked through arteries—sometimes as far up as the heart—and the drugs were dumped by this means into the cancerous site. In some cases, the procedure brought dramatically increased damage to the tumors. It had drawbacks, however; it was often painful.

Dr. Klopp, in one report, suggested that if one used a heart-lung pump to set up a second circulation exclusively through the tumorous area, the results of chemotherapy might improve.

Several years ago Dr. Edward T. Krementz of Tulane University, reviewing Dr. Klopp's paper, was attracted to the idea of setting up a secondary, or extracorporeal, circulation. Dr. Krementz, Dr. Oscar Creech, Jr., Dr. Robert F. Ryan, and others at Tulane felt that the best results might be achieved when the cancer was confined to a single area which could be isolated; an arm or a leg would be ideal. They carefully plotted the anatomical distribution of drugs via various blood vessels for several sites.

One of the early patients for this experimental procedure was a young man with melanoma of the left arm. Scores of these ugly black cancers extended from his shoulder to his wrist. The surgical team with clamps blocked off the blood supply at the shoulder, introduced a catheter into the artery and another into the vein at the shoulder and, with the heart-lung pump, started circulating drug-loaded blood through the arm. A little of the drug leaked back into the general circulation; but ten times the normally permissible dose circulated through the melanotic arm. Within the next week or two, the melanomas withered and fell away. The man was alive and well five years later.

The Tulane team charted other routes through other body areas. And so did surgical teams in other medical centers. At George Washington University, Dr. Brian Blades and associates have isolated a cancerous lung and perfused it with 200 times the concentration of drug that could be tolerated by the intravenous route. Two heart-lung pumps have been used successfully—one to perfuse the heart and other organs, while the second maintained general circulation.

Perfusion still is dangerous; under inexperienced surgeons, patient mortality can be extremely high. Where surgeons are properly trained in its use, however, it has yielded great benefit to a majority of patients whose cancers were confined to accessible sites. After several hundred perfusions with nine different drugs for cancers of the brain, throat, arms, legs, shoulder, thigh, lung, liver, abdomen, and pelvis, the Tulane group have reported particularly satisfactory results in sarcomas, melanomas, and cancers of nerve. Melanoma of the limbs has been controlled for up to six years in 44 per cent of the patients. Besides providing short or long remissions from the disease, the technique has shrunk a substantial percentage of inoperable cancers to the point where surgeons could remove them. Combined perfusion and surgery has controlled five of six limb sarcomas for four or more years.

With some success, widely disseminated cancers have been attacked by perfusing the entire body. The Tulane group have withdrawn marrow from the breastbone and hip bones, perfused the bodies with what ordinarily would be lethal doses of drugs, flushed out the drugged blood, replaced it with new blood and, six or eight hours after the transfusion, injected back into the patient his marrow, which then began to produce new blood.

Early in December of 1953, Dr. Jeanne C. Bateman of George Washington University interviewed a woman with inoperable recurrent colon cancer. The woman knew that she soon would die, but she wondered whether by some means she could be made well enough to travel from Washington, D.C., to Chicago for a final Christmas visit with her daughter. Dr. Bateman told her she had a new drug called Thio-TEPA which had cured transplanted rat and mouse cancers; they could take the gamble and try the new drug, if the patient so wished. The drug was tried. The patient had a happy Christmas season with her daughter; and, in 1961, when Dr. Bateman reported the case, the patient was not only alive, well, and without evidence of her disease, but her colostomy—an artificial opening in her side —had been closed and she was using her normal bowel.

Dr. Bateman, in other cases, tried injecting drugs, particularly Thio-TEPA, directly into tumors. The procedure has worked well in some cases; one inoperable breast-cancer patient was alive and without evidence of disease, and without surgery, five years following the injections. This technique has resulted in prolonged survival of a number of patients with cancer of the ovary who could not be helped by surgery or X rays. Dr. Bateman's five-year survival rate for ovarian cancer is 31.7 per cent in early cancers and 5 per cent for late ones. She feels that the technique may offer some hope for cancer of the pancreas, which usually is beyond help by other means.

Occasionally, leukemia invades the central nervous system, including the brain. Because of the "blood–brain barrier," drugs do not pass from the general circulation into the affected areas, and consequently there has been little relief of the nervous symptoms, which are among the most heart-rending of the many pathetic features of this disease. Dr. Joseph Burchenal of Memorial Cancer Center wondered whether methotrexate injected intrathecally—that is, through the barriers protecting nerve and brain— might help these patients. It did. Scientists at Ohio State University have applied the intrathecal technique to a series of children whose brain tumors had recurred or had been only partially removed; in four out of five, the severe headache, vomiting, and other symptoms were controlled completely.

The slow dripping, or infusion, of hormones and other preparations have increased their efficacy. The injection of drugs in heated blood has shown some promise in initial tests at Duke University; slowly dissolving pills and implanted pellets have extended the effectiveness of many preparations. Several other methods of giving drugs have improved the remission rate and degree of palliation in cancer patients, although they have not budged the negligible cure rate.

A Lahey Clinic group under Dr. Elton Watkins, Jr., and Dr. Robert D. Sullivan has found highly satisfactory a portable pump which infuses drugs into ambulatory patients twenty-four hours a day for weeks at a time. Small, weighing only eight ounces, the pump can be carried in a jacket pocket. Inside the pump is a replaceable plastic bag containing a five-day supply (25 cc) of 5-FU or another drug. When the supply runs low, the patient replaces it with a full bag. The tiny pump, which is wound every eight hours like a watch, is attached to a catheter. The catheter is embedded in an artery serving the tumorous area to be infused. Day and night, the drug drips through the catheter into the artery, while the patient plays, works and sleeps.

The technique so far has been most effective against primary or metastatic tumors in the liver. These tumors ordinarily indicate that the patient has only weeks or a few months at most left to him. Under this infusion therapy, some patients with liver tumors so far are living, and quite well, for as long as eighteen months. They are not cured, but their massively enlarged livers have shrunk and returned to normal function, pain has been relieved, and appetite and weight have improved. Because the liver detoxifies the drug after it has pervaded the cancers, liver infusion has had virtually no side effects. The catheter—usually inserted into the hepatic artery when the primary tumor is removed at surgery—often is left in place; infusion then can be started or stopped at will.

The Lahey group began its experiments in 1962. In 1964 it was extending them to cancers of the head and neck and a few other sites.

A decade or so ago, some in Washington were saying the way to produce the magic bullet for cancer was to appropriate one billion dollars for a crash program. That's the way the bomb was built. That's the way the United States would beat the Soviet Union in missile and space exploration.

Scientists winced. Everyone close to health research shuddered. It was one thing to build a bomb; the human mind already had established the proposition that $E = mc^2$, and the engineering and industrial materials and manpower could be mobilized by signing a document. It was quite another matter to establish an equation for cancer, when the disease itself, its cause, course, and countless other factors were all X's—unknowns. Additional laboratory space would help; animals and equipment were needed; but only the properly prepared and inquiring human mind could identify the thing called cancer and solve the problem it posed.

In 1953 Congress appropriated $1 million earmarked for chemotherapy. Some of the competent and conscientious civil servants responsible for the prudent disbursing of research funds predicted much of the money would be wasted. Obediently, however, they began searching for qualified scientists who could and would (and, in fact, did) use the windfall productively. The next year Congress raised its appropriation to $3 million, and since then the lawmakers have increased the funds prodigiously until in 1962 the chemotherapy appropriation amounted to $34 million, more than one-quarter of the entire budget of the National Cancer Institute.

There is a large difference between a billion-dollar and a $34 million program; some cynics on both sides said the difference was that of a crash and a thud.

For better or worse, however, the chemotherapy appropriation profoundly has altered the character of cancer research. Some scientists who had poked along on the country lanes of investigation, examining a little-known enzyme system of an obscure organism, were put on the now-congested freeway of chemotherapy; they began producing antimetabolites or applying analogues to the enzyme systems of a standard stock of cancer. Others who had been tracing tediously the matted strands of a phase of metabolism went to work on an assembly line which manufactured new-model molecules. There was nothing compulsory about these shifts in investigative interest; on the contrary, any scientist was completely free to pursue whatever line of study he wished—with the agreement of his academic superiors, of course. It was just a matter of funds being available in chemotherapy contracts, and not in less glamorous or less practical fields.

Big Research had been built. But even in Big Research, many scientists found it difficult or impossible to obtain support for studies closest to their hearts. With the growth of grants, it had become more and more difficult for the granting agency and the distinguished scientists who counseled it to become acquainted with all who applied for support. Well-known scientists and familiar ideas readily gained support; new scientists with new and offbeat ideas often had trouble winning a hearing.

What happened during a decade of Congressional indulgence? An impressive 200,000 chemicals were tested for anticancer activity, almost 200 of them in humans. Many of the new drugs cured transplanted cancers not only in mice but in rats and hamsters as well. All of them were toxic, and most of them were too dangerous for testing on humans.

Only time would tell whether any of the drugs produced under the chemotherapy program would cure any kind of human cancer.

There was the possibility in 1964 that a very few patients were being cured by one of the original modern anticancer drugs. The textbook definition of a cancer cure requires that the patient be well and without evidence of the disease five years after treatment. Some of the patients with a rare form of cancer, choriocarcinoma, had remained well and were without symptoms for more than seven years after Drs. Roy Hertz and Min Chiu Li of the National Cancer Institute in 1956 began treating them with Methotrexate. Choriocarcinoma is cancer which arises from a bit of the placenta left behind in the womb following childbirth; it responds to female hormones much as normal tissue does, and, like placenta, it produces hormones. The disease sometimes disappears spontaneously, but rarely after it has become metastatic. In all the Hertz series, choriocarcinoma had spread beyond the uterus, in fifty-one of the cases to the lungs, in others to the brain and other sites. Of sixty-three women who had completed a full course of treatment, thirty were alive and without evidence of cancer. Some patients who had relapsed and become resistant to Methotrexate again went into remission under treatment with vinblastine, actinomycin D or DON.

Beyond these sparse but spectacular triumphs, there was little evidence or prospect of a "magic bullet" for human cancer in 1964.

Even the cure of transplanted mouse or rat cancer, which had become routine with many preparations, left much to be desired. Of the two million mice now used annually in cancer research, relatively few bore spontaneous cancers; and with rare exceptions, the naturally occurring animal cancers were as incurable as human cancers. It became painfully apparent that there is an enormous difference in curing a transplanted mouse cancer by injecting poisons within a day or two of the transplant and curing mice of their spontaneous cancers. There is a much greater difference between curing transplanted mouse cancers and curing human cancers.

A notable but not widely noted exception to the incurability of spontaneous animal cancers was reported by Dr. W. Steele Livingston, a North Hollywood veterinarian, who wrote in the *Journal of the National Cancer Institute* that he had cured spontaneous cancers in dogs and cats brought to him by clients. He treated the animals with a curious mishmash which he called a "necrofiltrate"—an extract of a soupy, smelly mess of rotting placenta or flesh, infested with bacteria, fungi, and yeast, which he incubated under 25 pounds pressure and at 40–50° C, for three months. He injected into the veins or bellies of the animals a port-wine-colored fluid strained from the decaying material through unbleached muslin and filter paper. All three cats so treated were, when he made his report, (1) and (2) alive and well eighteen months and twenty-nine months, respectively, after treatment and (3) run over and, at autopsy, showing no signs of tumor. Of twenty dogs, eight were alive and tumor-free or dead and found to be without cancer from eighteen to sixty-five months following treatment; the rest died of or with their cancers. The cancers were of the breast, rectum, skin, blood vessels, and connective and lymphatic tissues. The work was reviewed by two critical authorities, Drs. Ian Macdonald and

Michael B. Shimkin and found to be worth pursuing. The "necrofiltrates" never cured a human; in clinical trials they were combined with X rays and so far have proved ineffective.

By 1962 there had set in a deepening disillusionment with the system by which candidate drugs were tested. The preliminary trial as prescribed, was against three kinds of transplanted cancer in mice—leukemia 1,210, mammary carcinoma 755, and sarcoma 180. Preparations passing this test were then tried against other transplanted animal cancers. Some critics pointed out that, under this system, many very useful drugs, like the British Myleran (busulfan), never would have gotten over the first hurdle. They recalled that the value of still other preparations was demonstrated not on cancerous animals but on normal animal and human systems.

A few of the most productive and experienced leaders in the field of cancer research already had issued cautions against the capricious or empirical use of anticancer drugs by physicians unfamiliar with dosage schedules, side effects, and other essential and delicate details. Dr. George E. Moore, Director of Roswell Park, and Tatsuhei Kondo reported that, on the basis of animal and human studies, chemotherapeutic agents, ill-advisedly used, could reduce the patient's resistance to cancer. As early as 1958, they said that whereas an injection of 100,000 cancer cells normally is required to give some animals cancer, when cortisone also is given only 10 cells are needed. They told of the accelerated tumor growth in 9 of 75 patients treated with TSPA and in 4 of 50 given actinomycin D. They reported that in animals they had increased the number of lung metastases from intravenously-injected cancer cells by treating the animals, following the injections, with small amounts of nitrogen mustard or actinomycin D (large doses decreased metasteses) and that preinoculation treatment with actinomycin D, nitrogen mustard or TEM strikingly increased the growth of transplanted tumors. "Although experimental results like these cannot be directly applied to clinical work," they reported, "they still serve as a warning that cancer chemotherapy that is inadequate because the dosage is insufficient or the drug is ineffective may sometimes be even less satisfactory than no chemotherapy at all." They speculated that the anti-cancer drugs may have caused tumors to release cells into the blood stream, knocked out local defenses of the tissues, or reduced systemic resistance to disease.

That some of the Moore-Kondo animal observations do apply to humans was indicated in a report of a two-year study of 2,000 lung cancer patients at fifteen Veterans Administration Hospitals. The death rate at eighteen months for cortisone-treated patients was almost 50 per cent greater than for placebo-treated patients. Patients given toxic nitrogen mustard fared very little better than those given nontoxic placebos. A group at Catholic University of Chile tested a combination of ACTH, dexamethasone and Nitromin on nineteen patients. Only six improved for from three to five weeks; then they, like the others, declined rapidly and died. Autopsy showed that almost every organ was riddled with metastases, presumably caused by adrenal hormones.

The published fact sheets on thousands of chemicals tested for anti-cancer activity leave no doubt about the monumental stature of the chemotherapy program. From the viewpoint of sheer statistical effort, no program in the history of science and medicine can approach the current drive for a drug which, hopefully, will help so many otherwise helpless humans. The many millions of dollars invested, when weighed against the economics of doctor and hospital charges, time lost from work, and other items on the nation's $12 billion annual bill for cancer damage, represent a modest sum. With one in four Americans now alive scheduled to come down with cancer at one time or another, the chemotherapy program costs about 75 cents per future victim per year. Those who know cancer best—those who have the disease or who have a relative or friend ill with it, and the scientists and physicians who are seeking a means of controlling it—understand the difficulties of equating the cancer deaths with digits in a Congressional appropriation. It is a pity that cancer control cannot be bought.

A possible waste of money is among the minor dangers of Big Research; it is axiomatic that waste necessarily increases with the size of an operation. The real risk intrinsic to a system of Organized Science and Organization Scientists lies in the probability that individuals, their ideas, and their creative imaginations may be trampled under as the scientific herd stampedes this way and that behind its leaders. Mass thinking or group brainstorming has yet to solve a serious scientific problem.

Perhaps even now one can detect a trend away from the healthy confusion of interests which has characterized unsupported, and consequently unorganized and unguided, scientific investigation of the past. It is completely possible, of course, that out of routine testing will come a cure for human cancer; it may come from the wartime blister or nerve gases, jet propulsion fuels, assorted dyes (like styryl quinolines), caustics, or any of the hundreds of analogues made by man as a counterfeit or facsimile of the compounds which comprise life. The large investment, not of money, but of scarce scientific manpower, on molecule manufacturing is symbolic of a great change.

The trend toward eliminating any subjective or personalized evaluations of agents is achieving its ultimate goal with computers taking over the function of the human mind; the damage done to tumors, as compared to the damage done to the host, now is assessed by calculating the days of survival of experimental and control animals as against the weight loss (representing toxicity) in both groups. The slide-rule system has more and more supplanted the appraising eye and judgment.

In the freshet of facts and figures, a few fundamentals of biology may have been lost sight of.

About 300 investigators throughout the world who have become attracted to the importance of periodicities within nature have been finding that plant, animal, and human metabolism rises and falls with the fidelity of tides, that cells observe seasons of synthesis and decay, and that systems follow a logical sequence in their respective activities.

Dr. Franz Halberg of the University of Minnesota, a leading scholar in the field of periodicity, has shown that in mice, alcohol or a drug taken at the height of diurnal metabolic activity will have little ill effect, whereas the same drug in the same dose will cause death a half-cycle—twelve hours—later. Dr. Dougherty and Dr. Leo Samuels of the University of Utah have shown, in independent studies, that the adrenals observe diurnal variations in producing stress hormones; when people rise in the morning their adrenals increase production of cortisone-type hormones which proceed to destroy an overnight accumulation of white blood cells (lymphocytes). Besides the female menstrual cycle, the human hormonal and other systems follow daily, lunar, seasonal, and annual changes. Some are governed by what Dr. Halberg calls circadien (almost, but not quite, daily) rhythms.

Big-time research, in its centrally directed, pressurized, assembly-line quest for the magic bullet for cancer seems to pay little attention to these simple biological findings. In doing so, it may be passing up methods of improving the existing means of controlling cancer. Presumably,

1. Drugs given to patients at the peak of their daily metabolic cycle—or, in the case of hormones, as indicated within the daily or monthly periods—would be metabolized rapidly; drugs given during the declining phase would have longer-lasting effect.

2. Radiation administered at the daily or monthly low point of normal cell division might spare the normal resting cells. (Dr. Halberg's studies showed the cancer cell observes no period.)

3. Surgery at periods other than the traditional early morning hours, when most people are least able to withstand stress, might be better tolerated by sick patients.

In the light of the widespread disregard for the biological status of the host at various times, it is no wonder that one clinician so often fails to confirm another's results, and it is a miracle that scientists who work with animals ever achieve comparable data. Most clinical and laboratory observations are valid for periods covering the investigators' working hours; what takes place during the other sixteen or so hours and weekends is speculative.

By providence and by caprice, the student of cancer has been given as clues a thousand significant facts and a thousand tantalizing and misleading artifacts.

Many of the most provocative stem from the field of chemotherapy.

Why is it, for instance, that so many substances used to treat cancer with varying degrees of (incomplete) success also cause cancer? Can it be that these agents merely grease the skids for a smoother descent to death, that they permit a strategic withdrawal to and over the brink of disaster? Do they, for a while at least, merely sicken the cancer more than they sicken the host? And why do anticancer agents, like cancer itself, weaken the host's immunity, or disease resistance?

If there be substance to these speculations, it may follow that the current search for a cancer cure is 180 degrees off course—that the toxic analogues, the antimetabolites, the antimitotics, and all the rest are, at best, a means of perhaps delaying but also of insuring eventual death from disease.

And if, by some chance, this should prove true, it might be expedient to turn attention to the other direction—toward finding and using natural, nontoxic chemicals in the right combination which would reform the wayward cell or fortify the host by stimulating his defenses against the disease?

Besides producing thousands of their analogues, biochemists have also produced in pure and stable form scores of the natural, vital chemicals themselves. They include hormones, vitamins, many enzymes, nucleic acids and their nucleotides, proteins and their amino acids, energy-transferring and energy-transforming compounds. They have traced some of the major pathways by which cells generate and transfer energy, by which they mature, work, age, and die. With chemicals now available, it may be possible to reconstruct almost an entire normal metabolic system.

In the living system, all chemicals are interdependent on others—on precursors, enzymes and coenzymes, hormones, electrolyte balancers, electron donors and acceptors, and many others—sometimes including their own products. It is possible now to administer to animals the equivalent of an entire metabolic sequence—a combination of natural chemicals that would compensate for any defect in the cycle. In physiologic doses, an entire combination of these might not prove as toxic as some of the single artificial blocks now used to treat cancers. And they might repair the presently unknown basic metabolic fault, or faults, known as cancer. This shotgun approach has not been tested in animals or patients, but if the present course of trying to correct one metabolic defect by creating more metabolic defects fails, it might be worth considering.

CHAPTER 27

COMBINATION THERAPY

In the 1930s, breast-cancer patients at the University of Edinburgh Medical School were treated by radical mastectomy. In this, as we have seen, not only the cancerous breast is removed, but also a part of the chest wall and extensive tissues in the armpit and other areas to which the cancer cells might have spread.

This operation, the conventional one when the cancer is removable, is a good treatment: 75 per cent or more of the women with presumably early breast cancers are alive five years after the operation (in the uncured, the cancer was not as early and as curable as it first appeared). With good surgeons, the operation will give at least five years to from 20 to 40 per cent of women whose cancers have spread a little beyond the breast, but not very far. All in all, of patients with early and moderately late cancers under skilled management more than 30 per cent will survive five years. The very advanced, obviously hopeless, are not included in these percentages.

Dr. Robert McWhirter, then a young Edinburgh surgeon, felt that radical mastectomy was not necessarily the best answer to breast cancer, not even when it was combined with X rays for patients whose cancers had spread to the armpit. In 1941, he began an experiment: instead of the massive operation which took about two or three hours of a good surgeon's time, he performed a one-hour simple removal of the breast, then, several days later, he irradiated the tissues to which the cancer might have spread. As time went on, Dr. McWhirter continued checking not only on his large series of patients but also on his statistics; both looked good.

Along the way, Dr. McWhirter concluded that this treatment was not for all patients. Radiation was proving risky following radical mastectomy; the tissue covering the operated chest wall was too thin to stand up under X-ray bombardment. Very fat women did not do well under this therapy, nor did those with circulatory disorders.

Nevertheless, more than 90 per cent of the operable patients could and did take the procedure. They were given the one-hour operation and then, starting on the tenth day after surgery, they were irradiated from four fields five days a week for three weeks for an average tumor dose of 3,750 r. The side effects were minor—a transient sunburn in about 50 per cent, occasional cough and difficulty in swallowing for a while (but negligible lasting damage to the esophagus, trachea, lung, or pleura) and some slight decalcification of ribs. On the credit side, the treatment showed several advantages over radical surgery: waterlogging of the arm was rare, dissemination of cancer cells in the operative wound was kept to a minimum, and convalescence and return to normal living were rapid.

When sufficient time had passed, Dr. McWhirter discovered that, under this procedure, the five-year survival rate of his patients was almost one-third higher than it had been in his own and others' patients who had undergone radical mastectomy. The ten- and fifteen-year survival figures became even more impressive.

Many breast-cancer specialists came to visit with Dr. McWhirter and to study his technique for a day or possibly two. Some returned home to try it, with certain modifications, on their own patients. Some of them felt it would be better to administer the X rays before the operation rather than after it; some felt the radiation should be given after a radical, rather than simple, mastectomy; others "improved" upon the operative procedures or the radiation dosage and schedule. They then reported that the McWhirter technique (with their "minor modifications") did not work.

Dr. L. Henry Garland, a Stanford University radiologist and a critic of many clinical practices, found the McWhirter technique satisfactory and the survival rate superior for patients with evidence of cancer spread to the armpit. He is of the opinion, however, that for patients with cancers still confined to the breast, radical mastectomy is the best treatment, and for those with more broadly disseminated cancer he recommends radiation alone.

Neither Dr. McWhirter nor Dr. Garland nor any of several other experimentalists in this area has had revolutionary impact on the conventional treatment of breast cancer in the United States. The cure rates are the same as they were in 1930.

In clinical experiments and in laboratory tests several combinations of treatments have been tried in efforts to improve the lot of the cancer patient. Some of them seem to have yielded percentage-point gains against human cancer; some of them have not helped at all; and a few turned out to be definitely detrimental to the interests of the patient and objectives of the physician.

The potential clinical and laboratory combinations already are many, and they are increasing at a rapid rate. Each new agent presents the possibility of a new multiple of combinations. The number of possible combinations now is astronomical.

Among the agents are several types of surgery, various hormones (or their elimination), other drugs, radiations, pressure, heat, cold and such physiological factors as diet and exercise. There may not be enough tumor-bearing plants, animals, and humans in the entire world to test all the combinations now possible, even though each tumor were given a tailor-made treatment.

The number of practical combinations is low, however, and the number of combinations actually under test are probably fewer than fifty. Seldom are more than two or three agents used simultaneously in any treatment.

Of all the elements involved in combination therapy, the time factor may be the most important. With proper timing, the beneficial effects of one agent may be multiplied by another; with incorrect timing, one agent may neutralize the effects of another—or, worse, enhance the toxic and death-dealing properties of the other.

Scattered observations on animals and humans, for instance, indicate that the good effects of radiation reach their peak a considerable time after exposure; to introduce a second agent too early after radiation may bring out the Mr. Hyde in X rays, and to introduce it too long after the optimal point may mean the loss of the additive or multiplying beneficial effect of the rays. The same seems to apply to radiation when it is used as the second agent; X rays too early after surgery, for example, may further deplete a patient who has not recovered from the stress of an operation, and radiation given too late following surgery may miss the opportunity to sweep up the cancer "crumbs" before they become too numerous, too well established, and too resistant for radiation to destroy them.

So little is known about the basic biological effects of radiation and other agents that time elements must be worked out the hard, hazardous, and tedious way—by trial and error. This, gradually, is being done. The physician who treats a patient with a combination of agents without first acquainting himself with the published experiences of others is gambling unnecessarily with the health and life of his patient. Whereas Dr. Mc-Whirter improved the lot of his breast-cancer patients with a treatment established by large, controlled and carefully studied trials, others have failed miserably with "modifications" of the technique. Dr. Thomas L. Dao of Roswell Park reviewed the fate of 364 patients given either simple or radical mastectomy and various schedules of postoperative radiation and found that not only was there no difference in their survival and that of unirradiated patients, but irradiation seemed to increase greatly metastases to the lungs and skin.

One of the professional hazards of experimental medicine is the high probability of being unconfirmed and often denounced by other investigators who modify the technique "slightly" and describe the method as unsatisfactory. (If things go well, it is usually the "modification" that works—not the original technique.) Happily, however, the facts are established eventually, although too often only after the original discoverer has gone to his ultimate reward.

Second, or third, agents are introduced into cancer treatment, fundamentally, for three reasons: (1) to enhance the therapeutic effect of the first, (2) to counteract the toxic effect of the first, or (3) to set up a second, independent, assault on the cancer.

Quite often there is a conflict of purpose: the secondary agent, which adds to or multiplies the tumor-destructive potential of the first, adds to or multiplies the toxicity as well, or weakens the tumor-destroying powers of the first treatment.

Radiation is sometimes employed after surgery has failed, and vice versa. This, however, is not true combination therapy; in many cases, the failure of the first treatment makes a cure more difficult for the second.

Enough success has been achieved in combination therapy to warrant the collaboration of an entire tumor board to consider each case; the team basically should be comprised of a pathologist, a surgeon, a radiotherapist, and an internist, all of them preferably with experience in a large number and variety of cancer cases. The participation of several other specialists, of course, is all to the good. Unfortunately, this type of guidance is available usually only at the larger medical centers.

Surgery and radiation constitute the commonest combination used against cancer. In some centers, various combinations of these have been used against different cancers with highly satisfactory results. Despite this, medicine as a whole is slow to adopt the techniques. The main reason for this is that there is no authoritative referee to rule on the merits of treatment, although the journals do their ineffective best.

Typical of the several lists of cancers which are indicated for a combination of radiation and surgery is one proposed by Dr. James E. Turner of Northwestern University:

Seventy-five to 100 per cent five-year survival: nonmetastatic semi-noma of the testis treated by castration and radiation of nearby nodes; and adenocarcinoma of the uterine lining by packing the uterus with radium tubes, and 6–12 weeks later, total removal of the uterus.

Fifty to 75 per cent five-year survival: eye cancer (retinoblastoma) and recurrent but nonmetastatic squamous-cell cancer of the anterior tongue, mouth, palate, penis, and lip and noninfiltrating transition cell cancer of the bladder.

Thirty-three to 50 per cent five-year survival: locally metastatic squamous cancer of the alveolar and inner-cheek mucous membrane, floor of the mouth and cancer of the pulpy, glandular part of the breast.

These and many other cancers are treated with various combinations of drugs, radiation and surgery—some of them with results superior to the above.

In 1955, four physicians at the University of Maryland began seeking a means of improving the low cure rate for the commonest and most rapidly increasing kind of lethal cancer—cancer of the lung. Conventional treatment, the surgical removal of a lung lobe or the entire lung, was curing only about 5 per cent of these patients, and radiation was yielding a five-year survival rate of 4 per cent or less, although it temporarily shrank up many of the tumors. With little to lose and much to gain, the Maryland team decided they would divide their patients into two groups: one they would treat with supervoltage radiation from a cobalt-60 "bomb" for five weeks; the second group would receive not only the vigorous cobalt-60 irradiation but also, six to eight weeks after it, removal of the lung and lymphatic tissue which cancer might have seeded. There was a risk in withholding surgery for so long; in that time, viable cancer cells might migrate to distant body sites, but the investigators were of the opinion that both the local and systemic effects were at their peak six or eight weeks after radiation and the gamble was worthwhile.

As time passed, they began to feel better about their experiment. When they operated on the radiated patients, they found the large tumor masses had shrunk up and the lymph-node metastases, which heretofore had made surgery impossible or futile, had been sterilized. Within six weeks, the bleeding tendencies induced by X rays had passed. There was no evidence of fibrosis in the normal lung, which had been shielded during radiation, or other serious side effects.

At forty-four months after the start of the experiment, fifteen of the eighteen patients given the combination treatment were alive, thirteen of them without recurrence of their cancers for periods ranging from ten to forty-four months. The results were definitely superior to those achieved in other "control" patients given surgery alone, radiation alone or surgery prior to radiation. In 1964, they still found their experimental treatment superior to any other.

The investigators—three radiologists, Drs. Fernando G. Bloedorn, Carlo A. Cuccia and Raul Mercado, Jr., and Chest Surgeon Dr. R. Adams Cowley—estimated conservatively that the procedure might double the 4 or 5 per cent cure rate. At six years, the survival rates of the patients were between two and four times that of patients given only surgery; and, as perhaps the most measurable of the results, twenty-five of twenty-seven who at first were inoperable became operable following the cobalt-60 therapy.

Radioactive gold (which emits short-range rays and has a half-life of only sixty-five hours) has been used by a few investigators as a sterilizing agent in connection with surgery.

Dr. R. H. Flocks and his associates at the State University of Iowa began employing radioactive gold about a decade ago in hope of overtaking and destroying cells shed by prostatic cancers into lymphatic channels. In Dr. Flocks' practice, this common kind of cancer in almost all cases had spread beyond the prostatic capsule by the time the patients came in for treatment. In one-half the patients, the cancers had settled in bones and distant tissues, and the best that could be offered them was palliative treatment. In the other half, however, the cancers still seemed to be within the lymphatic channels draining the prostate area, and it was in these cases the investigators felt prophylaxis might help. They injected colloidal radioactive gold into the prostate and lymphatics with a shielded syringe, applied an enzyme, hyaluronidase, which enabled the gold to spread rapidly through tissues, and then a few weeks later removed the prostate and the cancer-seeded tissues. The technique appears to have reduced the rate of cancer recurrence substantially in 3,000 patients.

Drs. Willard M. Allen, A. Norman Arneson, and Alfred I. Sherman of Washington University have introduced a similar technique in the treatment of cervical cancer. They inject colloidal radioactive gold into loose tissues around the uterus, implant radium into the cervix and vagina and, about a month later, remove the uterus and lymph nodes. While the procedure yields a very high cure rate for early cancer (as does surgery alone or radiation alone), its greatest value is in moderately advanced cases in which it appears to have reduced recurrences to one-fifth those following surgery and less than one-half after radiation alone. It is ineffective against widely disseminated cancer.

Radioactive iodine has been incorporated into rabbit antibodies against human fibrinogen and injected into cancer patients. In more than fifty patients so treated at the University of Rochester, the radioactivity localized in cancers of the cervix, rectum, esophagus and bronchus and in melanoma. Scientists at the University of Oregon have shown that the female hormone, stilbesterol, transports radioactive phosphorous to mouse breast cancers, and a fibrin-destroying enzyme deposits radioactive iodine in several rodent tumors.

For much more than a half-century, medical literature has recognized the seeding of surgical wounds with cells from cancers removed during operation. In the late nineteenth century, a few surgeons applied carbolic acid to the cancerous site when they finished removing a cancer. Generally, however, the problem escaped serious corrective attention until 1956, when Dr. Warren Cole of the University of Illinois was persuaded by a series of animal experiments that something could be done about it. He reported in 1959 that nitrogen mustard following surgery helped some breast-cancer patients. The director of Roswell Park, Dr. George E. Moore, confirmed the findings. Between these two, and many later recruits, a start has been made in controlling, for a while at least, this phase of iatrogenic (doctor-caused or treatment-caused) recurrence of cancer.

Various studies have shown that cancer recurs in the surgical wound in 10 per cent or more of breast-cancer patients, in from 17 to 43.6 per cent of patients with cancers of the head and neck and in a wide range of other types of cancer. It is a problem which costs many lives. Sometimes the cancer is implanted during careless handling by the surgeon; in cutting through the tumor, or the tissues harboring metastases, or the blood vessels serving the area, he may, despite numerous precautions, inadvertently carry the cells to their new nesting place by way of contaminated surgical gloves or instruments. Errant cancer cells need less than one hour to attach and establish themselves in tissue.

Even the simplest procedure of inserting a needle to remove a biopsy specimen sometimes is believed hazardous. Not uncommonly, new cancer colonies are found in the tract of the needle.

An intensive search for chemicals lethal to the loose cancer cells has turned up several effective compounds, including kitchen cleaners like Clorox, a solution of common table salt, the World War I wound disinfectant called Dakin's solution, a related commercial hypochlorous acid called Chlorpactin, the familiar embalming fluid known chemically as formaldehyde, and the anticancer drug, nitrogen mustard. Dr. Cole found, in rat experiments, that any of these depressed the local recurrence of cancer about 90 per cent. Dakin's solution was least toxic; nitrogen mustard was most effective, but it also proved more toxic than the others. Experiments with rats indicated that by bathing surgical wounds in the right solution, it may be possible to reduce the cancer recurrence rate in humans. The problem is to find the right solution.

Another problem in surgery is posed by cancer cells which become dislodged from the tumor, enter the bloodstream and migrate to distant sites. The available evidence shows that this occurs without the intervention of surgery, although in many cases an operation produces a shower of these cells. The evidence also is that something in the system very often destroys these cells before they can anchor in a distant capillary and establish new cancer colonies. Numerous case histories indicate that patients with cancer cells floating in their bloodstream following removal of the primary tumor were established as completely cured of cancer several years later.

The first substantial success of what Dr. Cole called "adjuvant chemotherapy"—that is, the use of drugs along with surgery—was reported late in 1961 by Dr. Moore, who chaired a study of 3,000 patients in thirty-nine institutions, universities, and hospitals. After three years of double-blind experiments—neither the doctor nor the patient knowing in each case whether the experimental drug was given or withheld—Thio-TEPA, had registered startling short–term success against breast cancer: only 5 per cent of the premenopausal patients given Thio-TEPA at their operation and for two days after it had suffered a recurrence as compared with a 54 per cent recurrence in the control patients over twenty-six months. During the same period, postmenopausal patients given Thio-TEPA registered a less spectacular, but still highly impressive, response: only 11 per cent recurrence as against 35 per cent among control patients. The results were preliminary (they covered only twenty-six months).

That adjuvant chemotherapy could be tricky—and risky—had been made clear in animal experiments. Dr. Gerald O. McDonald of the Cole group found that nitrogen mustard, while it did not increase the number of tumors in operated rats, greatly accelerated the development of these cancer colonies. Long ago the Mayo brothers recognized the value of cauterizing biopsy wounds with phenol, and others had recommended swabbing with a formaldehyde-soaked sponge. (Animal experiments indicate, however, that treatment of an area prior to disturbing cancer cells accelerates cancer growth.)

Dr. Moore's report on nationwide adjuvant chemotherapy also indicated that drugs were helpful at surgery for cancer of the ovary. On the other hand, at least at this stage of investigation, adjuvant chemotherapy offered nothing of promise to patients with cancer of the lung or colon.

Other studies showed that some commonly used cancer drugs increased the spread of cancer, sped its growth, and shortened survival. For this reason, new combinations tested outside large-scale, carefully controlled experiments are done at the patient's peril.

A group of physicians in experimental medicine at the Veterans Administration Hospital in Dallas, Texas, in 1961, injected hydrogen peroxide into cancer patients before irradiating their tumors; this, they felt, increased the amount of free oxygen in the cancer cells and, consequently, the lethal effect of the rays. At this writing, it is too early to tell how much impact this technique will have on cancer treatment; in the first fourteen cases, however, cancers often shriveled up and disappeared, at least for the time being. The procedure is being tested in a dozen other research centers. In 1964, the Dallas group was still happy with the treatment.

The dramatic, if preliminary, results in enhancing radiation effects with hydrogen peroxide are highly gratifying for several reasons. In the first place, this agent (the beauty secret of many blondes) is available and cheap—enough for an entire course of treatment can be bought for a nickel at the corner drugstore. Its effects, under radiation, are largely or entirely local; if one-half a tumor in a peroxide-treated patient is irradiated, only that half heals; the unirradiated half continues to thrive. No systemic toxic effects were noted among the first series treated, and the indications were that the drug would enable radiologists to lower their effective therapeutic doses of X rays and thereby reduce the dangerous effects of large doses. Preliminary trials showed that resistance to the treatment was slow in building up, signifying that patients might respond to the combination a second or third time following recurrence.

All these observations, however, await confirmation by more extensive testing. As a by-product of these studies, autopsy showed that the hydrogen peroxide erased cholesterol patches in atherosclerotic, or hardening, arteries.

Investigators at Children's Hospital, Boston, have employed a combination of the antibiotic, actinomycin D, radiation and surgery with a high degree of success against widely metastatic Wilms's tumor, a kidney cancer of children. The combination was suggested when an irradiated youngster was given the drug and showed a dramatic tumor regression. In the first thirteen children with widespread Wilms's tumors treated with surgery, X rays, and actinomycin D, the scientists said, eleven were alive and without evidence of cancer up to six years following completion of treatment.

Retinoblastoma, the inherited eye cancer, at one time was almost always fatal. Now, thanks to an increasing number of agents used to treat it, deaths from this malady have dwindled to fewer than 10 per cent of those afflicted. Early in the twentieth century, surgeons tried to cure retinoblastoma by removing the affected eye as soon as the disease was discovered in a child; this procedure failed in more than 90 per cent of the cases, because almost invariably the disease soon appeared in the second eye and killed the child. Surgeons then tried another procedure: they removed the affected eye and irradiated the second eye. This rescued almost one-half the children but left all the survivors completely blind.

In 1936, Dr. A. B. Reese of Cornell University Medical School removed the cancerous eye and shielded the lens while irradiating the second eye. The survival rate rose to 65 per cent, and of the survivors, 24 per cent retained useful vision and 13 per cent limited vision. Cataracts and eye hemorrhages were frequent, however. In 1953 Dr. Reese and his associates made another significant step in the control of retinoblastoma: they removed one eye, gave a small and nonblinding dose of X rays to the other eye, and administered an anticancer drug, TEM, to the patient. For lengthy periods, this treatment with three agents kept the cancer under control in 89 per cent of the patients.

A few years later Dr. Edward T. Krementz, who helped develop the technique of perfusing drugs through isolated areas of the body with a heart–lung machine, headed a Tulane team which applied perfusion to retinoblastoma. Their first patient was a boy three-and-a-half years old who came from a family with severe eye troubles but no history of eye cancer; his father and his father's father and three sisters were partially or totally blind, but the boy's three brothers and two sisters were in good health. The boy himself had a large tumor in the left eye and a small tumor in the right eye. The left eye was removed, and in August, 1958, the Tulane scientists introduced a threadlike catheter into the right carotid artery in the boy's throat, and through it poured TEM into the artery once a day for twelve days. The drugged blood was drained out through the jugular vein. A light dose of X rays was given. The small tumor disappeared, and vision returned.

In 1961, when the Tulane group reported, the first patient was alive, well, and enjoying good vision in his one eye; four others had gone more than one year without recurrence; one had just completed treatment, which seemed to be successful; and, in a sixth, cancer had returned to the remaining eye after nine months and the eye had to be removed. As late as 1964, the procedure had become the treatment of choice at Tulane. The results suggested the possibility of trying perfusion and X rays only, without removing even one eye. No doubt this will be attempted in an effort to save the sight in both eyes.

Several other combinations are now being tried in humans. Their ultimate efficacy, at this writing, is very much open to speculation.

From several centers, a combination of the drug, 5-FU, and X rays are showing promise against retinblastoma; but the many problems of dosage, timing and other all-important factors still are being worked out. Stanford scientists have reported that the combination seems to improve the lot of patients with various cancers of the lung, head, neck, esophagus, and a few other sites, but their treatment of choice in retinoblastoma is supervoltage radiation, which saves vision as well as lives.

Many drugs are under test for such help as they may be to patients operated upon or irradiated for cancer.

At this stage, the most promising techniques are being worked out in laboratory animals and cancer cells growing in laboratory dishes. The former are registering combinations more effective than anything yet tried on patients; the latter are establishing the biochemical principles which govern the action of X rays and drugs.

Some of the drugs add to the effects of radiation. Nitrogen mustard and TEM do this. They are radiomimetic—radiation imitating—in that they have the selfsame effects on the cell and the host that X rays do: they inhibit growth, cause cancer, produce chromosome inequalities when cells divide, block cell division, mutate cells, cause delayed cell death, induce an inflammatory reaction and skin blisters, kill viruses, smash nucleic acid molecules into small units, break up white blood cells, cause hair to gray, knock out immunity, destroy complement and other proteins, including enzymes, by inactivating sulfhydryl (sulfur-hydrogen) bonds, make monsters of embryos, concentrate red blood cells, induce nausea and vomiting, reduce the blood's clotting ability, and cause body wasting. The drugs sometimes are effective after the patient has become resistant to X rays; and they have several other advantages over X rays in their availability, cheapness, and control (with antidotes).

Other agents which have one or more of the properties of radiation have been used in combination with X rays against animal cancers. They include deuterium (the double-weight hydrogen) as a substitute for hydrogen in (heavy) water, actinomycin D, 5-bromodeoxyuridine, a thymidine analogue which when used to pretreat cells, enhanced radiation effects tenfold, the antivitamin, 6-aminonicotinamide, and an anti-nucleic acid drug, 6-mercaptopurine.

Investigators at the University of Wisconsin have combined 5-FU or 5-FUDR with radiation, and others at Stanford have catheterized tumor areas, injected methotrexate, and irradiated. These procedures are delicate ones, but, with safe and effective dosages established, they have made some tumors disappear for substantial periods.

Dr. Samuel Schwartz at the University of Minnesota found that injections of some porphyrins, when combined with X rays, seemed to help patients with cancers of the thigh, vulva, tongue, muscle, larynx, and lip, but their effects were unpredictable and sometimes completely contrary to expectations. Moreover, they often made patients light-sensitive for months; small exposure to sunlight resulted in serious sunburn effects.

Several dyes also sensitize tissues to the effect of radiations, including light and X rays. Other dyes arrest tumor growth in the absence of light and other rays. The mechanisms of action of these substances are becoming understood—they involve the addition or deletion of charged hydrogen atoms in enzymes and the nucleic acids of viruses and cells.

A generation ago, when Dr. Otto Warburg's finding of a fault in oxygen metabolism in cancer cells was exciting scientists throughout the world, the answer to cancer looked very simple. All one had to do was get more oxygen into the cancer cell. This could be done by placing the patient under two or three atmospheres of pressure in an environment of pure oxygen. Under those pressures, the amount of oxygen dissolved in blood plasma rises about fifteenfold. This idea was implemented in Cleveland with the construction of a six-story building costing $1,000,000 for the experimental treatment of cancer. The building was abandoned and the idea discarded when increased pressure failed to cure cancer.

In 1964, hyperbaric oxygenation, or "hybaroxia," as treatment with oxygen at pressure is called, once again became the darling of experimental medicine. Symposiums on its magic were held before overflow audiences. This time there was something to talk about—not particularly the treatment of cancer, but rather the rescue of patients from a dozen other perilous situations. The treatment, which dates back to nineteenth-century spas, was revived by Dr. Iete Boerema of Amsterdam, who felt that increased blood oxygen would slow down the process of blood poisoning. The oxygen, he believed, might keep tissues alive and safe from gangrene and inhibit the bacteria causing the trouble. He was right.

Hundreds of large and small hybaroxia units have been built throughout the medical world in recent years. They range in size from a sort of coffin to large rooms in which two or more surgical operations take place simultaneously. The procedure has been reported effective in preventing the spread of gas gangrene and consequent amputation, increasing the safety of operations for congenital heart conditions in infants, overcoming the effects of arterial insufficiency owing to injury and other causes, increasing survival from shock, resuscitating victims of carbon monoxide poisoning and the newborn from asphyxia, and helping those who have suffered heart attacks.

In 1953, Dr. L. H. Gray and his British associates showed that, when mice were compelled to breathe under increased oxygen tension, radiation made their transplanted tumors wither away rapidly. The oxygen greatly increased the sensitivity of the tumors (and normal tissue as well) to the rays. Dr. Ian Churchill-Davidson of St. Thomas Hospital, London, soon thereafter began irradiating cancer patients under three atmospheres if they were conscious, four when they were anesthetized. All the patients in his early series were in terminal stages of the disease, and, though there were no cures, the data leaves little doubt but that hybaroxic radiation had dramatically enhanced effects on some tumors. In 1964, facilities for hybaroxia, including radiation treatment for cancer, were being built in many American medical centers. Dr. Orliss Wildermuth, after treating 100 cancer patients by hyperbaric radiation at Seattle's Swedish Hospital, concluded that the procedure offered remarkable improvement in radiotherapy.

Like other medical miracles, hybaroxia holds its hazards. Besides presenting dangers of explosion, oxygen in too great concentration is poisonous. Because oxygen effects are similar to those of X rays (both form free radicals, inactivate sulfur enzymes, disintegrate nucleic acids, and break chromosomes), the two agents have an additive effect.

Dr. Curreri, who had pioneered the clinical use of 5-FU, said at the end of a long, futile fight to save House Speaker Sam Rayburn from death by cancer of the pancreas: "One of the overpowering problems with cancer drugs is their terrible toxicity. The population of New York City could be wiped out by dumping a few gallons of two cancer drugs in the city's water supply."

Many practitioners of experimental medicine have felt that had they dared risk near-lethal doses of drugs, they might have cured some human cancers. They were deterred by the fact that too often a semi-safe dose proves deadly.

At the other end of the scale, many scientists are seeking combinations of two or more drugs which will enhance antitumor effects without producing intolerable toxicity. The Tulane group have found that if they administer peroxides, which are a target of radiomimetic drugs, when they perfuse with such agents as nitrogen mustard, tumor damage is increased. Others are seeking preparations which will have potentiating, additive or synergistic effects when combined with anticancer drugs.

In a collaborative study by Dr. Julian Ambrus and his group at Roswell Park and another team working with Dr. Albert Segaloff of the Alton Ochsner Medical Foundation in New Orleans, patients are being given "double-barreled" drugs. These are compounds in which the active atomic groupings of two different anticancer drugs are welded into a single molecule. The first preparation was called AB 100; a blend of urethane and nitrogen mustard radicals, it cured several transplanted animal cancers, including leukemia. AB 100 had minor effect against human tumors; but two of its successors, AB 103 and AB 132, produced dramatic, if temporary, remissions in about one-fourth of a series of patients with lung cancer. The combination drugs are toxic, but some of them show fewer side effects than either of the two molecules from which they were produced.

The future of efforts to potentiate drug effects or protect the patient is very much in the hands of the basic biochemist who is studying the chemical targets of the drugs, the protection offered by administering the target chemicals during therapy, the feasibility of blocking cell metabolism with two or more analogues aimed at the same sequence of chemical reactions, and the practicality of striking simultaneously at two or more entirely independent chemical systems within the cell. This is a large research order, but a good start has been made by Dr. Howard E. Skipper at Southern Research Institute in Birmingham, Alabama, Dr. Van R. Potter at the University of Wisconsin, and Dr. Arnold Seligman at Johns Hopkins University.

Dr. Daniel S. Martin of the University of Miami has attempted for many years to increase the efficiency of analogues of dietary elements by deleting the natural food factor from the diet. In mouse experiments he has cured transplanted cancer by ridding the animals' diet of the vitamin, nicotinamide, while feeding them a potent counterfeit of the vitamin. In humans, this dietary procedure, while possibly increasing the anticancer effect of analogues, also has increased their toxicity.

The fear of atomic warfare, perhaps more than the desire to improve cancer treatment, has inspired considerable research into radiation effects and their prevention.

The most commonly used technique has been infusion of marrow following near-lethal doses of radiation. In some cases, marrow has been withdrawn from the bones of leukemia patients, refrigerated while the patient was vigorously irradiated and then returned to the patient intravenously; the marrow manufactured new blood elements which prevented radiation death. In other cases, donor marrow has been infused into the recently irradiated patient, but these foreign cells became parasitical and produced antibodies against their host's tissues.

The growing but still inadequate fund of information on the action of anticancer drugs and radiation on cell chemistry has supplied many new leads to the control of toxicity. To varying degrees, science has been able to prevent damage by supplying certain chemicals in advance, replenish the radiation-depleted chemicals or undo damage by repairing the injured chemical structures.

The observation that two of the prime molecular targets of radiation and radiomimetic drugs are sulfur bridges and sulfhydryl bonds which hold the protein molecule together has led to the use of many natural and artificial sulfur-containing compounds to offset radiation effects and the harm done by sulfur-attacking drugs. Among the natural sulfur-containing compounds which have a detoxifying action are the amino acids, methionine and cystine (and the latter's metabolite, cysteine), and glutathione. In some manner, they seem to permit the continued cell synthesis of nucleic acids which are needed for survival and growth. Hydroxyl amines alone or combined with these sulfur compounds exert substantial protection against radiation.

Artificial sulfur compounds also have helped overcome the poisonous effects of radiation and such drugs as nitrogen mustard; they include a potent preparation called AET (or S-(aminoethyl)thiuronium-bromide-hydrobromide) and its sulfhydryl form, called MEG, the analogue thiourea, and several others. AET is of particular interest, because it appears to protect normal tissues and not cancer; clinically, however, it has not shown great promise. Hydrogen sulfide, when applied to dry spores during irradiation, reduced the lethal effects 75 per cent and, after radiation, 50 per cent, presumably by scavenging highly reactive free radicals out of the system. Some of the nucleic acid segments, the pyrimidine nucleotides, when given after lethal radiation have stimulated the stalled DNA chemistry of mice and saved the animals' lives, and, as a Yale scientist has shown, RNA from commercial yeast has protected irradiated mice.

Unidentified chemicals in the spleen, liver, and perhaps other organs as well offer protection against radiation. University of Kentucky investigators found that fetal liver cells, quick-frozen in glycerol at $-176°$ F, and stored indefinitely at $-122°$ F, protected mice against lethal X rays up to 65 per cent. Dr. Richard C. Lillehei of the University of Minnesota, who has successfully grafted many major organs from one dog to another, found that a fine mince of spleen injected intravenously offered protection against radiation, but the transplant of an entire spleen did not. Others have found that a theoretical trypsin inhibitor (which restrains trypsin from disintegrating tissues and which can be induced by injecting trypsin into animals) is a highly effective safeguard against X rays.

One of the effects of radiation is to produce a bacteremia (bacteria in the blood), possibly by increasing the permeability of the lower intestine and allowing the microbes to escape into the system. Sulfa drugs and antibiotics (chlortetracycline) have helped prevent this complication and have made radiation much less lethal to several experimental species. Actinomycin D, added to the food of fruit flies, greatly reduced the number of radiation mutations. Still another cancer-fighting use for the tetracyclines is being developed by scientists at College of the Pacific and at Stanford: they are attaching to tetracycline molecules various atoms of boron, lithium, or uranium, feeding the doctored antibiotics to tumor-bearing animals and then—after forty-eight hours when the bomblike antibiotics are concentrated in cancers—exploding the compounds with neutron streams from atomic reactors.

Hormones, too, have influenced radiation effects. From the results of several scattered experiments, one might conclude that, due to hormonal effects, males are more vulnerable than females to radiation. In one series of experiments, castration helped male mice survive radiation effects; in others, estrogen helped; and, in still others, analogues (antiandrogens) designed to block the use of male hormones offset the lethal rays. One series of experiments indicated that male hormone increased sensitivity to radiation not only by normal tissues but by tumors as well. Adrenal hormones have been reported to have seemingly contradictory effects: Stanford scientists have found that a single large dose of hydrocortisone, even if given 100 days after a leukemogenic dose of X rays, suppresses leukemia in one-half the irradiated animals. A Salt Lake City scientist, on the other hand, found an additive effective in radiation and cortisone—when the two agents were used together they almost doubled the curative effects of radiation alone against transplanted mouse cancers of the breast and nerve. Preradiation parathyroid extracts have been reported to increase the survival of animals exposed to lethal X rays.

About fifteen years ago, Dr. Howard L. Richardson, then at the University of Oregon, and Dr. A. Clark Griffin, then at Stanford, teamed up to show that in some instances one carcinogen would cancel out another. They found that carcinogens which cause cancer of the skin blocked the carcinogenic activity of a dye product which induced liver cancer in rats. Dr. Richardson has shown that radiation, given a month or two before the carcinogen, prevents or inhibits liver cancers induced by the dyes; others have found radiation offsets the effects of other carcinogens, including two benzanthracene forms, although it has additive effects with still others. In these experiments, timing and dosage are all-important; it may be the radiation-rebound effects rather than the direct effects of radiation that afford the protection. At the Mayo Clinic, radiologists have reported that by spacing X-ray treatments over certain periods, they have improved five-year survivals of patients with cancers of the tonsil, nasopharynx, and anus from 300 to 400 per cent over that achieved by conventional radiation given day after day for an established period.

Many new offbeat and potentially important elements are being introduced to further complicate the already complex cancer-therapy picture.

There is the temperature factor, for example. Animals whose body temperature is raised to the fever range show an accelerated response to radiation, but, in the few experiments so far carried out, elevated temperature did not increase the cancer remission rate. Many years ago, Dr. Titus Evans at the State University of Iowa showed that by chilling animals, and thus slowing down their body chemistry, he could administer without great damage several times the lethal dose of X rays; now, at Northwestern University, there is a serious effort to combine chilling (or profound hypothermia) with radiation in an effort to cure animal cancers. More than a decade ago, Father B. J. Luyet at St. Louis University demonstrated that with ordinary antifreeze (ethylene glycol) heart tissue could be quick frozen in liquid nitrogen without the formation of ice, gradually thawed, and made to beat again. Recently, Dr. Stanley W. Jacob of the University of Oregon Medical School has employed hypothermia and enormous pressures (20,000 pounds per square inch), which prevent ice formation, to keep fast-frozen tissues viable (he has made refrigerated puppy hearts beat normally when transplanted to adult dogs) and test the applicability of cold to the treatment of animal cancer. Dr. James C. Owens at the University of Colorado has shown in dogs that the circulation in several areas can be clamped off safely for hours, under hypothermia, while extensive surgery or organ treatment is undertaken. These experiments could conceivably have implications for the treatment of cancerous organs outside the body or in the metabolically indolent body.

Hypnosis has been used in Fort Worth, Texas, to overcome some of the immediate effects of radiation (such as nausea and vomiting) and surgery (the need for narcotics has been reduced). The Cantarow-Paschkis group at Jefferson Medical College have shown that in exercised rats cancers grow and kill more slowly than in sedentary animals and that something extrated from fatigued muscle (which had been "exercised" in test tubes) slows the growth of cancer in animals. Just as oxygen tension —produced in chambers under high atmospheric pressures and by other means—has enhanced radiation effects, so has a stiff shot of whiskey depressed them. Ultrasonic radiation is recognized as a highly destructive agent; specific frequencies may be found to destroy tumors without damage to normal tissues. The great biological influence of radio waves and magnetic fields only now is beginning to be explored seriously; it is clear that they wield profound influence over the growth and regression of cancers, and they may act synergistically or additively with other agents. Direct-current electric potentials, used in the Soviet Union for anesthesia and in other countries to facilitate the regrowth of regenerating tissues and heal wounds, is yet to be tested against cancer. The many areas of the light spectrum are beginning to show critical influences on normal and cancerous growth. Infrared radiation and cold have made cells exposed to both factors highly vulnerable to X rays.

These are but a few of the many areas of great or small promise in the treatment of human cancer. Some which at the present time show little prospect of therapeutic value may in the future be combined with one, two, three, or more agents to effect cures now impossible.

While new treatments are being developed and favorable combinations are being worked out, a great deal can be done for patients with the means now at hand. It can be done best by dedicated doctors in centers concentrating on the control of cancer.

Drs. Nylene E. Eckles and Mary Sears at M. D. Anderson Hospital, Houston, specialize in the care of women with inoperable or metastatic breast cancer. They treat 250 new cases each year. On planned schedules, they treat each case according to the individual's needs and employ countless conventional and experimental therapies and combinations of therapies. They are determined not only to keep the patient alive, but to make the final months or years a period of comfort and activity.

Dr. Eckles outlined in 1964 some of the measures undertaken for 1700 hopelessly advanced breast-cancer patients treated during the past decade.

Narcotics are withdrawn from those who have become addicted. The patients are released from their habit within ten days by radiotherapy to areas of pain, intensive medical management of withdrawal symptoms, and psychotherapeutic assurance that much can be done to help the patient and that the time ahead offers pleasant and useful life. In this service, no new addictions have been formed, and old ones have been broken completely. This is in contradistinction to the practice of some physicians of putting their patients on narcotics when the case is recognized as incurable and keeping them addicted until death.

Plaster casts are promptly removed from broken bones of the hip, thigh, and upper arm, and the fractures are stabilized with rods, plates, screws, or perhaps a new metal head. The fracture is treated with radiation, and usually within ten days the patient walks again. In this service, even patients with only weeks to go are not permitted to be immobilized in plaster.

Eyes blinded by metastases are not removed; vision is restored by radiotherapy. Brain metastases are treated successfully in 80 per cent of the cases by X rays.

A large variety of hormones—old standbys as well as many new ones—are used. Only one-third of the patients respond to them. The other two-thirds are treated by radiotherapy, cleaning and healing their ulcers, draining effusions, and other measures. Hormone-producing glands are not removed from patients whose tumors are found to be hormone-independent. Ovarectomy is sometimes achieved with Thio-TEPA in the others.

Forty per cent of these patients were helped by pituitary stalk section. This surgical procedure, severing the nerve and blood vessels connecting the pituitary with the hypothalamus, is simpler than removing the pituitary and at least as effective. Many women undergoing stalk section lactated profusely.

A large variety of drugs is used here. Specialists—neurosurgeons, orthopedic surgeons, ophthalmologists, gynecologists, radiotherapists, and others—are called in on cases.

Meticulous records are kept, not only of each patient's response to drugs and other procedures, but also a day-by-day and month-by-month account of incidental observations, clinical oddities, facts about associated disease, epidemiological notes, and irrelevant material which often on review gives leads for future research.

These records—at this writing being run through a computer—should prove useful in charting new treatments. Meanwhile, in the lengthened survival of patients, in increased comfort, and in useful life, one thing has already been proved: good doctors in a good institution can do a great deal for their patients—even hopeless patients—with means now available.

CHAPTER 28

PREVENTION

Many authorities have said that the most effective way of reducing cancer deaths is to prevent the disease. Cancer, they say, is easier to prevent than to cure.

Nature has done this. In the last generation, the incidence and death rates for cancers of the liver, stomach, and uterus have declined 50–60 per cent. No one knows how—or why.

There are many ways of preventing cancer. Some are highly theoretical and, for humans, quite impractical. Three studies have shown, for instance, that women hysterectomized or ovarectomized before the menopause are less likely than intact women to develop breast cancer. Neither of these procedures is recommended as a prophylactic measure.

Some preventive measures call for good and prompt attention, such as the surgical removal of precancerous lumps and sores. It takes an alert person and an informed doctor to detect most of these conditions, but this detection is possible and practical.

Some measures are of an immunological nature, and most of them are on scientists' drawing boards for possible future application to humans. They include vaccination against the things which cause cancer and against cancer itself. Many of these procedures are successful against specific cancers in animals.

The means of preventing some cancers are at hand; they are available and have been for years. They merely call for avoiding known carcinogens in our environment. Cigarettes have been shown by statistical, chemical, and biological means to be one of the most common sources of carcinogens affecting man. If it were spinach rather than tobacco, there would be no problem. But, because cigarette smoking is attractive to many adolescents and addictive to adults, the solution is not an easy one.

As indicated in earlier chapters, a large number of carcinogens or chemicals suspect of carcinogenic activity have been reported to exist in the air we breathe, the food we eat, the water we drink, the drugs we take, the medical treatments we are given, the jobs we hold, the products we handle, our nation's defenses against enemies, and the habits we form.

Only some of them can be avoided; in most cases, the individual has no choice. To a degree, and often to a ridiculous degree, however, one may select his class of carcinogens. He may move out of smog-bound cities to the country, for example, and face up to the hazards of close contact with fertilizers and pesticides. He may quit his job as a garage mechanic to avoid exposure to carcinogens in oils, become a doctor or dentist—and then face the carcinogenic and leukemogenic dangers of X rays. Or, if he wishes to make a career of dodging cancer, he may, by dint of great ability, commendable application, and some luck, become a very rich man and avoid the numerous cancers which predominate among those of the lower socioeconomic status. Dr. Breslow, it will be recalled, has found that poor people come down with cancer 25 per cent more often than rich people, are less than 50 per cent as likely to have their cancers diagnosed while still curable, and are notoriously laggard (or financially unable) in taking and completing treatment.

It often is difficult to determine where sound suggestions of carcinogenic dangers end and where fantasy and hypochondriac appeal begin. For this confusion there are several reasons. First and foremost is a lack of clear and reliable information on environmental carcinogens. While more than 500 chemicals are known to cause animal cancers, few have any idea as to what products they are in; and, for one reason or another—usually because of the damage the information might do to industries and commercial products—little is said about them. It can be pointed out that comprehensive lists of chemicals found to be carcinogenic are published every now and then in the scientific literature; but, without identifying the sources of exposure, the lists are meaningless to the public. When all the laboratory information is available—the kinds of cancer produced in experimental species by various routes of administration and the doses needed—it is still debatable as to how applicable animal findings are to humans.

Human data, too, can be unreliable to a degree. A study at Memorial Cancer Center in New York has shown that patients often tend to lie when giving a history. They say they eat what they know they should eat, rather than what they actually do eat; they deny having had a venereal disease; they understate the amount of alcohol and tobacco they consume; they hide the emotional stresses in their work and home life; and they list as their habits and hobbies wholesome pursuits about which they know little. Only when compensation is allowed for these degrees of bias, can data be regarded as reliable.

Complicating the picture still further is the fact that carcinogens also prevent cancer. With evidence of this phenomenon mounting rather rapidly, it appears that in some cases small prior doses of a carcinogen will neutralize later large carcinogenic doses of the very same agent. An increasing number of instances have come to light showing that one carcinogen often will offset another one—ethionine and trypan blue, which cause different kinds of liver cancer in rats, virtually cancel each other out when given together; X rays have been found to prevent the mouse lung cancers induced with urethane; 4-nitroquinoline N-oxide, which causes skin cancer in mice, prevented or retarded skin cancers by two other carcinogens, benzpyrene and 1,2,5,6,-dibenzanthracene.

Dr. Charles Huggins of the University of Chicago has reported that each of at least forty hydrocarbons—almost all of them noncarcinogenic—when taken orally prevent the activity of some of the most potent carcinogens known. He has urged that this be explored intensively with a view to producing pills which might someday permit man to smoke his cigarettes and expose himself to other carcinogenic sources with impunity. As with most suggestions that principles established in basic research might well be applied to human health problems, his proposals stimulated no positive action. With great success, Dr. Huggins has applied other basic research to clinical cancer. (As mentioned earlier, he was the first to castrate and give estrogens for prostatic cancer and the first to adrenalectomize, a boon to many breast-cancer patients.) His cancer prevention proposal, however, would have to be tested in many laboratories and, as its benefits and limitations became clear, on a large segment of the population—a job too big for any one scientist.

Happily, a number of measures can be taken by the individual to prevent some kinds of cancer; most of them entail neither the breaking of an addiction nor offending a strong and sensitive industry.

A lot of skin cancer can be prevented, for example, if light-skinned people will keep their exposure to sunshine within reasonable limits. Young bronzed Adonises and Venuses may have a leathery skin in their thirties, keratoses in their forties, and skin cancers in their fifties.

Additional caution by the patient, as well as the doctor and dentist, in medical X rays would help prevent several kinds of cancer. Doctors and dentists tend to resent the public's being warned against excessive and unnecessary radiation. They argue that warnings may deprive some patients of necessary diagnostic and therapeutic measures. Nevertheless, the patient has reason to be wary of unnecessary or excess radiation on two counts: (1) it is the patient who develops the cancer, and (2) the record of misuse of radiation, of dangerous equipment, and of careless practices is so well documented as to warrant caution.

Pending the issuance of a list of carcinogens and substances strongly suspect of carcinogenic action by the government or another responsible agency, one would be well-advised to avoid unnecessary exposure to coal-tar products, paraffin, lubricating oils, arsenicals, and other suspect substances indicated in earlier chapters. An authoritative, comprehensive, and comprehensible list of dangerous and avoidable substances is long overdue.

By the same token, it would be helpful to the medical profession if some of the doubts and disputes on carcinogens and preventive measures were resolved by a competent, deliberative body with adequate objectivity and authority to be believed and obeyed. Evidence which would dispel much of the confusion and ignorance over the safety of certain drugs, the pesticide practices, and the advisability of numerous sugrical operations for precancerous conditions for some time has been obtainable from a careful evaluation of the literature and consensus of specialists in various scientific and medical areas. No one seems to be doing much about it.

Back in 1947, Dr. Frank E. Adair of Memorial Cancer Center proposed many different measures for the prevention of various cancers. They were suggested by a careful review of the literature, discussions with experts in several fields, and Dr. Adair's own broad experience as a leading cancer surgeon. A decade later, Dr. R. J. Samp of the University of Wisconsin and the Wisconsin Division of the American Cancer Society began a four-year poll among 1,400 physicians to ascertain their professional feelings toward the proposed preventive measures. The results were published in the March 31, 1962, issue of the *Journal of the American Medical Association,* with Dr. Samp's comment that, "The idea of preventing cancer seemed vague and doubtful to the [physician] audience as a whole. Added to this discouragement is the fact that not one idea, lead or theory on cancer prevention was suggested by the entire professional audience."

Wisconsin, with splendid medical education facilities, is generally regarded as superior to most states in the quality of its physicians.

In the poll, physicians were asked to give one of five grades to each measure, most of them practiced in the best medical centers, a few of them of doubtful value. The top grade indicated merely that the doctor felt the measure had definite merit, the lowest grade, no merit.

The highest number of top grades (1,014 of a possible 1,400) was accorded to "avoidance of unnecessary X-ray and radioactive exposures" and the lowest (90) to "routine vaginal douching in cases of chronic, nonspecific discharge."

The measures, in the order of their importance, given top rating by 700 to 999 of the 1,400 physicians were: total hysterectomy, rather than sub-total; removal of polyps from bowel and bladder; removal of large ovarian cysts and solid growths; prompt treatment of all erosions and chronic infections of cervix (biopsy first); Pap testing of all adult females to screen out atypical uterine tissues; removal of thyroid nodules, especially single ones; examination of all surgical specimens microscopically to note tissue changes warranting further follow-up.

Given top rating by from 300 to 699 were: removal of areas of leu-koplakia; excision of suspected single masses in adult female breast; isola-tion, enclosure, or sealing off of areas where aniline dyes, chromate vapors, or asbestos dust are present; removal of gallstones; removal (grafting) of exfoliative areas of irradiation or arsenical dermatitis; warning and guarding against inhalation of industrial toxins, chemicals, and fumes (gas masks, ventilation system); excision of skin moles in areas of irritation; resection of colon with advanced ulcerative colitis; removal of duct papillo-mas of the breast; repairing of postpartum lacerations of cervix; grafting of areas of deep skin burns that do not heal; circumcision of male infant; correction of chronic oral infections and dental disease; excision of per-sistent areas of localized chronic mastitis of breasts; control or restriction of use of therapeutic drugs with suspected carcinogenic action (e.g., hormones, arsenic); surgical correction of undescended testicle; elimination of or protection against everyday carcinogens (dusts from asphalt and tar roads, truck exhaust, food additives); avoidance of tobacco in all forms; avoidance of skin contact with tar and petroleum products; removal of senile keratoses; cleaning up of city atmosphere (smog, pollution); prompt surgical or medical management of gastric ulcers, chronic gastritis, perni-cious anemia; avoidance of overexposure to, or protection from, sunlight.

And top-rated by 100 to 299 were: promotion of oral and dental hygiene from infancy; reduction of female cervical cancer by eliminating exposure to male smegma (circumcision, better male hygiene); avoidance of ingestion of excessively hot foods and drink; correction of avitaminosis (Plummer-Vinson's syndrome, Laennec's cirrhosis); addition of iodine to diet in areas with iodine-poor soil; maintenance of regular bowel habits; avoidance of purgatives; encouragement of mothers to breast-feed babies; conservative use of alcohol and "hot" spices.

While the entire study was significant in indicating many physicians' casual attitudes toward cancer prevention, it is surprising that only 942 top-graded the need for microscopic examination of surgical specimens, that only 711 showed great concern for protection against industrial toxins, 485 against drugs with suspected carcinogenic activity, 401 against to-bacco, 436 against smog and 149 against iodine deficiency.

Of equal interest were the numbers who gave a grade of zero—no value whatsoever—to such prophylactic measures as removal of senile keratoses, 489; cleaning up air pollution, 555; prompt management of ulcers, gastritis, and pernicious anemia, 612; avoidance of excessive exposure to sun, 323; circumcision and male hygiene, 785; correcting vitamin deficiency, 606; iodine supplements in goiter belts, 801; conservative use of alcohol and hot spices, 984; and vaginal douching for chronic discharge, 1,083.

Dr. Samp found some of the response consistent with the unproved anti-cancer value of the measures (douching, hot foods, and spices), Wisconsin's conditions (smog and industry) and government, rather than medical, responsibilities (drugs). Other scores (on tobacco, excessive sunshine, removal of keratoses and other data-supported measures) persuaded him that "there is much to be done in educating the profession."

In 1962 and 1963 the Food and Drug Administration, armed with new responsibilities and new powers, seemed to be making headway in protecting the public against dangerous drugs. As was to be expected, considerable confusion attended the changeover to more effective action. It remains to be seen whether public servants under multiple pressures of the industry, politicians, press, and medical profession will be able to find an equitable and equable way of resisting enthusiasms for new drugs until they are explored for booby-trap effects, of limiting the use of old ones of doubtful utility, of enforcing a reasonable discrimination in the prescribing and taking of medicines, and of permitting competent investigators to bring new useful drugs into experimental medical practice. One government survey showed that 53 per cent of pregnant women take a variety of drugs; in 41 per cent of the cases, neither the patient nor the physician was able to identify the drugs taken. This finding symbolized the problems posed by a drug-happy population.

In public health, the sins of commission may be no greater than those of omission in the detection and prevention of cancer. Cancer calls for the best that medicine has to offer. New methods of measuring the performance of various glands and other vital organs and tissues in humans often are beyond the competence or concern of the average physician and the means of the average citizen. Some useful tests are available in only a few centers of research and experimental medicine. Some of the simple tests, like the Pap smear, are little used by most doctors, studies have shown. Tests for thyroid inadequacy—probably the most common defect in older people, the most readily remedied, and the most frequently ignored—usually are not made.

When current medical services leave so much to be desired, perhaps one would do well to discount liberally the advances in basic research as a portent of medical miracles of the immediate future.

Cancers in laboratory animals have been prevented or retarded by many means. Breast cancer in susceptible mice has been prevented by a combination of growth hormone and either ACTH or lactogenic hormone; transplanted mouse leukemia has been prevented with the ingestion of benzene, intravenous injections of carcinogenic hydrocarbons, or vaccines or testicular extracts; antioxidants, which suppress the formation of free radicals, have been reported to decrease the cancer incidence in mice, delay the aging process, and extend the animals' life spans between 15 and 26 per cent.

While the above measures may never offer help to humans, there are a few things people can do for themselves. Common sense and common cleanliness need no prescription; both of them offer some defense against cancer. Somewhere in the area between fanatical food faddists and their equally emotional detractors is a middle ground in which intelligent people take the vitamin and mineral supplements they find missing in their regular diets. People can keep their weight down to a reasonable figure and lower the numerous health risks that go with excess flabby flesh.

Sometime in the future man may be able to counteract the effects of carcinogens with chemicals specifically designed for that purpose. This is possible now in animal experiments. The carcinogenic effects of butter yellow, which causes liver cancer in rats, can be overcome merely by adding the vitamin riboflavin to the animal's diet. Niacin offsets the effects of an artificial vitamin, 3-acetylpyridine, a carcinogen-suspect in cigarette smoke.

Drs. Paul Kotin and Hans A. Falk, then at the University of Southern California and now at NCI, showed a few years ago that several common carcinogens could be made into anticarcinogens by the addition of a couple of hydrogen atoms to the molecule; the altered molecules, if administered to animals anywhere from a couple of weeks before, until a week after, exposure to the carcinogens, prevented cancers from developing. Drs. James and Elizabeth Miller and Charles Heidelberger at the University of Wisconsin have been charting the charges in various areas of carcinogenic molecules to determine which electronic configurations made them cancer-causing; they have destroyed the potency of some carcinogens by inserting an atom, like fluorine, into the molecule. Dr. Murray Shear of NCI found that common lard given with the carcinogen (benzpyrene) reduced the incidence of animal cancers from 58 to 2 per cent. A derivative of DDT has eroded the cortex of normal and overfunctioning adrenal glands; and a close relative of it, called perthane, has prevented mouse cancer—by action on the pituitary gland.

At this stage, few if any would or should volunteer to be injected with carcinogens, other potentially dangerous chemicals, or even seemingly innocent ones on the off-chance that the treatment might prevent some kind of cancer from arising in the future. Yet only a large population treated over a long time would prove the prophylactic value of nonspecific drugs. Some relatively safe measures, however, are suggested for people peculiarly subject to certain kinds of cancer.

A few chemicals have been studied in humans to determine whether they would prevent skin cancer, which plagues fair-skinned people in the sunniest parts of the world. Among them was squalene, a component of sebum, the oily substance which naturally coats hair and skin. One demonstration that it detoxifies methylcholanthrene, a common laboratory carcinogen, suggests that it might be useful in the oil and other industries where skin cancer is a high hazard. Paraaminobenzoic acid, a vitamin, also protects against the sun's rays. Chloroquine, an antimalarial sometimes used to treat connective tissue diseases, has been tested in humans against sun-induced basal cell cancers; it cut the incidence by 80 per cent of the cancers appearing in controls in one trial.

Epidemics of a few cancers in various parts of the world have inspired highly speculative reports as to their causes and prevention. One Costa Rican investigator has blamed stomach cancer, common throughout Central America, on the practice of softening tortilla corn meal prior to cooking in kitchen ashes; he has said this cancer is not common in areas where the meal is softened with lime. The high rate of cancers of the digestive and upper respiratory tracts in the Calvados area of Normandy has been blamed upon the natives' great liking for the applejack they produce there under the name of calvados. The suggestion is that these cancers can be prevented by abstaining, or drinking other liquor.

In December, 1961, Dr. Bertil Bjorklund of the Caroline Institute and Immunology Research Laboratory, Stockholm, injected himself and 120 healthy volunteers between sixty and seventy years old with a vaccine which, he felt, might show whether people produced antibodies against cancers— possibily all kinds of cancer. Because the volunteers were at the peak of the cancer age (that is, within a very few years a substantial percentage of them could be expected to develop the disease) the Swedish scientist had reason to believe that he soon would have an indication as to whether or not a vaccine might prevent cancer. If the results were favorable, he intended vaccinating a great many volunteers against cancer in a definitive test of the vaccine. By late 1963 he found that some of the people did show anticancer antibodies. None of the subjects had had any untoward effects, and none had developed cancer—although, statistically, a few should have.

On the face of it, the vaccine was harmless. It was prepared from chemicals extracted from the membranes of human cancer cells which had been killed with ultraviolet radiation, stored in a frozen and dried state and suspended in salt water. In earlier tests, the vaccine had been injected into patients between seventy and eighty years old with noncancerous diseases; the vaccine had caused no harm and seemed to be effective in stimulating the production of antibodies and other anticancer chemicals in the blood.

For decades, scientists had talked about a cancer vaccine. Some believed an effective one never could or would be produced; some felt that vaccines—a different one for each kind of cancer, perhaps—might be achieved at some distant date. Only a few felt that a vaccine for many or all kinds of cancer was conceivable. Here and now was a vaccine which actually was being tested for its possible prophylactic effect in cancer—human cancer—all kinds of human cancer.

His peers did not take kindly to Dr. Bjorklund's experiments. He was accused of being premature, of conducting potentially harmful experiments on people, of producing an ineffective preparation based upon the untenable immunological preface that human cancer cells contain a common antigen or common antigens. At scientific conferences, the bland Swedish scientist, like D'Artagnan, fenced with each and all of his hostile and sometimes irate critics, met each lunge and parried with his own experimental results.

The proof of the merit or folly of this approach will be apparent eventually, if Dr. Bjorklund is permitted to carry on his work. The U.S. Public Health Service, his principal supporter, found technical reasons for withdrawing its aid when the controversy reached its peak. This was followed by efforts to oust him from his laboratory and sever his academic and scientific affiliations.

The hostility was not surprising. Almost every notable advance in medical science—and, to be sure, many pseudo-advances, as well—had met with similar cynicism, skepticism and opposition. Nevertheless, this case served to remind science once again that there often is a practical side to basic research and that its application to medical problems saves lives—the sooner it is applied, the more lives saved.

In recent years it has been demonstrated time and again that it is possible to immunize susceptible animals against transplanted cancers. In most cases, the immunization was effective against only a single, specific cancer; in a few cases, vaccination prevented a wide range of tumors.

Animal experiments are necessary—and they have proved valuable. Several principles seem to be emerging from the experiments at this writing; some of them are departures from the prevailing principles established for immunization procedures for nonmalignant diseases. Dosage, timing, route of administration and, of course, composition of the vaccine are criti-

cal factors which spell the difference between immunization, failure to immunize, or the development and acceleration of cancer.

A group at the University of Minnesota—Drs. J. Bradley Aust, Carlos
Martinez and the late John J. Bittner—vaccinated mice by injecting live
cancer cells in their tails and then, after a period of several days, amputat-
ing the tails. If they cut off the tail ten days after inoculation, the mouse
was immunized against later transplants of that cancer. After twelve days
there was not much point in removing the tumors, which by then had
metastasized widely. If they transplanted a second cancer to the supposedly immunized animal at any time before the seventeenth day, it
"took," and killed the mouse. When they surgically joined a tumor-
susceptible mouse with a tumor-tolerant mouse, in the manner of Siamese
twins, the tolerant mouse became resistant. Another member of the
Minnesota group, Dr. Herbert M. Hirsch, feels that the experiments with
vaccines of transplanted mouse tumors have little bearing on the problem of
a vaccine for human tumors or for spontaneous tumors of any species.

A good many scientists hold, however, that the possibility of producing
a vaccine against spontaneous cancers, including human, is a lively one.
A number of vaccines have proved effective against chemically induced
cancers in animals.

Dr. Richmond T. Prehn of the University of Washington has vaccinated
successfully against many cancers—spontaneous, transplanted, and induced by such agents as methylcholanthrene, dibenzanthracene and plastic
films inserted into tissues. Many of the tumors had only weak antigens. The
faster the tumors grew, the greater their potency as a vaccine. He feels that
the carcinogens induced an antigenic change in cell membranes which made
the cancer cells subject to attack by immune lymph cells. A group working
with Dr. George Klein at the Caroline Institute in Stockholm also found
that sensitized lymph cells attacked and destroyed methylcholanthrene-
induced cancers.

Dr. Charlotte Friend of the Sloan-Kettering Institute has immunized
mice against a leukemia virus with two vaccines: (1) one of them made of
leukemia viruses killed when mixed with formalin, and (2) viruses killed
when mixed with the blood serum (antiserum) of rabbits previously injected with the virus.

Dr. Vittorio Defendi of Wistar Institute has shown that while animals
can be immunized against free viruses, the immunity will not affect viruses
which already have entered cells, nor will it affect the infected (now
cancerous) cells themselves.

Dr. Alex Novikoff has spun out of rat liver cancer cells the tiny particles,
microsomes, which serve as cell protein factories. The material, comprising
6 per cent of the cell, did not itself induce cancer when injected into rats

but, on the contrary, effectively immunized the animals against later transplants of the liver cancer.

Cancer cells (Ehrlich ascites) have lost their carcinogenic potency after being incubated at high fever temperatures for ninety minutes. Charles A. Apfel of Pondville Hospital found that five or ten injections of (5–10 million) inactivated cells gave mice 100 per cent immunity to that kind of cancer. Dr. Ralph N. Baillif of Tulane discovered that injections of fewer than three million untreated ascites cancer cells failed to produce cancer; when he gave mice four weekly injections of 50,000 cells, the animals became completely immune to the disease.

Dr. Ralph W. McKee has subjected mouse cancer cells to high doses of X rays and used them as a vaccine. With an original and seven booster shots of the specific vaccine, he has protected mice against the ascites cancer and two kinds of leukemialike lymphomas. He has noted that in unvaccinated animals, the blood content of properdin drops sharply and remains low following the transplant of a cancer; in vaccinated animals, the transplant also causes the properdin level to plummet—but on the third day it rebounds and remains high thereafter.

A few surprising events in recent years have suggested that a vaccine might not have to be specific to give a high degree of protection against cancer.

Dr. David Weiss of the University of California, for instance, discovered that he could fortify mice against the transplant of a variety of cancers by injecting them first with either living or killed tuberculosis bacilli. In these experiments vaccine dosage proved to be of the utmost importance; too much or too little weakened or abolished the protection. The vaccination inhibited cancer growth anywhere from 10 to 100 per cent; and, at last report, it had worked to some degree against every cancer employed— transplants of cancer of mouse uterine tissues, liver and bone, and two types of breast cancer. In some cases the vaccine was effective when applied after the transplants had started to grow. In these instances, it killed the growing transplants or prevented metastases and prolonged survival. The vaccine also offered protection against plague bacteria, some types of pneumonia, and staphylococcus infection.

A few years ago an epidemic of unknown origin swept through the rat colony at the Medical College of Virginia. The animals came down with a severe hemolytic anemia, which lasted several weeks and then cured itself. Dr. Jerome Sacks discovered that all the recovered animals were resistant to cancer; he tried to transplant six different tumors, to all of which the rats normally were susceptible, and found that the tumors wouldn't take. He infected other rats with serum from the sick animals, and they too took sick, eventually recovered and became resistant to cancer.

Only in newborn animals did the anemia (possibly caused by a virus) fail to protect against cancer. The limitations of this cancer-prophylactic procedure—whether it prevents or even cures induced and spontaneous cancers in other species—are yet to be reported.

Others have found that a number of endotoxins produced by bacteria, a fraction (zymosan) of the yeast cell wall, and fatlike chemicals from B. pertussis, a relative of the whooping cough organism, boost general resistance to disease, particularly to cancer. Dr. Julia McCain Lampkin-Hubbard of the University of Oklahoma extracted the small nuclear proteins, histones, from human cancers, injected them into rabbits, and, after four weeks of inoculations, treated cancer-susceptible mice with the rabbit antiserum. When the mice, simultaneously or later, were grafted with mouse lymphomas, the cancers failed to take.

Immunized lymph cells also have given a high degree of protection against cancer. Dr. Frederick W. Preston of Northwestern University withdrew lymph cells from rats which had been inoculated with a (Bagg) sarcoma and which had recovered; he injected the lymph cells into susceptible rats and found the injection protected three-fourths of them against later tumor implants. The lymph cells were effective even when they had been frozen for a few weeks and then revived by thawing.

Several investigators have reported that the effect of a vaccine can be enhanced if an antiserum to it, or immune lymph cells, are administered along with the vaccine. One risk is that the reaction may be so vigorous as to induce anaphylactic shock. The technique, however, offers a possibility of strengthening the effects of a weak vaccine.

Dr. Sven A. Bach of the U.S. Army Medical Research Laboratory in Fort Knox reported that he has improved greatly the efficiency of specific antibodies (gamma globulin molecules) by exposing the molecules to certain temperatures, to specific radio frequencies and to electrical energies. Under the correct conditions, the spherical antibody particles unwind somewhat, exposing a number of additional reactive sites and greatly increasing the antibodies' ability to destroy viruses and microbes.

The discovery that DNA digests of lymph cells contain a substance which causes the antibody-manufacturing lymph cells to multiply has opened a new avenue to boosting natural immunity by chemical means. The discovery by Dr. Werner Braun and others at Rutgers has had some interesting immediate results. When the digest substance was given to irradiated animals, radiation damage was repaired; when it was administered to aging cancer-prone mice, their breast cancers were delayed or failed to appear.

With all the advances in recent years, the field of immunity, and particularly cancer immunity, is only beginning to open up. Some seemingly incredible events have been observed, and, no doubt, many more will follow. Dr. David A. Salzberg of the Palo Alto Medical Research Foundation, for instance, has found that if baby rats which normally develop liver cancer when fed butter yellow are nursed by rats naturally resistant to the cancers, the baby rats also become resistant. One could guess at a transmissible anticancer agent in the milk.

Dr. Howard L. Richardson found that when resistant rats were housed near susceptible rats they, too, became susceptible to liver cancer. The implications of these studies are that a virus, as well as the butter-yellow diet, are involved in these cancers. Now Dr. Richardson is examining what may turn out to be a much stranger phenomenon: when he housed the cancer-susceptible rats next to guinea pigs (which are naturally resistant to the liver cancer), the rats too became resistant. He is examining the possibility of a transferred immunity—possibly something excreted by the guinea pigs which reach the rats through the air.

One of the possibilities in cancer immunology is a vaccine against the chemicals that cause cancer. If this dream should come to pass, immunized industrial workers would be protected against carcinogens in their shops, smokers could puff away on cigarettes with impunity, carcinogenic additives in food and carcinogens in other sources of environmental exposure would be unable to cause cancer.

For many years, Dr. Hugh J. Creech of the Institute for Cancer Research, Philadelphia, has sought to find a means of vaccinating against carcinogens. His work—with well-known fluorescent chemicals and in animals only—has met with a measure of success but has not yet reached the point where his techniques can be applied to human populations.

Carcinogens generally are small molecules, too small by themselves to incite antibody attack. Dr. Creech uses them as haptens; that is, he attaches them to large protein molecules in the hope that antibodies will form against the strange "bump-on-a-log" proteins. He has managed to attach scores of carcinogen haptens to a single protein (usually serum albumin) molecule; and in certain hapten concentrations, the molecule becomes highly antigenic. When fewer than twenty-five are attached, the molecule tends to lose antigenic activity; with more than thirty-seven, the immunizing effect weakens. One happy discovery is that carcinogens, when bound to protein, do not cause cancers in animals. In these studies, Dr. Creech has discovered that some anticancer drugs, like nitrogen mustards, following their injection into patients, combine with proteins and become antigenic. In these cases, antibodies are produced against them—thus knocking out the therapeutic effects of the drugs.

Drs. E. H. Byers and Russell H. Wilson of Dallas obtained partial immunization against the carcinogen, methylcholanthrene, by first injecting their animals with a mince of tissues which had been incubated with methylcholanthrene.

A great many developments in research with possible application to the cancer problem are taking place. Sometimes the implications of the work are not noted immediately. Dr. Jacqueline Verrett and Dr. Joseph M. Laughlin, Jr., of the Food and Drug Administration, for instance, have reported that teratogenicity (the ability to produce congenital defects or monsters) of drugs, food additives and other substances has been reflected in the test substance's effects on chick embryos. When a teratogen is injected into the yolk of a fertilized chicken egg, it kills or damages the chick embryo. Dr. Farber, it will be recalled, discovered that something in the blood of cancerous animals and patients has similar effects on the chick embryo. Other research has brought the suggestion that many teratogens are carcinogenic, and many carcinogens are teratogenic.

It may not be too wild a guess to suppose that some day one may be able to identify some substances as carcinogenic by their effect on the chick embryo. This sort of development—if it ever came to pass—would greatly facilitate identifying carcinogens in environment. Man then would know what to avoid to prevent cancer.

Dr. Jonathan E. Rhoads of the University of Pennsylvania a few years ago proposed a mathematical equation to guide surgeons in performing operations designed to prevent or cure cancer. In it, the risk of killing or harming the patient was weighed against the chance of preventing or curing the cancer. He concluded, "Clearly if the ratio of the lives saved to those lost is less than one, the procedure is contraindicated. How much above one the ratio should be to constitute a sufficient, as well as necessary, condition for the preventive surgery is at present a matter of judgment. The author's judgment would place the figure at not less than two. . . ."

There is a large area between the extremes of undertaking a foolhardy and patently harmful experimental procedure on the one hand and abdicating the professional and moral obligation to preserve life by all possible means, on the other. Each individual practitioner in conscience and within his competence must draw his own equation of risks and chances. Perhaps for medicine as a whole, the urgent application of the fruits of basic research to the experimental detection, prevention and treatment of cancer may offer bargains—rates much better than a life for a life.

In animal and test-tube experiments, perhaps a thousand studies have suggested ways of preventing cancer. Most of the suggestions are probably impractical. Some of them seem worth pursuing for such benefit as they might bring humans. With one exception, however—the vigorous campaign against cigarette smoking—there is no really strong and effective effort to apply the fruits of research to the prevention of cancer in humans.

CHAPTER 29

CONTROL

Cancer control is a term that means whatever one wants it to mean. In this text it means eliminating cancer from the ten leading causes of death.

Cancer control is completely possible. It conceivably could—but won't —come tomorrow. The means of cancer control may have been at hand for some time; it may be buried in the mountains of scientific literature; it could be in the minds of investigators too timid to undertake the experiments necessary to prove it, or too unpopular to be financed.

Some spokesmen for the movement have said that great progesss has been made and is being made toward cancer control. This euphoria has soothed much of science, the medical profession, and the public. Current complacency is the greatest deterrent of all to cancer control; so long as satisfaction exists, science and medicine well may continue to pursue the familiar paths which experience has shown lead only to small advances.

A much better course might be to contemplate the many things that are wrong with efforts to control cancer. All of them can be corrected.

The failure of cancer-control efforts can be measured. The sternest standard shows that more people are developing cancer than ever before, and the number of deaths continues to increase steadily—in the United States estimates set the 1964 deaths at 6,000 more than in 1963. This rise in deaths is taking place despite a phenomenal decrease—unmanaged and not understood by science and medicine—in the incidence of common cancers of the stomach, liver and uterus.

One can take scant comfort from the gradual rise in cures, mostly of accessible and slow-growing cancers, if the disease and its rising toll cancel out these modest advances. More than two million deaths (290,000 of them in the United States) are estimated as the 1964 score of failure. By general admission, between one-third and one-half of these deaths are completely unnecessary; they measure the ineptitude of programs for the education of the public and the inadequacy of the medical profession and system.

Unless drastic improvements are made, these sorry scores will worsen. At least 48 of the 190 million Americans now alive will develop cancer, and more than 30 million eventually will die of it.

A great many measures have been proposed for the prevention of cancer. With one notable exception—the investigation of cigarette smoking as a cause of lung cancer—little has been done to ascertain the merit of the proposals and still less to try to prevent the disease. There has been virtually no effort to validate scientific suspicions of human cancer dangers in environmental factors. The committees which have met appear to have been forgotten, along with their recommendations. Most of the measures proposed for physicians are largely ignored—if indeed they were ever noted in the first place. Little thought is given to application of leads to prevention emerging from basic research.

The enormity of the problem of hazards was acknowledged by the Committee on Environmental Health Problems, set up by the Surgeon General, U.S. Public Health Service in 1961. This group, the CEH, recommended an immediate and sweeping change in existing programs, and it proposed new legislation. It reported the increasingly severe air pollution, and, in water, a steady rise of unwanted tastes and odors, the indestructible chemicals with immediate lethal and unpredictable long-range effects on health and, now, radioactive wastes. It warned that pollution of the air, water, and land resources presents "threats of an insidious nature, a form of creeping paralysis which, if not recognized and corrected can lead to urban stagnation and death as surely as the most violent epidemic." It contended that frank occupational disease persists and is confounded with the normal mental and physical deterioration of aging; it said that of the nation's 70 million civilian laborers "probably more than one-half have some degree of physiological impairment which could be greatly reduced if adequate knowledge were available." The committee estimated that more than one-half of the nation's industrial plants lack basic hygiene control measures.

Little or nothing has been done to correct these situations.

The Food and Drug laws candidly permit known carcinogens to be swallowed regularly by humans. These substances cause cancer when *injected* into animals. If they do not cause cancer when *eaten* by experimental animals, they are deemed safe for human fare. Under these laws humans are subject to exposure to a variety of carcinogens—trace doses, to be sure, but each of which may add to or multiply the effects of another.

Even the test animals are not subjected to these complex dangers; they usually are given one carcinogen and one only. Humans have no way of knowing whether the combinations of multiple carcinogens to which they are exposed cause cancer in experimental animals when given orally or by needle. Efforts to test the effect of multiple carcinogens have been very few, and those that were made involved combinations of two or three at most. Humans regularly eat mixtures of many carcinogens, and they ingest them daily as long as they live.

While recent drug laws scrupulously insist that the toxicity of new preparations be established before they can be put on the market, the life-long carcinogenicity of many new and old preparations has not been determined. The dangers of drugs used during pregnancy, when they may predestine the fetus to congenital disease or future cancer, were pointed up by the thalidomide incident at a cost of several thousand babies. It is unlikely, however, that either this or anything else has greatly deterred physicians from prescribing and pregnant women from taking other drugs with more subtle—possibly carcinogenic—effects. Dr. Bongiovanni, who has made many studies of congenital disease and childhood cancer, has told physicians, "The use of hormones during pregnancy should be reserved for clear and compelling indications. Never use a potent drug during pregnancy unless the indication is clear; then use a minimum dose. And if treatment involving a fetal hazard is necessary, keep in mind the anticipated effects so that any malformation can be recognized and corrected early." Cancer, coming to an offspring years later, seldom can be traced to a mother's indiscreet use of a drug during her pregnancy.

While the number of states adopting laws regulating the registration and inspection of X-ray machines is gradually increasing, the laws are weak and their enforcement lax. There has been no serious effort to restrict the use of these sources of powerful carcinogenic rays to trained and responsible operators; the majority apparently continue to spray themselves, their patients, and their neighbors with radiation. When even the most highly trained radiologists show a significant excess of leukemia and other radiation-induced diseases, there can be little hope that the relatively untrained physicians, dermatologists, dentists, chiropractors, osteopaths, physiotherapists, and shoe clerks will show more consideration for their patients and customers or caution for themselves. This lack of responsibility is reflected on all levels—from the clerk who uses X rays to fit a child's shoes to the venturesome scientists who have altered the Van Allen belt girdling the earth with an ill-considered space explosion of a hydrogen bomb and were surprised at the durable distortion they inflicted.

While there is excellent evidence in experimental animal work to indicate that the stress of emotions may play a prominent role in the genesis and course of cancer, this enticing field of investigation is left largely to the enthusiasms of Freudian psychologists of little stature or competence. The hard-headed, practical people who control research funds and seem convinced that psychosomatic and somatopsychic phenomena are on a scientific par with necromancy have discouraged competent examination of this problem.

Hormones, one of the mechanisms of emotions, have been investigated intensively but not as extensively as the problem requires. Some hormones which have been available for a long time—notably thyroid hormones—have had only the sketchiest testing in animals, and almost none at all in humans. The combinations of hormones tested against human cancers have been simple, few, and (with exceptions) marked by an incredible lack of imagination. Whereas all experimental evidence indicates a strong interdependency of most or all endocrine glands, laboratory and clinical testing has been done pretty much with a single preparation, often with the idea of blocking a hormone. While the removal of glands has brought palliation to a minority of patients, these operations have yet to cure a cancer arising elsewhere in the body. Equally difficult to understand is the failure to try to anticipate relapse and prophylactically treat the patient having a hormone-responsive cancer while still in remission; the custom is to wait until the patient gets so deeply into trouble that even the most drastic measures have slight chance of success. Only elaborately-controlled clinical experiments can suggest ways of prolonging remissions and suppressing the disease; and under the prevailing leave-well-enough-alone philosophy this is not possible.

The best virologists have considerable respect for the particles with which they work. They are acutely aware of the unsolved mysteries of virus behavior and of the staggering potential of danger in ill-advised adventures in the molecular cosmos. Others walk boldly where virologists fear to tread; a majority of Americans had been inoculated before it was discovered the polio vaccines contained cancer viruses. While at this point it may be expedient and comforting to contemplate the different susceptibilities of laboratory animals and humans and to hope that humans, unlike animals, will not develop cancer as a result of these blunders, prudence and new knowledge dictate that the entire practice of prophylaxis be reviewed carefully and critically.

Of particular interest is the universal program of vaccinating against smallpox. It has been some years since a single case of smallpox originated in the United States—thanks to the efficacy of these vaccines. On the other hand, the rise in cancer generally parallels statistically the use of smallpox vaccines. It is known that vaccinia greatly enhances the potency of carcinogens in mice; and, in humans, cancers have developed in vaccination scars too often for mere coincidence. Vaccinia can be particularly virulent in the very young; there is one case in which a mother was infected by the virus from her vaccinated son and passed it on to her eighteen-week-old fetus, which was born dead and deformed ten weeks later. If the infant has acquired antibodies from the mother, the vaccination is worthless; if it hasn't, and if it cannot yet produce antibodies, animal studies indicate the child may be made tolerant of the agent for all its life.

The support for immunization procedures involving risk is matched only by the opposition to others which someday may control cancer.

An increasing number of scientists have reported that cancers, both animal and human, are antigenic; that is, they contain unique molecules which, if isolated and purified, might be the basis for an effective vaccine. Against this still small but rising tide of hope there is a counterreaction which is difficult to understand. The few clinical experiments which have been undertaken with vaccines to prevent cancer in elderly people, and vaccines and antisera to treat cancer advanced beyond help by other means, have met with bitter and sometimes brutal opposition. The fact that these experiments have been without serious sequelae—that the procedures have been much milder, in fact, than the anticancer drugs now used—has not deterred opponents from castigating the scientists and sometimes jeopardizing their jobs and academic standing. In some cases, the reported results of therapeutic immune measures are superior to those achieved in advanced cancer by conventional treatment.

There has been partial success in vaccinating animals against carcinogens, using the carcinogens as haptens attached to protein molecules as a vaccine. This, however, is under study by very few people. Also largely ignored is the possibility of administering noncarcinogenic analogues, natural or artificial, of known carcinogens to which the public is exposed. Some preventive measures might be tested on large groups of prisoner volunteers who have smoked heavily for thirty years or more; within a relatively short time one might learn whether hapten vaccines and vitamin and other carcinogen-analogues would reduce the high rate of lung cancer to be expected in this population. Workers strongly exposed to industrial carcinogens have much to gain from experiments in prophylaxis.

Numerous studies have shown that for some kinds of cancer early detection is a life-and-death matter. The value of regular checkups is reflected in two sets of figures offered a few years ago by Dr. Hugh F. Jewett of Johns Hopkins. In his own hospital, prostatic cancers were only 19 per cent curable; in the Army, on the other hand, where semiannual examinations were a must, prostatic cancer proved 54 per cent curable. Capt. Robert B. Brown of Bethesda, Maryland, has offered equally impelling figures for lung cancer discovered among Navy personnel: 88 per cent of all lung cancers detected during routine examinations and 71 per cent of those found during special examinations turned out to be operable, and 20 per cent of these men survived five years; only 4 or 5 per cent of civilians survive five years after diagnosis of lung cancer.

Few civilians, unfortunately, have good semiannual or annual check-ups, and for them a blood test would be a godsend. Relatively few can afford the $100 or more charged by some groups for a first-class cancer-detection examination. Routine chest X rays have yet to prove their value as a means of detecting early and curable lung cancer. In Phila-delphia, where more than 6,000 men reported for chest X rays every six months for more than ten years, the tests failed miserably to reduce death rates. The investigators concluded that the lung abnormalities of noncancerous cigarette smokers were so similar to those found in men with lung cancer that they couldn't tell the difference; they said that, so far as the X rays showed, either most habitual smokers had latent lung cancer or the abnormalities found in the lungs of cancer patients did not really represent cancer. In the Philadelphia studies the first indication of lung cancer came not from X-ray pictures but rather from symptoms —most commonly chronic cough and difficulty in breathing.

Lung cancer is not the only cancer—nor, indeed, is cancer the only disease—which is poorly diagnosed. Dr. Barkev F. Sanders, research consultant to the U.S. Public Health Service, told the 1963 meeting of the American Public Health Association that only 40 per cent of all diseases of clinical importance now are diagnosed, and only one-half of these diagnoses are correct. He cited a study of North Carolina general practitioners whose abilities ranged from those that would be acceptable in the outpatient clinic of a university hospital to "some whose practices would have been unsatisfactory in a senior medical student."

Considering the importance and difficulty of detecting early cancer and the paucity of good cancer diagnosticians and tumor pathologists, one would suppose that science and health agencies would conduct an aggres-sive search for blood, urine, and other tests for cancer. This has not been the case. On the contrary, virtually all the tests which have been proposed, including the Papanicolaou smear technique, have met initially with either hostility or apathy. An objective and systematic re-check on some of the tests reported in the literature, including some which were hastily and ineptly checked and called no good, might be well worth doing.

Dozens of tests have been advanced for cancer generally. Others are for cancer of various sites. The electrophoretic mobility patterns of red cells have been proposed by researchers at St. Vincent's Hospital, New York, for gastrointestinal cancers; others suggest the determination of adrenalin and related hormones in urine for neuroblastoma. Blood levels of lactic dehydrogenase together with analyses of white-cell concentrates and marrow aspirates, according to one report, have enabled Loma Linda investigators to predict lymphomas and leukemias anywhere from two to twenty months before onset of symptoms—a remarkably useful test if it can be reproduced regularly.

An old skin-resistance method for locating tumors should be checked. About fifteen years ago Dr. Curt P. Richter of Johns Hopkins found that tumors interfered with the passage of a light (22- or 90-volt) current along sympathetic nerve pathways. By attaching one pole to the patient's ear and running the other pole over the skin surface, he located tumors (and occasionally other impediments) by the resistance (up to 45 million ohms) they set up. This procedure should be tested for its value in pin-pointing cancers whose general presence is indicated by a smear, blood, or urine test. Drs. Henry M. Lemon, Langdon Parsons, and Peter H. Mozden, of the University of Nebraska, Harvard, and Boston University, re-spectively, have applied new and highly sensitive equipment in measuring the electric potential of the human vagina. One electrode contacts the vaginal skin; the other is placed against the belly skin. A voltmeter registers great changes in vaginal electric potential during various phases of the men-strual cycle, at ovulation, before and after the menopause, in hormone-associated diseases, and during hormone therapy. One hope is that the technique will serve as a test for the diagnosis of uterine and breast cancers and the patients' response to treatment. Outside this and a few other groups, there is little interest in this promising field of inquiry.

Proposed prognostic tests also should be rerun by able and objective groups. Some of these are chemical (blood levels of cortisol or lactic de-hydrogenase, for instance), some are immunological (the presence of scavenger and other defense cells in the tumor area), and some are physical (the response of normal and tumor cells to radiation). Valid tests might well indicate what type of treatment to employ and when to use it.

A whole battery of tests on large patient populations should show in short order the dependability and limitations of each procedure.

The person who has persistent cancer symptoms faces a serious prob-lem. He stands in urgent need of the best medical attention he can get.

Even small skin cancers require specialized management. Whereas the best men in this field cure almost 100 per cent of simple basal-cell car-cinomas with minimum disfigurement, the inexpert, with inadequate treatment, can cost the lives of more than 10 per cent of these patients and subject many more to eventual mutilation and pain. Too often the specialists are presented with skin-cancer patients only when repeated unsuccessful treatments elsewhere have left them with a large part of the face ravaged.

It is much more important to bring internal cancers at once to the attention of physicians who specialize in their treatment. If there is any chance of cure at all, the opportunity quickly slips away while the inexpert waits to see what happens or undertakes incorrect treatment.

An undetermined but certainly very high proportion of the 33–50 per cent of cancer deaths deemed unnecessary is due to the ineptitude of the first physician to see these cancer patients. Because of their unfamiliarity with cancer, dilatory tactics and poor treatment, some doctors may sacrifice more lives to the disease than they save. The custom by some family physicians and some non-cancer specialists of referring their cases only when there no longer is a possibility of cure is generally resented in good medical centers. In many cases, earlier inferior treatment of once-curable cases has made it impossible to offer the patient a decent chance even of palliation.

Patients with persistent cancer symptoms who do not receive prompt and adequate attention from the first physician they visit will do well to have the doctor refer them to an established cancer center, if that is at all possible.

The problem of recommending physicians best fitted to treat specific kinds of cancer is a ticklish one. The patient's first or family physician has the prerogative and the responsibility for referrals. Many physicians refer patients to nearby doctors with little competence in treating cancer. One study has shown that by and large doctors who have cancer are about as unsuccessful in seeking effective medical help as is the general run of patients; the doctors' doctors usually are just about as slow in detecting and diagnosing cancers and as unsuccessful in treating them as are those treating the nondoctor patients. It is unlikely that doctors have more luck in referring their patients than in finding help for themselves. If there were sufficient demand on the part of the profession and of the public, agencies like the American Cancer Society, the National Cancer Institute, and surgical and radiation societies might be persuaded to draw up a list of centers and specialists particularly interested and skilled in treating specific kinds of cancer.

Not all the great surgeons and others with a special talent in certain kinds of cancer are in the major medical centers, but, generally speaking, these centers offer the uninformed patient his best chance of cure. Cancer patients often require the attention of several specialists, and the large medical centers have teams to serve their varied needs.

Many of those who excel in certain fields will consult on cases; and sometimes the cost of this excellent advice is no greater than the price of a long-distance telephone call. Consultation can be particularly valuable in the utterly hopeless cases which can best be treated by a properly counseled family physician. Few situations in cancer are more tragic than those posed by patients who, having fallen into the hopeless category, nevertheless migrate from doctor to doctor and center to center in search of a miracle.

The physician's fees are not by any means a criterion of the quality of his services in detecting, diagnosing and treating cancer. For those who are fortunate enough to qualify, some of the best cancer services are rendered reasonably or free by many of the public agencies—military and VA hospitals, federal, state, county, and city public institutions, and state and other medical schools. Among these, of course, are wide differences in the quality of services. Congressmen, including those who bitterly oppose public health bills, have their own serious illnesses treated in federal hospitals—not only because it is free but, perhaps more so, because the services are generally superior to those available elsewhere.

In a few centers, particularly those with an active clinical research program, some cancers generally considered incurable are yielding to new methods of treatment. Sometimes the cures are made possible by new equipment, more often by an ingenious technique or great skill. The secrets of new success in treating certain cancers often are not passed along quickly to the profession at large, nor are they made available to all patients. Occasionally with more caution than is commendable, originators of new treatments will wait for five-year or ten-year results before reporting on their work, oblivious to the fact that some people in this time are dying unnecessarily of their cancers. Beyond this, medical communications are in such a mess and overworked physicians read so little, reports may pass unnoticed for a long period. More and more, physicians are learning of medical discoveries from newspaper clippings given them by their patients.

The cancer patient who places himself in the care of a physician unfitted to treat him not only reduces his chances of cure but runs a very real risk of being disabled unnecessarily, thus adding iatrogenic pain and distress to the miseries of his cancer. This is true whether the physician is a general surgeon or other specialist with scant familiarity with the specific cancer, a part-time radiologist or a general practitioner. Just as a plumber might be able to do a rough job in carpentry, many doctors can do a rough job outside their specialty or usual practice. In cancer, a rough job isn't good enough.

Dr. Loyal Davis of Northwestern University, in his 1962 presidential address to the American College of Surgeons, pointed out that

the holders of a medical license in various states are legally qualified to undertake hypophysectomy, pneumonectomy, prostatectomy, gastrectomy. . . . They are legally qualified to administer a "shot" of penicillin after a quick-look diagnosis and prescribe a physic. The license may not be revoked for undertaking a procedure for which the holder is totally unqualified by education and training. The only restraining influences are the doctor's own conscience and the more effective and material danger of a suit for malpractice. We all know that many surgical operations are performed in the United States today in hospitals of varying sizes by doctors who have not been educated and trained progressively in their postgraduate years to be surgeons. No one knows how many of these operations are bungled, and by no means do all of them result in disaster. . . . Many doctors may become deft, skillful performers of operations which proceed routinely. However, the patient may suffer grievously if the operation is unnecessary, if it is not preceded by careful pre-operative studies and evaluation, if the wrong procedure is employed, or if the postoperative management is inadequate because of ignorance or lack of a surgical conscience.

Dr. Davis' forthright lecture was in consonance with those of his predecessors in office. The College since its founding has served not only the cause of better medicine but also, compassionately, the interests of the public, who become the beneficiaries of improved practices and are the victims of the bad ones.

There are few doubts but that abuses within surgery are matched by others—at least as numerous and as serious—among physicians who, without adequate training, employ radiation. Qualified radiologists are less inclined to discuss these failings among themselves or with the public, however. The great damage done by ill-advised or improperly administered radiation often is slow in showing itself and sometimes is difficult to trace to treatment.

Equally abused is the art of giving pills or injections in chemotherapy. The faithful old family doctor or the high-priced internist who doesn't abide by indications and contraindications nor adhere to dosage schedules, who doesn't closely follow the patient's reactions to drugs, and who has not learned that a drug used for years finally has been found to be dangerous is inclined to attribute to the natural course of the disease a drug-induced relapse and speedy death. Or if he becomes aware of an irreversible and unforgivable error, he may find it expedient to abandon the dying patient and go off on a vacation.

With all its faults, and they are numerous, American medicine compares favorably with medicine practiced anywhere in the world. Individual doctors and groups in the United States have initiated many of the most valuable procedures in worldwide clinical use today. The brilliance of its great doctors and the competence and conscience of its many good doctors, in large centers and in the hinterlands, have given American medicine gigantic stature. Unfortunately, many cancer patients do not see the famous figures or even the good doctors; they patronize the materialistic and the mediocre or worse because they are conveniently located or because the patient feels one physician is as good as another.

As a rule, the talented practitioners welcome the opportunity to advise the public candidly on the problems and progress of medicine. This is opposed eloquently by those who are uncertain or ashamed of their own professional performance and who feel that the profitable and priestly status often accorded physicians might be diminished by revelations of the shortcomings, the scandals, the politics, and the sociological and economic pressures of organized medicine and individuals' ineptitude. There is a good deal of personal and professional security in the philosophy that the patient has no right to know what manner of man his doctor is, providing, of course, that the philosophy can survive in a society of ever-increasing sophistication.

Under a cloak of privileged semisecrecy, shoddy and antiquated medical practices equivalent to quackery have been able to flourish despite opposition by perhaps the majority of dedicated and able doctors. The ills of medicine are deep-rooted. Because of this, it will be a long time before all cancer patients will be given the treatment they need.

The control of cancer is inextricably involved with the general state of science, as well as medicine. The faults of science are as numerous as those of medicine, and both are too complex to be documented in detail here. Until they are corrected, however, the problems of cancer—and of public health in general—can be solved only in small part.

Perhaps the first step toward solution of the cancer problem, and that of the nation's general health, lies in a realistic appraisal of the situation as it now exists.

Money is uppermost in the minds of those who control public health programs. The real money problem is not how much to spend on science and health but rather *how* to spend it. There is a serious question as to whether there have not been progressively diminishing returns on the rocketing sums poured into science and health since the beginning of the science explosion fifteen or twenty years ago.

The Health Insurance Institute estimates that the American people spent $22.7 billion in 1962 (a 7.6 per cent increase over 1961 and double the 1952 expenditure) on the costs of sickness. Broken down, these costs included $7 billion on hospital treatment, $6.6 billion for doctors, $5.6 billion for medicines, $2.2 billion for dentists, and $1.3 billion for nursing homes, the services of nonprofessional practitioners and other medical services. The investment in medical research should be made with these costs in mind. Successful research, applied to clinical problems, tends to reduce the costs of bills for the one-in-seven Americans who spend time in the hospital each year, bills for an average of five doctor visits annually, and other costs, including time away from work. As against these non-productive outlays, the U.S. Public Health Service total annual budget runs about $1.6 billion and health research funds from other governmental, public and private sources a few hundred million dollars.

Research expenditures of all sorts have soared in the last two decades. Federal funds for research and development and related education rose from $73 million in 1940 to $2 billion in 1953 and more than $15 billion in 1963. This was to be expected. A great revolutionary new era has opened, and there is no choice but to promote research or perish. The problem is not one of producing the funds, but rather of producing the scientists who can use the funds productively.

With money goes power. In financing research—Big Research—money can pose a threat to the people it is supposed to serve and the ends it is to attain. Much depends on the character of the people who control the purse strings.

The principal controller of the public's purse strings in the American economy is Congress, a body of men understandably ignorant of scientific procedures and naturally responsive to the pressures of medicopolitical groups and scientific and quasi-scientific advisers. The medicopolitical groups counsel vigorously against the extension of public health services to elements of the citizenry hard-pressed or unable to finance decent medical care; and the quasi-scientific advisers mount ridicule against research into the brain glands of cockroaches, the chromosomes of fruit flies, and other projects which seem absurd on the surface, but which have yielded rich lodes of information related to human health and welfare.

Beyond Congress, there are a host of purse-string controllers with at least an opportunity to learn the problems of science. These are the officials of various granting agencies. In many cases, they have sufficient influence to gain support for a man and his work, to halt a project, or to endanger the scientist's academic standing by condemning his work and impugning his character.

The fact that there are a number of granting agencies offers a degree —but only a degree—of protection against scientific stagnation. It offers some—and only some—assurance of support to scientists with ideas more progressive than the usually conservative standards of those who administer the grants and, indeed, those who spend them. A diversity of agencies and granting systems is a protection, and again only to a degree, against discrimination because of age (over 65), race, creed, and youthful political indiscretions and a wide range of other prejudices—personal, professional, and scientific. Fears that multiple agencies make for duplication of research are groundless: a dozen competent scientists starting work on the same problem are quite likely to head off in a dozen different directions and possibly all wind up with a dozen different and useful results. A much greater danger is that the prejudices of one agency may be transmitted, through too close collaboration, to other agencies, resulting in the general blacklisting of scientists or their ideas.

While some granting officials are intelligent, hard-working, and dedicated to solving the health problem they are concerned with, others leave something to be desired. The latter often have left lusterless careers in science or medicine for the heady power and higher pay of investigating grants and grantees and recommending or condemning men and their work for agency support. They are notably reluctant to apply principles developed in research to urgent health problems. Some introduce a strange sense of musty decay and standards of discipline and rank into what should be a free and ebullient field of investigation. Some of their conclusions seem to be reached through clairvoyancy. They are intellectually far behind the men they judge.

Agency investigators make their findings known to a series of panels, counsels, or committees, usually of first-class scientists who examine the applications and make formal recommendations to the granting agencies. Some of these counsels are comprised of a mélange of perhaps a dozen different specialists—biochemist, biologist, pharmacologist, physicist, physician, immunologist, anatomist, and so forth—only one or a few of whom may understand the technical nature of each project proposed and, in the present scientist population explosion, none of whom may ever have heard of the applicant or talked with him.

Under these circumstances, scientists find it expedient to play a grim and cynical game called grantsmanship. One grantsman's version goes like this: A scientist is kind to his dean, the granting agency man, and a few members of the counsel. He gets his grant, buys his equipment, acquires a larger laboratory, hires a bigger staff, and starts to build his empire. He and his staff produce enormous numbers of scientific papers dealing ambiguously with trivia. He attends large and small meetings in far places, sits on councils and committees, holds conference after conference with distant or visiting scientists, shows granting agency representatives through his shining laboratories, files long reports in quadruplicate—and does very little research. He instructs his aides to pursue quiet and conventional lines of pointless inquiry which will please the conservative tastes of granting-agency investigators, produce inoffensive papers, and attract more money to buy more equipment, hire more staff, build more laboratory space, finance more travel, and make it more impossible for more scientists to do worthwhile work.

Occasionally a scientist bucks the system and does notable work. He is taken care of. They make him head of the department, dean, chancellor, or president of the university, in which position he is so burdened with administrative duties, money-raising, handshaking, and speechmaking that he never again enters a laboratory.

By 1963, it had become painfully apparent that the bartering of scientific freedom for funds under the government's system of Big Research was a bad bargain. While the leaf-rakers and the empire-builders within science fared well under ever-tightening government controls of research, individual scientists with new ideas and work to do became bogged down in the discipline, the directions, the instructions, and the red tape that became the price of their financal support. In cancer research, the chemotherapy program—under which many scientists became technicians under instructions from government offices in Bethesda—was the prototype of new programs dictated by the masters of Big Research. In an unprecedented move, the membership of the American Association for Cancer Research at its 1963 meeting voted unanimously to "express its deep concern that the recently issued Grants Manual of the National Institutes of Health contains specific and general modifications of earlier directives which threaten the presently existing helpful and profitable relationship between the Federal administrative agency and the scientific community and also threaten the rapid and efficient prosecution of the research objectives which we all recognize." The membership asked the National Academy of Sciences to intervene against "the implicit and explicit modifications in freedom of scientific inquiry."

The biting by cancer researchers, organized biochemists, and others, of the hand that fed them was strange and encouraging. The fact that the National Academy of Sciences rebuked the government which had created it in President Lincoln's time and which it advises on scientific matters was a hopeful sign.

A special Public Policy Committee of the Academy reported in 1964 that it had reviewed the complaints. It made recommendations for correcting abuses, not only at the government level, but in universities as well. By implication, the report concerned all granting agencies.

The Academy committee conceded that American science had reached a position of world leadership with federal government help. But, it added:

the emphasis on large programmatic ventures and laboratories which has been manifest in recent times must not lead to a loss of emphasis on individual scientists; the individual investigator has been and will remain the source of strength in American science.

It proposed expansion of study sections and advisory panels of scientists on a short-term, rotating basis; higher-quality scientists on agency staffs; more administrative duties and less influence in research by administrative employees; more responsibility for universities—and less for scientists—

in administrative detail of grants and contracts, reversing "the recent trend toward unnecessary restriction of scientific freedom and increases in the bookkeeping chores of scientists"; more latitude in spending grant funds; less accounting for days and hours spent in research; more money and freedom for young scientists and more restrictions for entrenched scientists who thrive on multiple grants from various agencies; encouragement of research in weaker institutions; and, on the part of scientists, conscientious use of funds and a responsibility to serve on panels, educate the young, and advance scientific knowledge.

The report served to bring into the open a festering sore within science. It by no means touched on all the inequities, but it made clear the fact that the inquiring mind could not be replaced by government funds and direction.

This action and the conditions which brought it about seem to have been missed by the popular press. It was of considerable importance, however, to every citizen interested in a strong America, in general scientific advance, or in cancer control.

There is no easy solution to the cancer problem, and there may be no considerable headway made until by some means the many growing pains of science and the decay of medicine are remedied. There is need for a great expansion of undergraduate education, many more professional colleges, a thorough revision of the anachronistic aspects of medical and scientific education and practice and continuing postgraduate work, particularly for the physician. The medical profession, rich in material rewards, nevertheless is attracting relatively fewer students and students of decreasing academic stature; and there is every indication that the present shortage of doctors will become more intense and the quality of doctors deteriorate further. While the ranks of students entering science as a career are swelling, it is doubtful whether the pressures and disciplines of Big Research will permit the average to attain the production reached by scientists of bygone free and easy days.

A major and still-growing problem in science and medicine is communications. This is the gap which prevents a scientist from knowing what work has been done and is being done on the project he is contemplating. It prevents the physician from knowing that his "minor modification" will lead to the rapid decline and death of a patient doing well on an experimental treatment. The communications fault lies not in a paucity of information but rather to a plethora of it. The estimated 20,000 journals dealing with biological subjects are studded with precious and semiprecious gems of knowledge buried in tons of dross and drivel which no one has time to examine.

For some time it has been apparent that the great research emphasis placed on cancer in mice is not very helpful in controlling cancer in humans. Drugs which affect the three standard mouse tumors often are useless clinically; by the same token, drugs discovered by other means to help humans often have no effect on the mouse cancers.

One of the great achievements of the chemotherapy program has been to increase during a few years the number of mice for research from 150,000 a year to 2,000,000. Of these, about 800,000 animals eventually are given or come down with cancer. About 800,000 people in the United States also have cancer and are available for study; most of them are beyond cure by conventional means. In the care of skilled practitioners of experimental medicine, this tremendous population of sick people would offer a magnificent opportunity to study the inherited and environmental causes of cancers, the biochemical and emotional characteristics of cancer patients, the value of blood and other tests for cancer, improved diagnosis, the efficacy of types of surgery and doses of radiation, and the true value of various drugs, immune procedures, and combinations of therapies.

If the federal, state, local, and other public and private health agencies were to move into modern health centers, staff them with the best doctors and researchers, and invite the 800,000 cancer patients to undergo conventional and experimental medical care, cancer control might be achieved in record time. Some incurable patients might be cured; and all would receive expert attention. The libraries of reliable information rapidly gained could be applied to the salvage of cancer patients next year and the year after.

A large-scale study of this sort would be costly, but in all likelihood much less expensive than the present practice under which families mortgage their futures in a usually losing fight against cancer. It would relieve many private physicians of the responsibility for the dreadful delays, the scandalous misdiagnoses, the improper treatments, and the pitiable deaths due to their incompetence.

The alternative to such a system is the present practice and the plodding pace, via endless and largely fruitless mouse experiments, to cancer control in the distant future. This is a system in which quacks compete quite successfully with many family doctors and in which controversial treatments, condemned by federal authorities and respectable medicine, quite naturally become a popular cause célèbre.

The matter of cancer control—including the intimately-related problems of science and medicine—is worthy of the most careful attention of the National Academy of Sciences. Its National Research Council, which since 1916 has mobilized the major scientific and technical organizations in matters of major scientific moment, would find cancer control an urgent and important subject for review. Cancer claims as many Americans each year as were lost in battle during the entire course of World War II.

The problem also concerns all citizens. In lives and money, they pay the bill. In each family of four, cancer will come, on an average, to one member. In every other household, it will kill one person. More than 250,000 school children are without mothers, and an additional 300,000 are without fathers because of cancer. Many parents mourn the loss of one of their children to cancer—a steadily mounting toll. An interested, informed, and intelligent citizenry can do much to speed cancer control. The agencies concerned need their help. The American Cancer Society courts it in a program of public education.

This is the beginning—not the end—of the story of cancer and cancer research. Cancer control, like many seemingly impossible achievements of recent history, can and will come to pass. How soon depends on the wisdom and vigor with which the problem is attacked.

INDEX